G000069411

CHEMICAL ENGINEERING METHODS AND TECHNOLOGY

PHOSPHORUS

PROPERTIES, HEALTH EFFECTS AND THE ENVIRONMENT

CHEMICAL ENGINEERING METHODS AND TECHNOLOGY

Additional books in this series can be found on Nova's website under the Series tab.

Additional E-books in this series can be found on Nova's website under the E-book tab.

BIOCHEMISTRY RESEARCH TRENDS

Additional books in this series can be found on Nova's website under the Series tab.

Additional E-books in this series can be found on Nova's website under the E-book tab.

CHEMICAL ENGINEERING METHODS AND TECHNOLOGY

PHOSPHORUS

PROPERTIES, HEALTH EFFECTS AND THE ENVIRONMENT

MING YUE CHEN
AND
DA-XIA YANG
EDITORS

Nova Science Publishers, Inc.

New York

NOTICE TO THE READER

The Publisher has taken reasonable care in the preparation of this book, but makes no expressed or implied warranty of any kind and assumes no responsibility for any errors or omissions. No liability is assumed for incidental or consequential damages in connection with or arising out of information contained in this book. The Publisher shall not be liable for any special, consequential, or exemplary damages resulting, in whole or in part, from the readers' use of, or reliance upon, this material. Any parts of this book based on government reports are so indicated and copyright is claimed for those parts to the extent applicable to compilations of such works.

Independent verification should be sought for any data, advice or recommendations contained in this book. In addition, no responsibility is assumed by the publisher for any injury and/or damage to persons or property arising from any methods, products, instructions, ideas or otherwise contained in this publication.

This publication is designed to provide accurate and authoritative information with regard to the subject matter covered herein. It is sold with the clear understanding that the Publisher is not engaged in rendering legal or any other professional services. If legal or any other expert assistance is required, the services of a competent person should be sought. FROM A DECLARATION OF PARTICIPANTS JOINTLY ADOPTED BY A COMMITTEE OF THE AMERICAN BAR ASSOCIATION AND A COMMITTEE OF PUBLISHERS.

Additional color graphics may be available in the e-book version of this book.

Library of Congress Cataloging-in-Publication Data

Phosphorus : properties, health effects, and the environment / [edited by] Ming Yue Chen and Da-Xia Yang.
    p. cm.
  Includes index.
  ISBN 978-1-62081-399-7 (hardcover)
  1. Phosphorus--Environmental aspects. I. Yue Chen, Ming. II. Yang, Da-Xia.
  QD181.P1P485 2011
  546'.712--dc23
                        2012008874

Published by Nova Science Publishers, Inc. † New York

CONTENTS

Preface   vii

Chapter 1   Aminophosphonates: Synthesis and Practical Application   1
                Ivan I. Stoikov, Olga A. Mostovaya, Alena A. Vavilova,
                Joshua B. Puplampu, Igor S. Antipin
                and Alexander I. Konovalov

Chapter 2   The Role of Phosphorus Ligands in the Homo-and Co-
                Polymerization of Vinyl Monomers   53
                Giovanni Ricci, Anna Sommazzi, Giuseppe Leone,
                Aldo Boglia and Francesco Masi

Chapter 3   Effects of Phosphorus Doping on the Electrical Properties of
                Diamond and Carbon Nanotubes   95
                Qingyi Shao, Aqing Chen, Guangwen Wang and Juan Zhang

Chapter 4   Limiting Nutrient and Eutrophication in Aquatic Systems -
                The Nitrogen/Phosphorus Dilemma   117
                Lars Håkanson

Chapter 5   Study on the Environmental Response of Sedimentary
                Phosphorus of Shallow Lakes to Anthropogenic Impact in Lixia
                River Basin, China   145
                Ying Zhang, Ling Liu, Chengpeng Lu and Bao Qian

Chapter 6   Application of the Standards, Measurements and Testing
                Programme and X-Ray Powder Diffraction
                to Study Phosphorus Speciation in Sediments
                from Baihua Lake, China   163
                Mei Jin, Jiwei Hu, Liya Fu and Miao Jia

Chapter 7   Phosphorus Complex of Porphyrins   179
                Kazutaka Hirakawa

Index   195

PREFACE

In this book, the authors present topical research in the study of the properties, health effects and environmental issues relating to phosphorus. Topics discussed in this compilation include aminophosphonate synthesis and applications; the effect of phosphorus doping on the electrical properties of diamond and carbon nanotubes; limiting nutrient and eutrophication in aquatic systems and the nitrogen/phosphorus dilemma; the environmental response of sedimentary phosphorus of shallow lakes and the anthropogenic impact; and the phosphorus complex of porphyrin.

Chapter 1 - There is an increasing interest in amine derivatives of phosphonic acids. The α-aminophosphonates, organophosphorus analogs of natural amino acids are most studied and attracted for the specialists in various branches of chemistry - biochemists, pharmacologists and synthetic chemists. Phosphonates containing the amine group in the β-position are less studied but recent studies suggest they may be useful as bioactive species and receptor compounds. Phosphonic acid derivatives are not only biologically active compounds but also effective extractants and membrane carriers for various substrates (metal ions, organic and inorganic acids, etc.). Many of these advantages are due to the combination of several different binding sites, namely, proton donating (NH) and two proton accepting groups (P=O and a lone electron pair of the nitrogen atom), as well as the possibility of varying the lipophilicity and sterical loading of the binding site. The acceptor phosphoryl group of the β-aminophosphonates is farther away from the nitrogen than that of the α-aminophosphonates. Hence the increased basicity of the nitrogen atom leads to the peculiar transport properties of these compounds. This chapter discusses the main methods for synthesizing α- and β-amine derivatives of phosphonic acids, their biological activity and the application of these compounds as extractants and membrane carriers.

Chapter 2 - A breakthrough in the field of olefin, cycloolefin and diolefin homo- and copolymerization was, at the beginning of the '90s, the discovery, by both academic and industrial groups, of a new generation of catalysts based on transition metal and lanthanide complexes with a wide range of ligands having N, P, O or other donor atoms. The use of these novel systems permitted to obtain novel polymer structures with unique properties other than those existing, even in the well-studied field of vinyl monomer homo- and copolymerization. Among the wide range of ligands used, phosphines played a relevant role; it is well known, in fact, that phosphine steric and electronic properties strongly depend on the type of substituents on the phosphorus atoms, and that changing substituents can cause marked changes in behavior of the free ligands and of their transition metal complexes.

Among the major discoveries, the authors can mention:

i.   perfectly alternating olefin/carbon monoxide copolymers obtained with catalysts based on palladium(II) complexes with bidentate chelating phosphorus ligands;
ii. polybutadienes and polyisoprenes having different microstructure, obtained with catalysts based on cobalt and chromium complexes with mono and bidentate phosphines;
iii. stereoregular polynorbornenes obtained with catalysts based on bidentate phosphine chromium complexes.

This paper provides an overview on recent progress in the homo- and copolymerization of vinyl monomers with catalysts based on transition metal complexes with phosphorus ligands.

Chapter 3 - Phosphorus as the n-type dopant, is widely used in the semiconductor industry. As a potential dopant, it is also possible for application in the nanoelectronics industry in the future. However, phosphorus is highly toxic, can cause harm to human health, and brings the corresponding environmental pollution. A brief review is given on the theoretical and experimental works devoted to the phosphorus doping of diamond and carbon nanotubes (CNTs). The doping usually has an important effect on the chemical and physical properties of diamond and CNTs. In order to better understand the bonding mechanisms of the phosphorus-doped diamond films, and the influences of the phosphorus-doped concentration on the diamond lattice integrity and conductivity, the authors calculate the electronic structures of the phosphorus-doped diamond with different phosphorus concentration and the density of states in the phosphorus-doped diamond films with a vacant lattice site by the first principle method. The calculation results show the phosphorus atom only affects the bonds of a few atoms in its vicinity, and the conductivity increases as the doped concentration increases. Also in the diamond lattice with a total number of 64 atoms and introducing a vacancy into the non-nearest neighbor lattice site of a phosphorus atom, the authors have found that both the injuries of the phosphorus-doped diamond films and the n-type electron conductivity of diamond films could be improved. The characteristics of phosphorus-doped and boron /phosphorus co-doped single wall carbon nanotubes (B-PSWNTs) are also studied by using the First-Principle method based on density function theory (DFT). The formation energy of the P-doped single carbon nanotube increases with its diameter. The total energy of the P-doped single carbon nanotube in the same diameter decreases with the increasing doping rate. The position of impurity level may depend on the C-P-C bond angle. It is feasible to substitute a phosphorus atom for a carbon atom in SWCNT. P-doped carbon nanotubes are n type semiconductors. Mayer bond order, band structure, electron density and density of states are calculated in B-PSWNTs. It concludes that the B-PSWNTs have special band structure which is quite different from B-N co-doped carbon nanotubes, and that metallic SWNTs will be converted to semiconductor due to B/P co-doping which breaks the symmetrical structure. There are more sp3 hybridizations in B/P doped SWNT than those in intrinsic SWNT. The band structure of B-PSWNTs is special owing to the special band structure of P doped SWNTs. Besides, Mulliken charge population and the quantum conductance are also calculated to study the quantum transport characteristics of B-PSWNT hetero-junction. It is found that the position of p-n junction in this hetero-junction will be changed as the applied electric field by the Mulliken charge population analysis, and it performs the characteristics of diode.

Chapter 4 - Remedial methods to lower eutrophication should not focus on nitrogen, but on phosphorus, because there are many major uncertainties related to (a) the quantification of atmospheric N_2-fixation by cyanobacteria, (b) wet and dry deposition of nitrogen, (c) the algorithm regulating the particulate fraction for nitrogen and hence also (d) sedimentation of particulate nitrogen and (e) denitrification. Occasional very high concentrations of cyanobacteria may may be quantitatively explained by high total phosphorus (TP) concentrations, high temperatures (higher than 15 °C) and/or low TN:TP ratios (lower than 15 by weight). So, there are no general validated mass-balance models for nitrogen which have been tested for independent coastal systems and been demonstrated to yield good predictive power for N only for P. Any N-model can be tuned, using different calibration constant sets for different systems, to give perfect descriptive power, but such tuning may obscure the true aspects of how natural systems work, just like a deodorant covers a bad smell. Because plankton cells include both nitrogen and phosphorus (given by the standard composition $C_{106}N_{16}P$), because both nutrients are transported to water systems by the same rivers, and because there is in many systems a potential for phosphorus-driven atmospheric N_2 fixation by cyanobacteria, one generally finds a marked co-variation between P- and N-concentrations in aquatic systems. Primary production (e.g., in g C per m^3 per day) cannot be predicted from concentrations (e.g., in mg per m^3) of dissolved nutrients, such as DIN (dissolved inorganic nitrogen), DIP, phosphate, nitrate or ammonia which are frequently below detection and have very high coefficients of variation (CV), but can only be predicted well from total concentrations of nutrients (TN or TP), i.e., from the total pools of the nutrients in the system.

Chapter 5 - The Lixia River Basin in China has been seriously affected by long-term intensive industrial, urban and agricultural activities. The fractionation of phosphorus (P) in five lakes sediments from Lixia River Basin have been investigated by SMT methods for the first time in order to understand the environmental response mechanism of sedimentary P to anthropogenic impact and the eutrophication status of these lakes. The results showed that the non-apatite P (NAIP) and organic P (OP) were more sensitive to the anthropogenic impact than other fractions of P. Furthermore, NAIP had significant relationship with fishery pollution and OP had significant relationship with other polluted from basin inflow respectively. Considered the results of other biogeochemical elements (carbon and nitrogen), the viewpoint "Three Stages" of the lakes in Lixia River Basin sedimentary environment was proposed, which can define three periods, before 1970s, from 1970s to 1990s and after 1990s. The first period was considered as the background period of the lakes in study area. The second period was the time when industry and agricultural begin to develop, the surface area of lakes decreased significantly and pollute material flowed into lakes more and more. During the third period, the industrial, agricultural and fishery developed quickly, the lakes in Lixia River Basin had been subjected to various pollutant sources and led to the serious pollution and hyper-eutrophication.

Chapter 6 - The distribution characteristics of phosphorus speciation in 17 surface sediment samples collected from Baihua Lake, one of the five drinking water sources for Guiyang City in southwest China, were investigated using the Standards, Measurements and Testing (SMT) programme and X-ray powder diffraction (XRD). In the study area, the total phosphorus (TP) concentrations varied from 591.57 to 2374.80 mg/kg with the mean concentration of 1604.02 mg/kg (dry weight), and it was evident that the phosphorus level in the sediments was generally higher than in other eutrophic lakes such as Chaohu Lake and Xihu Lake. The results of the two methods, the SMT and XRD, demonstrated the presence of different phosphorus species in the lake sediments. The results of the SMT protocol indicated that the average percentages of inorganic phosphorus (IP), organic phosphorus (OP), iron/aluminum-bound phosphorus (Fe/Al-P) and calcium-bound phosphorus (Ca-P) were 67.33%, 30.53%, 39.38% and 27.41%, respectively. Notably, the concentrations of inorganic phosphorus (IP) were higher than that of OP, and the IP consisted mainly of Fe/Al-P. The high concentrations of Fe/Al-P, a major and direct source of phosphorus release, might play an important part in accelerating eutrophication of water bodies. The present XRD analysis showed that $AlPO_4$ was found in all sediment samples among phosphorus species. Further statistical analyses of the results revealed significant and positive correlations between phosphorus species in sediments, and the four cluster levels were obtained. Additionally, remediation measures were briefly evaluated for the lake considering its pollution conditions and distinctive environmental features.

Chapter 7 - Phosphorus complexes of porphyrins demonstrate unique character. Porphyrin, a macrocyclic compound, is an important ligand for most atoms. Various metal ions are captured by the central nitrogens of a porphyrin ring through a coordinate bond. Some nonmetallic atoms can also bind to the central nitrogens. Phosphorus is an important nonmetallic central atom of porphyrin and can form a relatively stable complex. In general, the structure of a phosphorus complex of porphyrin is sterically hindered. Phosphorus porphyrin has a relatively small redox potential of one-electron reduction. Therefore, the photoexcited state of a phosphorus porphyrin is a strong oxidant. This electron accepting ability is advantageous for a photo-induced electron transfer reaction. In addition, porphyrins are used as photosensitizers of photodynamic therapy, which is a promising treatment of cancer. Since phosphorus porphyrins can oxidize biomolecules, such as protein and DNA, through photo-induced electron transfer, they have been studied as potential photosensitizers for photodynamic therapy.

In: Phosphorus: Properties, Health Effects and the Environment   ISBN: 978-1-62081-399-7
Editors: Ming Yue Chen and Da-Xia Yang   © 2012 Nova Science Publishers, Inc.

Chapter 1

AMINOPHOSPHONATES: SYNTHESIS AND PRACTICAL APPLICATION

Ivan I. Stoikov[1,2,], Olga A. Mostovaya[1], Alena A. Vavilova[1],
Joshua B. Puplampu[1], Igor S. Antipin[1] and Alexander I. Konovalov[1]*

[1]Organic Chemistry Department, A.M. Butlerov Chemical Institute, Kazan (Volga Region) Federal University, Kazan, Russian Federation
[2]Kazan Institute of Biochemistry and Biophysics, Russian Academy of Sciences, Kazan, Russian Federation

ABSTRACT

There is an increasing interest in amine derivatives of phosphonic acids. The α-aminophosphonates, organophosphorus analogs of natural amino acids are most studied and attracted for the specialists in various branches of chemistry - biochemists, pharmacologists and synthetic chemists. Phosphonates containing the amine group in the β-position are less studied but recent studies suggest they may be useful as bioactive species and receptor compounds. Phosphonic acid derivatives are not only biologically active compounds but also effective extractants and membrane carriers for various substrates (metal ions, organic and inorganic acids, etc.). Many of these advantages are due to the combination of several different binding sites, namely, proton donating (NH) and two proton accepting groups (P=O and a lone electron pair of the nitrogen atom), as well as the possibility of varying the lipophilicity and sterical loading of the binding site. The acceptor phosphoryl group of the β-aminophosphonates is farther away from the nitrogen than that of the α-aminophosphonates. Hence the increased basicity of the nitrogen atom leads to the peculiar transport properties of these compounds. This chapter discusses the main methods for synthesizing α- and β-amine derivatives of phosphonic acids, their biological activity and the application of these compounds as extractants and membrane carriers.

Keywords: Chemistry of Organophosphorus Compounds, Membrane Technology, Drug Delivery

---

[*] Corresponding author: E-mail: Ivan.Stoikov@mail.ru, Tel: +7-8432-315462; Fax: +7-8432-752253.

INTRODUCTION

The chemistry of functionalized organophosphorus compounds has recently attracted much attention due to the practicality and useful properties of these compounds. They are used as insecticides, fungicides, plasticizers and stabilizers for polymers, additives for flame retardant materials, extractants, catalysts and pharmaceuticals.

A particular attention is currently devoted to amino derivatives of organophosphorus compounds because of their similarity to many biological molecules. Aminophosphonates have an interesting combination of several binding sites of different nature, in particular, the proton donating (NH) and two proton accepting (P=O and a lone electron pair of the nitrogen atom) groups. Presently, extensive experimental data on the synthesis and application of such compounds has been obtained.

SYNTHESIS OF α-AMINOPHOSPHONATES

Almost all the current methods proposed for the synthesis of aminophosphonates are based on one of four strategies presented in Scheme 1.

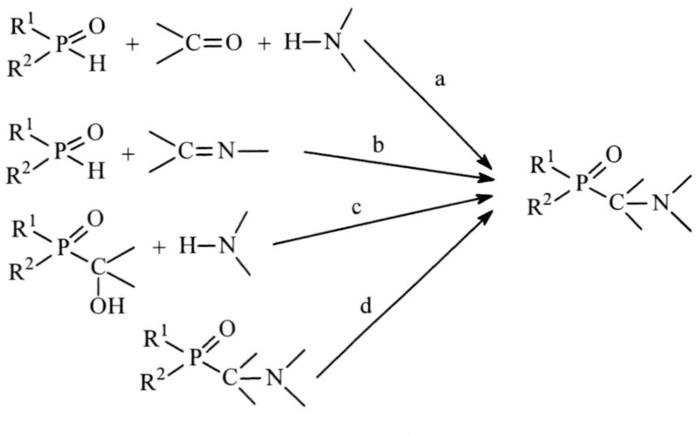

Scheme 1.

The Kabachnik-Fields reaction is mostly used for synthesis of aminophosphonates. It proceeds in a three-component system including amine, carbonyl compound and dialkylphosphite (path a). A lot of research has been devoted to this reaction. Identification of its synthetic potential as well as the reaction mechanism is of great interest. These issues have been completely covered in the review [Cherkasov et al. 1998]. The synthesis of α-aminophosphonates is often carried out by the Pudovik reaction, which involves a catalytic or non-catalytic addition of hydrophosphoryl compounds to imines (path b). Generally, dialkylphosphites are very active toward multiple bonds, e.g., C=C, C=O in addition reactions (Abramov reaction leading to hydroxyphosphonates formation). Also, nucleophilic amination of hydroxyphosphonates is used to obtain the derivatives of aminophosphonic acids (path c). By their nature, paths b and c are individual stages of two (or more) stepwise processes, as in the Kabachnik-Fields reaction.

Methods for obtaining α-aminophosphonates are widespread, and based on the strategy presented in the Scheme 1 as path d (C-, N-, P-modification). This strategy involves the use of the previously obtained combination of phosphoryl, α-carbon and amine fragments as key synthons. The synthesis of the target α-aminophosphonates, including peptides, is carried out by the introduction of the desired functional groups to the α-carbon atom (C-modification), the nitrogen (N-modification) or phosphorus (P-modification) atoms.

Kabachnik-Fields Reaction

The Kabachnik-Fields reaction discovered by Kabachnik [Kabachnik et al. 1952] and Fields [Fields 1952] independently in 1952 is one of the most common methods for obtaining α-aminophosphonates. For a long time, two hypotheses about the mechanism of this reaction existed. The first one assumed the addition of a dialkylphosphite to the carbonyl compound resulting in the formation of a hydroxyphosphonate followed by its reaction with an amine. The second way involved initial interaction of an amine and carbonyl compound yielding imine formation followed by subsequent addition of dialkylphosphite by the Pudovik reaction. The initial formation of imines was confirmed by IR spectroscopy [Keglevich et al. 2011] based on the appearance of the peak at 1646 cm^{-1} characteristic for the C=N bond. Thus, the reaction of diethylphosphite, benzaldehyde and propylamine proceeds with the imine formation at the first stage.

Increasing attention to environmental pollution called for the development of "green chemistry" approaches, e.g. the use of reactions which did not require organic solvents but use low toxic media like ionic liquids or water. Iranian scientists proposed the Kabachnik-Fields reaction to be performed in water with the yields of [1] exceeding 90%. Cu phthalocyanine tetrasulfate was used as a catalyst [Sobhani et al. 2008].

SbCl$_3$ adsorbed on Al$_2$O$_3$ also showed high catalytic efficiency in the Kabachnik-Fields reaction [Ambica et al. 2008]. Other examples involve ytterbium perfluorooctanoate Yb(PFO)$_3$ [J. Tang et al. 2011], TiO$_2$ [Hosseini-Sarvari 2008], CeO$_2$ nanoparticles [Sandeep et al. 2011], and FeCl$_3$ [Rezaei et al. 2009]. The use of the easily reusable H-beta zeolite as a catalyst provided significant reduction of the time of synthesis, increased product yield, and its equally efficiency for both aldehydes and ketones as well as aromatic and aliphatic amines [Tillu et al. 2011]. Good yields were obtained for the reactions carried out in water in the presence of β-cyclodextrin as a catalyst [Kaboudin et al. 2007]. Among catalytic function, cyclodextrins allowed separating enantiomers of aromatic aminophosphonic acids [Rudzinska et al. 2002; Rudzinska et al. 2007].

Chinese authors described the reactions performed in the absence of organic solvents. Besides environmental protection, this significantly accelerated the process and simplified the instrumentation required. The target products, i.e., 5-aminophosphonate [2] substituted pyrimidine nucleosides were obtained from 5-formyl-20-deoxyuridine and 5-formyluracil with high yields (75-90%) at 60-80 °C within 2-3 hours. This method proposed seems very convenient. The isolation procedure described by the authors is very simple and includes washing the product with ethanol [Zhang et al. 2010].

R=Ac, H

The use of ionic liquids in the Kabachnik-Fields reaction is very promising. They can significantly reduce the duration of the process and also avoid the use of a catalyst. Thus, good results were obtained with ethylammonium nitrate which is also environmentally friendly, easy to regenerate, and rather inexpensive. It provides very good yields of the reactions carried out at ambient temperature for 2-5 hours [Dake et al. 2011]. 1-Butyl-3-methylimidazolium hexafluorophosphate [Jin et al. 2006] and 1-butyl-3-methylimidazolium chloride [Reddy et al. 2011] are also mentioned for this purpose.

Sonication of the reaction mixture significantly reduced the duration of the synthesis and increased the yield of the target aminophosphonates [Song et al. 2006]. The reaction was mostly completed in the absence of the solvent with boron trifluoride etherate as catalyst.

The Kabachnik-Fields reaction was used in the synthesis of aminophosphonates based on calix[4]arene. The selective alkylation of two hydroxyl groups of *p-tert*-butylcalix[4]arene [4] by chloroacetonitrile with the subsequent reduction of nitrile groups to amine resulted in the substitution of the macrocycle with two aminophosphonate groups at the lower rim [Antipin et al. 1999]. The acetone added as a reactant (carbonyl compound) also played role of the solvent.

The macrocycle [6], 1,3-disubstituted at the upper rim with aminophosphonate groups was obtained by regiospecific amination of the calixarene following the introduction of the phosphorylalkyl groups [Antipin et al. 1999; Stoikov et al. 2000].

Tetraaminophosphonate in *cone* configuration was synthesized in a similar way from corresponding tetraamine derivative of the calixarene. An analog compound in the *partial cone* configuration [9] confirmed by ^{1}H and ^{31}P NMR spectroscopy was obtained by the interaction of the calixarene [8] with O,O-diethyl-1-(N-benzyl)-aminomethylphosphonate [7] and formaldehyde by the Mannich reaction [Stoikov et al. 2010].

$$(H_5C_2O)_3P + CH_2O + H_2NCH_2Ph \longrightarrow PhCH_2NHCH_2P(O)(OC_2H_5)_2$$
$$7$$

Fluorine containing α-aminophosphonates [10] exerting anti-cancer effect were synthesized without any solvent and catalyst by the Mannich reaction from fluorobenzoaldehyde, 3-amino-5-methylisoxazole and dialkyl phosphite under sonication [Song et al. 2005].

R^1=2-F, 4-F R^2=Me, Et, *n*-Pr, *i*-Pr, *n*-Bu

The authors observed the decrease in the yield of the target aminophosphonates in the reaction with *para*-substituted benzaldehydes against *ortho*-isomers. This was explained by the formation of an intramolecular hydrogen bond between the F atom at position 2 of the aromatic ring and the H atom of the imine bond. The increase in the positive charge on the carbon atom of the imine bond makes it more active in reaction with nucleophilic dialkylphosphite.

The interaction of the trivalent phosphorus chloride with carbonyl compounds and amides carried out in 1978 is also one of the alternatives of the Kabachnik-Fields reaction [Oleksyszyn et al. 1978; Oleksyszyn 1980].

It is believed [Oleksyszyn 1980] that the process starts from the condensation reaction of an amine with the carbonyl compound leading to alkylidenebisamide [11] as an intermediate. Then phosphorylation to aminophosphonate [12] and sequential hydrolysis leads to aminophosphonic acids [13].

The scheme shows:

$$R^1R(C)=O + H_2NCOOR^2 \xrightarrow{\substack{1.\ AcOH,\ PCl_3 \\ 2.\ H_2O}} R^1-C(R)(NH_2)-PO_3H_2 \quad \mathbf{13}$$

with $-H_2O$ pathway leading to

$$R^1-C(R)(NHCOOR^2)-NHCOOR^2 \quad \mathbf{11} \xrightarrow{PCl_3/AcOH} R^1-C(R)(NHCOOR^2)-PO_3H_2 \quad \mathbf{12}$$

and $\mathbf{12} \xrightarrow{H_2O} \mathbf{13}$

The method was extended to a wide range of amides and carbonyl compounds of P(III) chlorides [Seebach et al. 1989].

Reactions in two-component systems lead to aminophosphonic acids and their esters and involve the interaction of the hydrophosphoryle - imine and the hydroxyphosphonate - amine pairs which are inherent stages of the Kabachnik-Fields reaction. Strictly speaking, it is often impossible to distinguish between three- and two-component systems. It may depend on the sequence of mixing of the components of Kabachnik-Fields reaction.

Moreover, it has been many times indicated that performing the reaction in stages has in most cases an advantage over one-pot three-component process. Chemical yield and *de* of aminophosphonates are generally higher in the two-component protocol.

Addition of hydrophosphoryl compounds to imines discovered simultaneously with the Kabachnik-Fields reaction and sufficiently discussed in the literature is a type of the Pudovik reaction [Pudovik 1952].

The predetermined preference in choosing a strategy for the synthesis of α-aminophosphoryl compounds is traced to two important tendencies that favor the "imine" method: the desire to diversify the variations of N- and C-functional groups in the potential aminophosphonate, and the creation of conditions for maximum stereoselectivity, for the addition reaction of hydrophosphoryl compound to C=N bond.

The interaction of hydrophosphoryl compounds with the Schiff bases investigated in detail by Pudovik [Pudovik 1952] continues to attract the attention of researchers. This results from the reaction conditions and useful properties of the aminophosphonates obtained [Kraicheva et al. 2012].

$$R^1-C_6H_4-CH=N-C_6H_4-R^2 + \underset{H}{\overset{O}{>}}P< \longrightarrow R^1-C_6H_4-CH(P(=O)<)-NH-C_6H_4-R^2$$

The "imine" method is widely used in the synthesis of hetaryl derivatives of aminophosphonates. Moreover, the structure of the heterocyclic fragments can be greatly varied at the C- and N-centers. A series of C-pyridine derivatives was obtained by the addition of diethylphosphite to the corresponding Schiff bases [Boduszek 1996].

The variety of possibilities for the synthesis of aminophosphoryl compounds by the "imine" method is due to variation of substituents not only in the imine, but also in the phosphorus containing ligand. Inorganic phosphorus acids and various silylated organophosphorus compounds were used for the synthesis of aminophosphonic acids [Liboska et al. 2008; Bongini et al. 1994].

By the Pudovik reaction, phosphonate fragments reacted with Schiff bases obtained from ethylene diamine and 3-pyridinecarboxaldehyde or benzaldehyde, followed by subsequent hydrolysis to aminophosphonic acids using hydrochloric acid to form an effective chelator of metals [Gałezowska et al. 2009].

Also, in order to create the analogue of the plant growth regulator (morphactin), the fluorenecarboxylic acid, 9-aminofluorenephosphonic acid derivatives [15] were obtained by the addition reaction of dialkylphosphites to imines [14]. To obtain the corresponding aminophosphonic acids, their diethyl esters were heated with the concentrated hydrochloric acid for about 6 hours. It should be noted that after heating for half an hour, monoesters of phosphonic acid were first synthesized. After prolonged heating, aminophosphonic acids decomposed to the initial carbonyl compound, amine and phosphoric acid [Gancarz et al. 1980].

$R^1 = n\text{-}C_4H_9, Ph$ $R^2 = H, Cl, Br, NO_2$ $R^3 = Cl, Br, NO_2$

The Pudovik reaction was used to synthesize the aminoboronbenzylphosphonates containing formylphenylboronic acid substituents [Młynarz et al. 2011]. Without further purification, the tris (trimethylsilyl) phosphite obtained from trimethylphosphite and bromotrimethylsilane was added to the initially obtained imine [16]. Hydrolysis of the resulting aminophosphonate to an acid [17] easily occurs in aqueous methanol.

Amination of hydroxyphosphonates as an intermediate stage of the Kabachnik-Fields reaction is less commonly employed. Substitution of the hydroxyl group on the amine proceeds in the case of hydroxyphosphonates quite easily due to the neighboring phosphoryl group. The reaction starts with a nucleophilic attack of the α-carbon atom of phosphonate (activated by the neighboring acceptor, a phosphoryl group) by amine [Kiss et al. 2012]. Further, the hydroxyl group migrates to the phosphorus atom with the formation of a zwitterion [18]. Subsequent proton transfer from nitrogen to the oxygen atom of the phosphoryl group and the elimination of water lead to the formation of aminophosphonates [19].

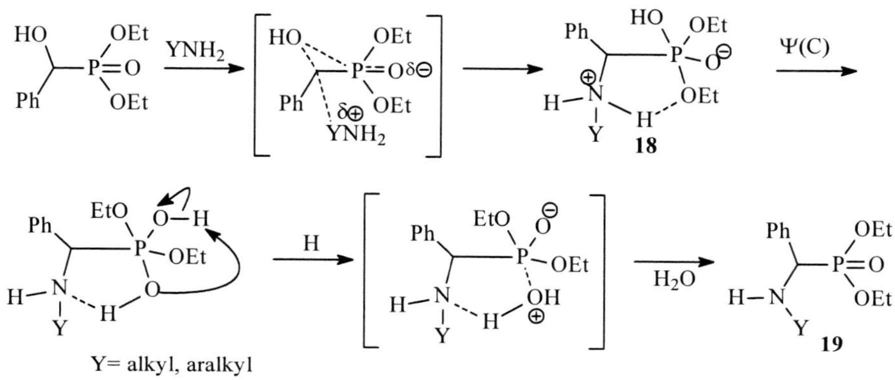

Y= alkyl, aralkyl

C-Modification

It is known that the carbon atom bonded to the phosphoryl group with pronounced electron accepting properties possesses an anionoid character. It is widely used in organic and organoelemental synthesis.

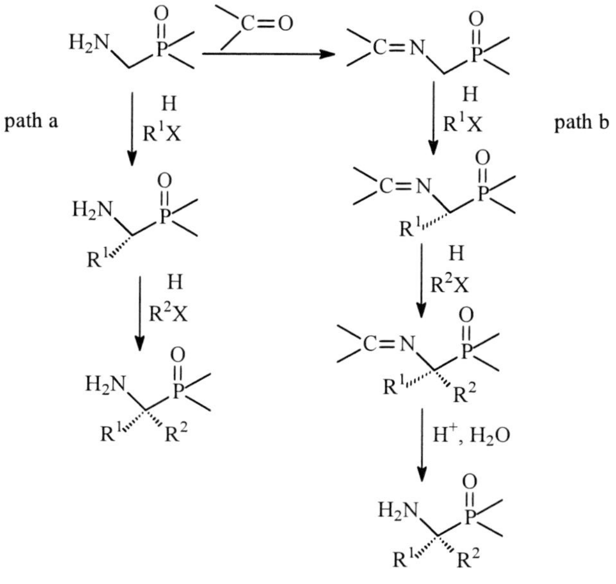

Scheme 2.

C-alkylation of acyclic aminophosphonates (Scheme 2, path a) is hardly used, obviously, because of their relatively weak CH-acidity [Bordwell 1988]. Probably, the accepting phosphoryl and donating amine groups do not provide sufficient stability of the α-phosphoryl carbanion.

However, the introduction of methyl, thiophenyl, trimethylsilyl [McNulty et al. 2008; Gulea-Purcarescu et al. 1996] and other heteroatomic groups to the α-carbon of aminophosphoryl compounds [20] (THF, -70 °C) have recently been described.

R= SiMe₃, SnBu₃, SPh, Me

Good effect is achieved by using iminomethylphosphonates (Scheme 2, path b). The delocalization of the charge by two acceptor substituents (imino- and phosphoryl groups) reduces the carbanion energy.

Secondary processes that occur following the electrophilic C-modification of aminophosphoryl compounds enhance the synthetic potential of phosphorylated imines [21]. More often, the product of alkylation [22] is converted to an acid [23] by acidic hydrolysis, for example [Genêt et al. 1992].

Note that the carbonyl compounds, from which the imine synthons were obtained, can be regenerated as a result of acid hydrolysis of phosphorylimines [Kukhar' et al. 1993]. The strategy described for aminophosphonate synthesis based on the phosphorylated Schiff bases has been applied [Groth et al. 1993] to isocyanidphosphonate [24].

α-Aminocyclopropylphosphonates were obtained by alkylation of the carbanion with alkylene oxide; terminal hydroxyl of phosphonalkanol [25] etherified by mesitylchloride, followed by cyclization under basic conditions and then methanolysis in acidic medium leads to the target product. Other examples of such reactions are presented in [Kukhar' et al. 1993].

N-Modification

This type of reactions for aminophosphonates is responsible for their inhibitory effect in relation to the corresponding substrates [Kafarski et al. 1991; Cheng et al. 1991; Bartlett et al. 1990], and also ensures the participation of aminophosphonic acids and their esters in the peptide synthesis.

Easy proceeding N-acylation of aminophosphonic acid [26] under the influence of the ethyl formate [Zymanczyk-Duda et al., 1996] gives a mixture of N-formylamino- [27] and N-ethoxymethylenimino- [28] derivatives of alkylphosphonic acids.

The reduction of phosphorylated imines [29] to the corresponding aminophosphonates [30] carried out with catecholborane is described [Rassukana et al. 2009].

The well-known technique for increasing the nucleophilicity of the nitrogen atom by introducing the trialkylsilyl group (the "silyl activation") has been successfully employed in peptide synthesis [31] for N-acylation with benzylchloroformiate [Mucha et al. 1995], as well as in the synthesis of phosphorus analogues of glycine containing dimethylphosphine oxide group [32] [Kankorat et al. 1996].

The addition of N-silylated aminophosphonates [33] to acetone, benzaldehyde and *para*-brombenzaldehyde is performed at ambient temperature [Pudovik et al. 1997]:

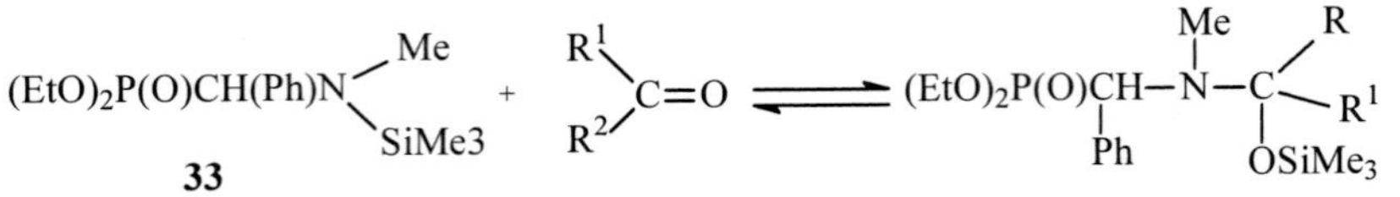

While rectified, N-(siloxyalkyl)methylphenylmethylphosphonate decomposes to the initial aminophosphonate and carbonyl compounds.

An efficient method for the synthesis of N-formyl-1-aminoalkylphosphonate [35] diphenyl esters from corresponding aminophosphonates [34] by treatment with acetic and formic anhydride has been presented [Sieńczyk et al. 2006].

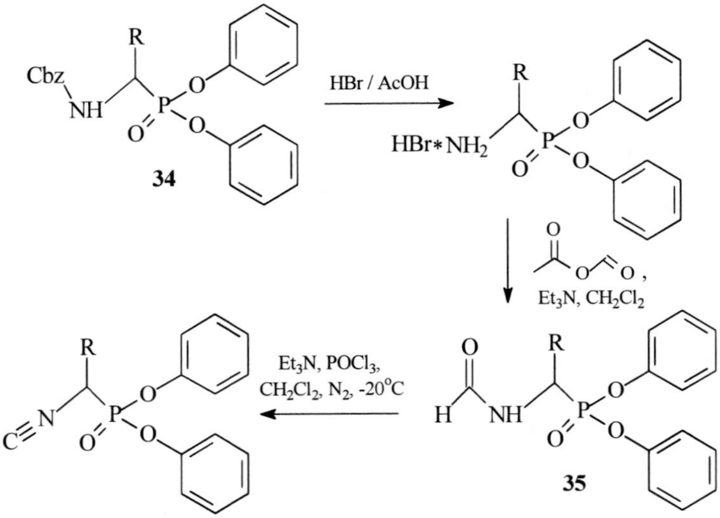

Nucleophilic reactions of the nitrogen atom of aminophosphonate involve not only substitution but also other reactions characteristic for primary, secondary and tertiary amines. Among them, well-studied quaternization of aminophosphonates, in particular, addition to unsaturated compounds is described [Khailova et al. 2003; Palacios et al. 1999].

P-Modification

These types of reactions in the chemistry of aminophosphonates are the usual processes of saponification and esterification of phosphorus acid derivatives. Esterification of aminophosphonic acid [36] occurs selectively on one acidic group with formation [37], even with sterically hindered alcohols using bromotris(dimethylamino)phosphonium hexafluorophosphate (BroP) or N,N,N',N'-bis(tetramethylene)chlorouronium tetrafluoroborate reagent (TPySIU) [Galleotti et al. 1996].

Other Methods

The reduction with various hydrogenating agents of unsaturated nitrogen-containing organophosphorus compounds with α-aminophosphonate skeleton is most simple and frequently used method for the synthesis of the aminophosphonates.

In this way, α-nitrophosphonates [38] can be easily converted into aminophosphonates [39] [Hatani et al. 1996] at room temperature with about quantitative yield.

Aside the widely used Pudovik reaction for imines, the phosphorylation of unsaturated compounds containing a double bond in the α-position to the nitrogen atom (enamines and other similar compounds) is another rarely used but promising strategy for the synthesis of aminophosphonates.

Until the end of the 1980s, the hydrophosphorilation of enamines was never successful in classical conditions of the Pudovik reaction, which is a type of base-catalyzed addition reactions. Only with the discovery of the electrophilic variant of Pudovik reaction characteristic for vinyl ethers, enamines and other electron rich alkenes, as well as for five-membered cyclic alkylenephosphoric acids [40] with enhanced proton donor capabiliteis, a simple one-stage method has been developed for the aminophosphonate [41] synthesis [Ovchinnikov et al. 1985; Safina et al. 1990; Safina et al. 1992].

R= $CH_3CHCHCH_3$, $CH(CH_3)CH_2$, $C(CH_3)_2C(CH_3)_2$, $CH_2C(CH_3)_2CH_2$, o-C_6H_4
R^1= alkyl, aryl
R^2= H, COOEt, COMe
R^3_2= $(CH_2)_5$, $CH_2CH_2OCH_2CH_2$, Me_2

Amidophosphonates [42] were also obtained by the interaction of the cyclic chlorophosphites with amides. Their acidic or basic hydrolysis results in formation of the aminophosphonic acids [43] or their monoesters [44] and [45], respectively [Swamy et al. 2005].

$$R^1 = Ph,\ 4\text{-Me-}C_6H_4,\ CHMe_2,\ 3\text{-Me-}C_6H_4,\ CH=CH-Ph$$

$$R^1 = Ph,\ 4\text{-Me-}C_6H_4,\ CHMe_2$$

Preparation of the α-aminophosphonic acids [47] is possible by the interaction of nitriles with phosphoric acid [46] [Chai et al. 1980.].

$$H_3PO_3 + CH_3CN \longrightarrow H_3C-\underset{\underset{NH_2}{|}}{C}-P(O_3H_2)_2$$

46   **47**   85 %

α-Aminophosphonates were prepared with a very good yield by the interaction of amine, carbonyl compound and trialkylphosphite in the presence of catalytic amounts of (bromodimethyl)sulfonium bromide at room temperature [Kudrimoti et al. 2005].

Recently, α-aminophosphonates [49] were synthesized by oxidative phosphonylation of amine [48] in the presence of the oxidizing agent, 2,3-dichloro-5,6-dicyanobenzoquinone [Wang et al. 2012]. The reaction takes place in mild conditions, preferably in acetonitrile solution. 1,4-Benzoquinone as catalyst was found to be less effective in this reaction.

By the interaction of the products of Beckmann rearrangement promoted by phosphorus oxychloride with typical phosphorus nucleophiles (di-and triethylphosphites) from the oximes [50] and [52] α-aminomethylenebisphosphonates [51, 53] were obtained with low yields (40%) [Yokomatsu et al. 1994]. The obtained aminophosphonates can be easily transformed to the corresponding aminophosphonic acids by treatment with trimethylsilylbromide.

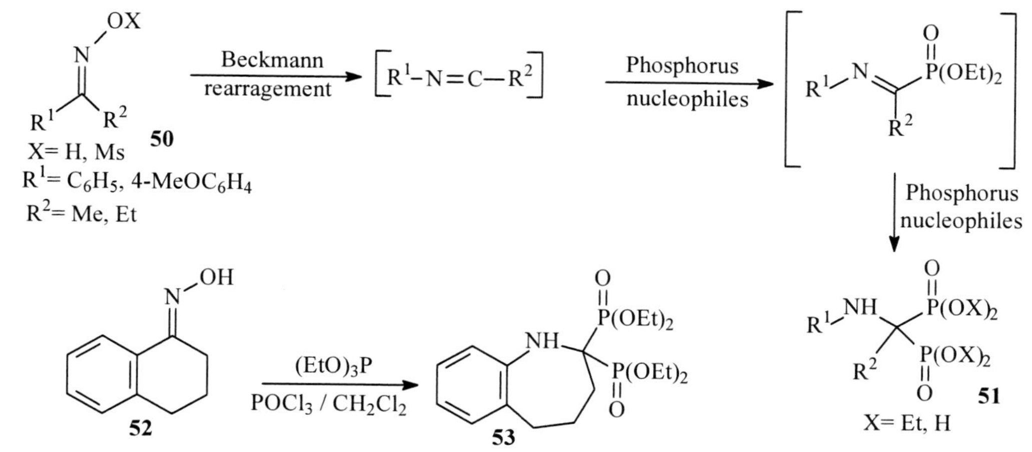

The use of oximes [55] and [57] in the synthesis of α-aminophosphonates was also proposed [Berlin et al. 1968]. In these works, oximes were obtained from corresponding α-ketophosphonates [54]. Their subsequent reduction to aminoalkylphosphonates [56, 58] was carried out by diborane in tetrahydrofuran. Unfortunately, this method gives quite low yields of the target products which did not exceed 10-20%. The reduction by aluminum amalgam also did not lead to high yields. Significantly increase of the yield of the target products was achieved by the oxime hydrogenation on palladium/carbon catalyst, or in a mixture of zinc-trifluoroacetic acid [Kudzin et al. 1980].

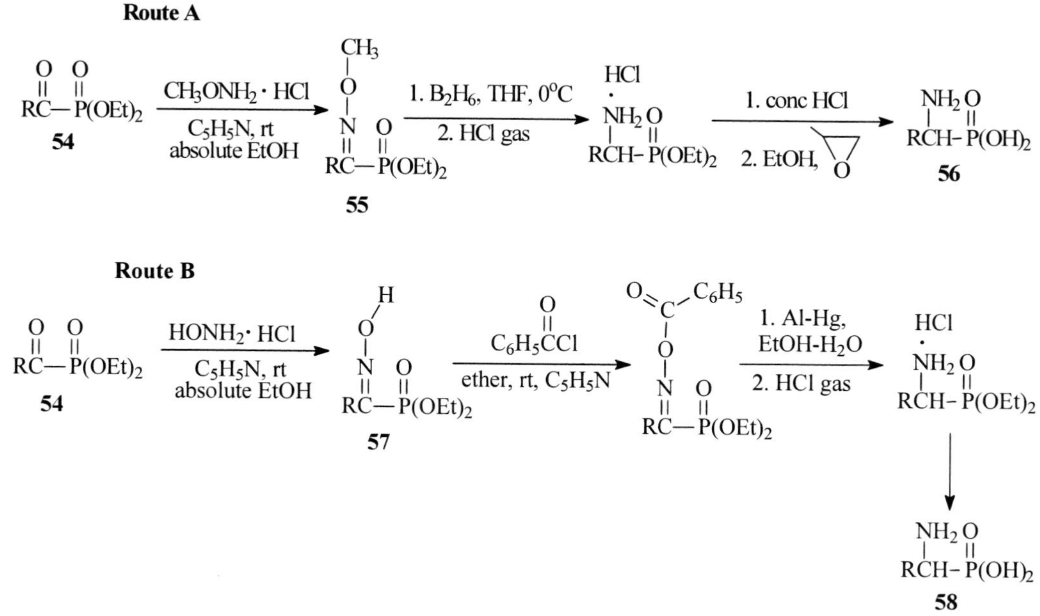

Route A

Route B

α- and β-Aminophosphonates were obtained in three stages by the condensation of aminoaldehyde [59] with diethylphosphite [Pousset et al. 2002]. The variation of the reaction conditions provided rich diastereomeric α-hydroxy β-aminophosphonates [60, 61], then subsequently converted to the N-Boc aziridines [62]. The hydrogenation of the cycles obtained on Pearlman catalyst unexpectedly resulted in opening of the C-C bond and formation of α-aminophosphonates [64]. The use of catalytic amounts of palladium on carbon changed the direction of the reaction. The C=N bond opening took place, and [63] was formed with high enantiomeric purity.

$R^1 = C_6H_5CH_2$, $tBuOC_6H_4CH_2$, C_3H_7, $(CH_3)_2CHCH_2$, $(CH_3)_2CH$

Reactions of Neutral Phosphites

Reactions of natural amino acids with trialkyl- and triarylphosphites have long been successfully employed in peptide synthesis via non-classical Arbuzov reaction.

Three-component system trialkyl(aryl)phosphite - carbonyl compound - amine was successfully applied in a number of studies for the synthesis of aminophosphonic derivatives of urea and thiourea.

Triethylphosphite mixed with an aldehyde and phenylurea condenses under reflux in toluene solution to the corresponding aminophosphonate [65] in the presence of boron trifluoride etherate [Huber et al. 1977].

A similar reaction of thiourea [Oleksyszyn et al. 1977] and N-substituted thioureas [Kudzin et al. 1978] occurs with triphenylphosphite in the presence of glacial acetic acid. Under specific conditions, both amino groups of thiourea can take part in this interaction.

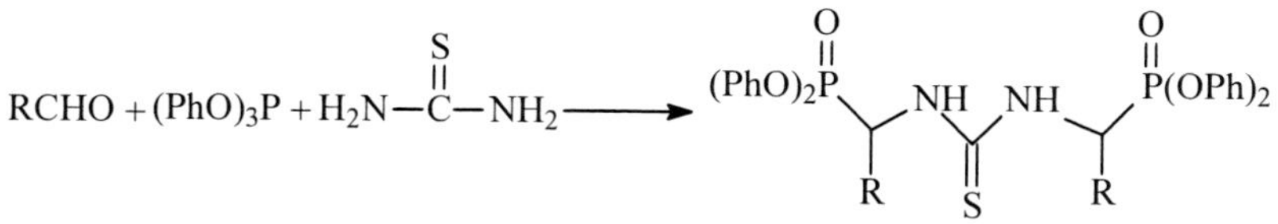

$$RCHO + (PhO)_3P + H_2N-\overset{\overset{\displaystyle S}{\|}}{C}-NH_2 \longrightarrow$$

(PhO)₂P type structure with R, S, NH—NH, P(OPh)₂

Recently, the synthesis of fluorinated phosphonates [66] by the interaction of trialkylphosphites with perfluoroalkanethioamides has been performed [Mykhaylychenko et al. 2011].

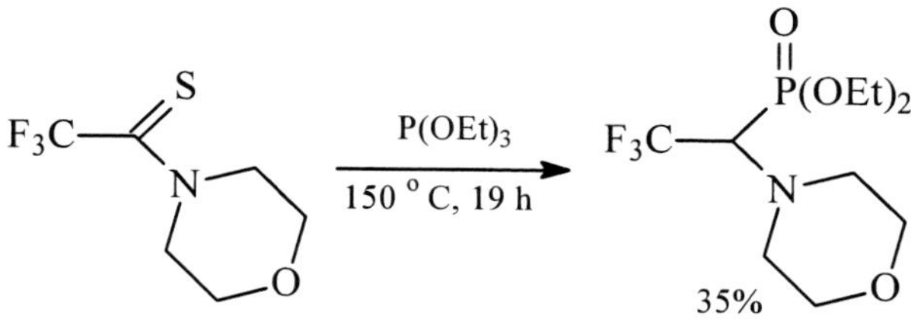

35%   **66**

Probably, the reaction starts from a thiophilic attack of the sulfur atom of thioamide by the phosphite with the formation of a zwitterion [67], which is subsequently cyclized to form the compound [68]. Its nucleophilic attack by trialkylphosphite presumably leads to the elimination of thiophosphate and the formation of ylide [69]. The formation of the final product [66] is possible in the case of intramolecular proton transfer and the release of ethylene. The proposed scheme of the reaction mechanism is shown below.

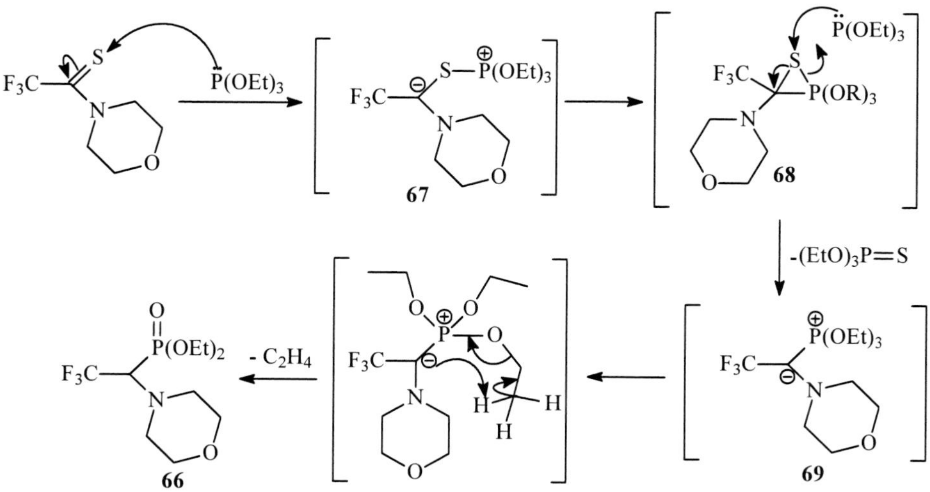

SYNTHESIS OF β-AMINOPHOSPHONATES

Easily proceeding nucleophilic addition of ammonia and amines to vinylphosphonic esters by the double bond is one of the most developed approaches to the synthesis of β-aminophosphonic derivatives. Such reactions were investigated first by A.N. Pudovik in the 1950s [Pudovik et al. 1953].

Ammonia and amines usually fuses with the vinylphosphonates in the presence of sodium ethylate. In some cases, the reactions proceed successfully in the absence of catalysts. The addition reaction of NH_3 to vinylphosphonic ester in alcoholic solution in the presence of a small amount of alcoholate results in β-diethylphosphonoethylamine formation with a good yield [Pudovik et al. 1953]. Previously, ethylaminophosphonic acid was synthesized by the complicated Finkelstein method from the ethyl ester of β-diethylphosphonopropionic acid [Finkelstein 1946], and by Kosolapov by interaction of β-bromoethylphthalimide and triethylphosphite followed by saponification of the reaction product [Kosolapoff 1947].

In the study of the addition reactions of secondary amines to vinylphosphonic ester, the ease with which fatty secondary amines fused with it was noted [Pudovik et al. 1953]. Dimethylamine and piperidine fuse to the vinylphosphonic ester [70] in the absence of the catalyst while aniline requires sodium methylate as a catalyst. The addition of amines to the vinylphosphonic ester is presented on scheme [Pudovik et al. 1953]:

$$CH_2{=}CH{-}\underset{\substack{\|\\O}}{P}(OC_2H_5)_2 \;+\; \underset{R'}{\overset{R}{\diagdown}}N{-}H \longrightarrow \underset{R'}{\overset{R}{\diagdown}}N{-}CH_2{-}CH_2{-}\underset{\substack{\|\\O}}{P}(OC_2H_5)_2$$

70   **71**   R= H, Me, Ph, etc.

The reaction with diphenylamine does not give satisfactory results: additions in the presence of sodium ethylate occur quite vigorously. But the authors did not succeed in isolating the product which did not crystallize while standing and decomposed in distillation under high vacuum [Pudovik et al. 1953].

β-Aroxyethylamines [72] react with dialkylvinylphosphonates [73] in refluxing the mixture in absolute ethanol due to sequential participation of both N-H bonds in the reaction [Reznik et al. 1999].

$$\text{[72]} {-}O(CH_2)_2NH_2 + H_2C{=}CHP(OR')_2 \longrightarrow \text{[74]} {-}O(CH_2)_2NH(CH_2)_2P(OR')_2$$

72   **73**   **74**

R=Me, MeO,
R'=Me, Et, Bu

The reaction product [74] then fuses with dibutylvinylphosphonate to form N,N-bis[β-(dibutoxyphosphoryl)ethyl]-N-[β'-(2-methoxyphenoxy)ethyl]amine [75] in refluxing the mixture of reagents in absolute ethanol in the presence of catalytic amounts of sodium ethylate:

$$\text{[74]} {-}O(CH_2)_2NH(CH_2)_2P(OBu)_2 + H_2C{=}CHP(OBu)_2 \longrightarrow \text{[75]} {-}O(CH_2)_2N\underset{(CH_2)_2P(OBu)_2}{\overset{(CH_2)_2P(OBu)_2}{}}$$

74   **75**

In this reaction, methyl-β-[methyl-β'-(2-methylphenoxy)ethylammonio]ethylphosphonate [76], a product of alkylation of the nitrogen atom by the methyl radical in the initially formed dimethyl-β-[β'-(2-methylphenoxy)ethylamino]ethylphosphonate [74], was also obtained.

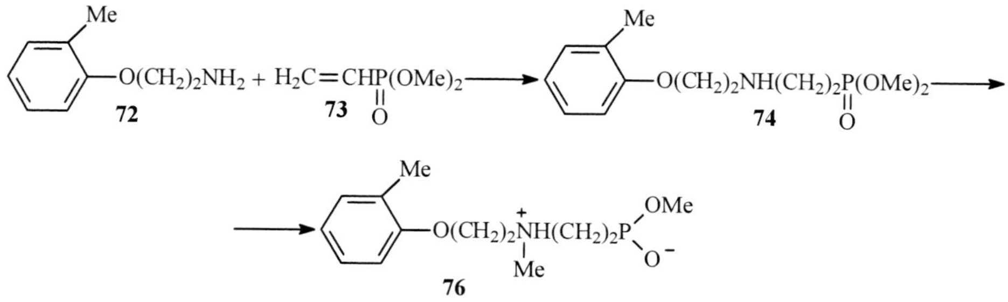

The formation of salt structures [77] by dealkylation of the initial phosphonate was observed during the interaction of alkylamines with vinylphosphonates substituted at the α- or β-carbon atom [Gubnitskaya et al. 1989]:

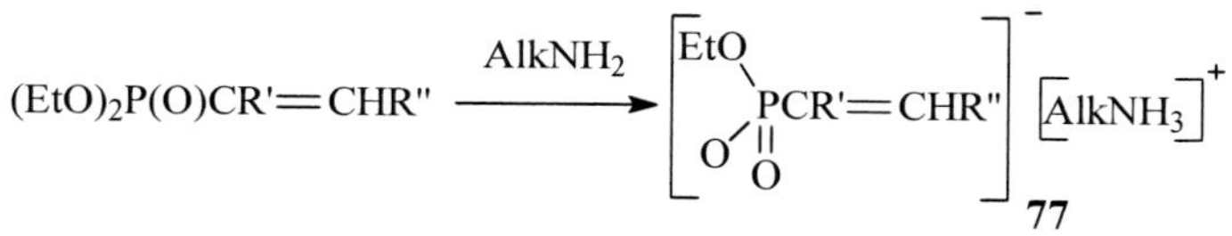

N-Arylpiperazines with diethylvinylphosphonate interact under heating with the formation of corresponding ethyl-β-(N-arylpiperazino)ethylphosphonates [78] [Reznik et al. 1999]:

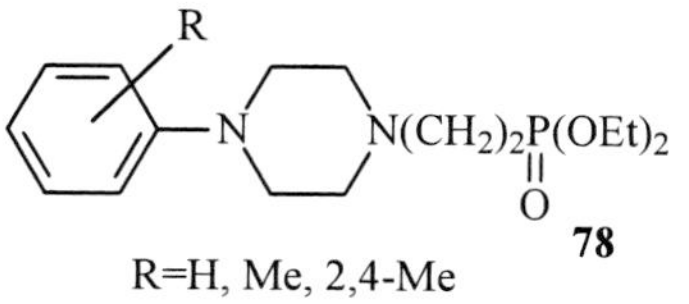

R=H, Me, 2,4-Me

During the study of the interaction of vinylphosphonates with compounds having primary and secondary amine groups each of which are able to fuse with the C=C double bond [79], the products of addition to the primary amine group, N-[β-(methoxyphenoxy)ethyl]-N'-[β-(diethoxyphosphoryl)ethyl]-α,ω-diaminoalkanes [80], were only isolated in high yields under reaction conditions [Reznik et al. 1999].

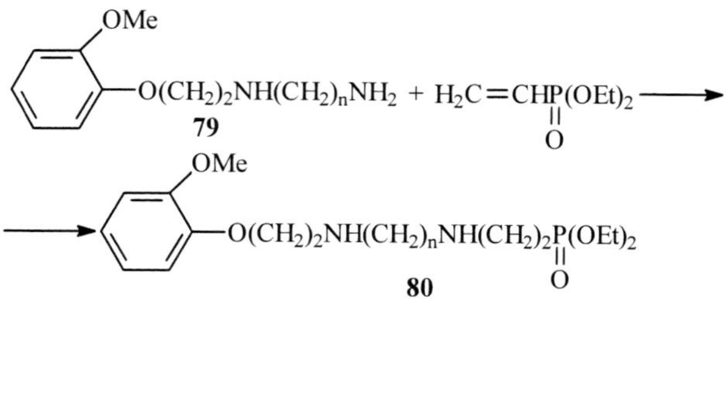

The results of the reactions were explained by the spatial availability of the lone electron pair of the nitrogen atom of the primary amine group. The steric availability of the NH-group, by contrast, is hindered because of the presence of bulky 2-methoxyphenoxyethyl radical, capable to form intramolecular hydrogen bonds with amine groups. The biological activity of the obtained β-aminophosphonates was studied and high hypotensive and α-adrenolytic activity established.

Kabachnik and co-workers studied the reaction of various vinyl phosphorus derivatives with amines and found that the reactivity of unsaturated compounds decreased from four- to three-coordinated phosphorus derivatives in the following sequence [Kabachnik 1964]:

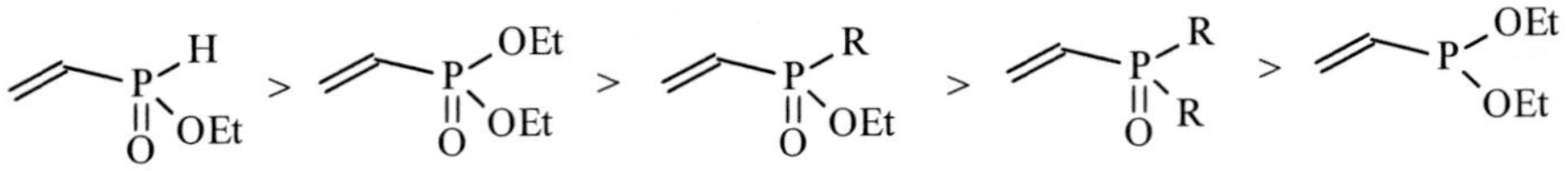

In all the cases, the addition of amines to vinylphosphonates occured through the β-carbon atom of the multiple C=C bond in accordance with its polarization. The authors explained the addition in the β-position by the displacement of electrons under the influence of the electron acceptor phosphoryl group or by the formation of a transition complex [Kabachnik 1964].

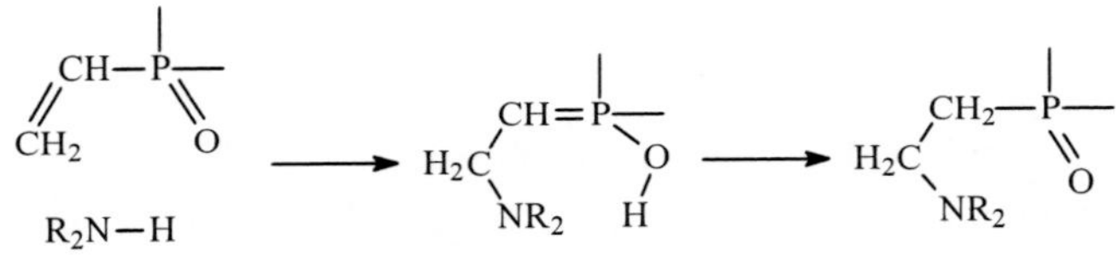

Secondary amines fuse without a catalyst [Pudovik et al. 1953; Märkl et al. 1981], the primary amines require basic catalysis in the excess of the amine under heating [Pudovik et al. 1953; Gubnitskaya et al. 1989]. Recently, it has been shown that the formation of β-aminophosphonates in aza-Michael reaction is significantly accelerated by using water as a solvent, and the reaction can be easily performed even at ambient temperature [Matveeva et al. 2008].

While heated, α-bromovinylphosphonate reacts with the concentrated aqueous ammonia followed by hydrolysis of the ester groups with hydrochloric acid and the formation of corresponding β-aminoethylphosphonic acid [Zygmunt 1985].

Reaction of ethylidene-bis-phosphonic acid with primary amines and diethanolamine proceeds in water, alcohols or solutions of acetic acid at 100-120°C with the formation of 2-amino-1,1-bis-phosphonic acid with the yields of 70-100% [Matveev et al. 1998].

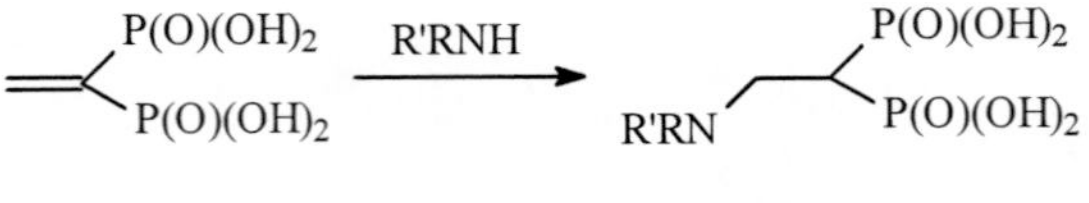

Similar reactions of tetraethylethylidenebis-phosphonate showed that benzylamine, methylbenzylamine and ethylenediamine gave stable adducts of 1:1 composition [81]. In the case of methylamine, the 1:2 adduct [82] was obtained [Bailly et al. 1994]:

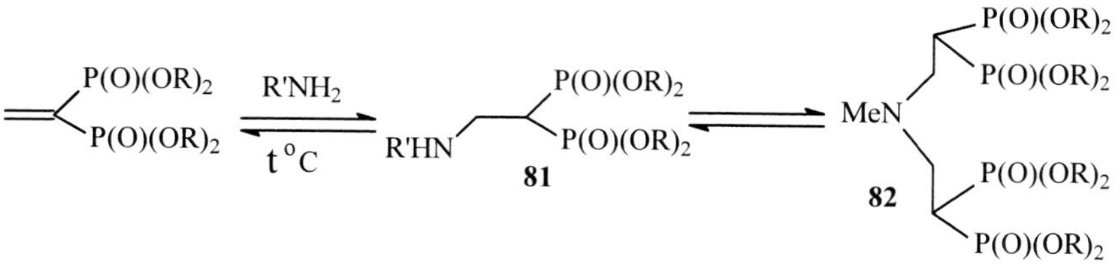

Recently, polyfunctional organophosphorus compounds have started to gain attention. In order to obtain such compounds with an amino group in the β-position, the addition reactions of alkanolamines to unsaturated derivatives of the four-coordinated phosphorus acids were investigated [Khusainova et al. 2009]. The product of monoaddition [83] was mainly obtained together with small amount of the 1:2 adduct by the interaction of vinylphosphonate with ethylene diamine. The reaction of 2-aminoethanol with vinylphosphonate in the absence of catalysts led to the product of amine addition to the β-carbon atom of the phosphonate [84]. Under stronger conditions (no solvent, heating at 150 °C), the dealkylation of phosphorus to zwitter-ionic compound [85] was achieved.

$$(EtO)_2P(O)CH=CH_2 + H_2NCH_2CH_2NH_2 \longrightarrow (EtO)_2P(O)CH_2NHCH_2CH_2NH_2 +$$
$$\textbf{83} \quad \text{major}$$

$$(EtO)_2P(O)CH_2NHCH_2CH_2NHCH_2CH_2P(O)(OEt)_2$$
$$\text{minor} \quad \textbf{84}$$

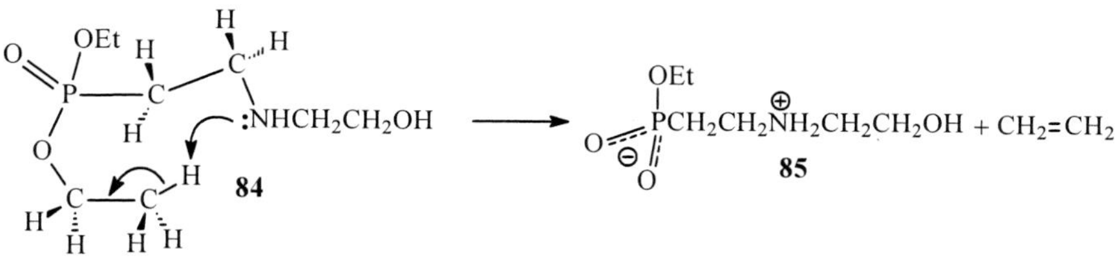

Such a dealkylation with the formation of salt structures has been previously observed by a number of authors [Reznik et al. 1999; Gubnitskaya et al. 1989]. All the above mentioned compounds are crystalline substances with high melting point, insoluble or poorly soluble in organic solvents, and have the following structure [Khailova et al. 2003]:

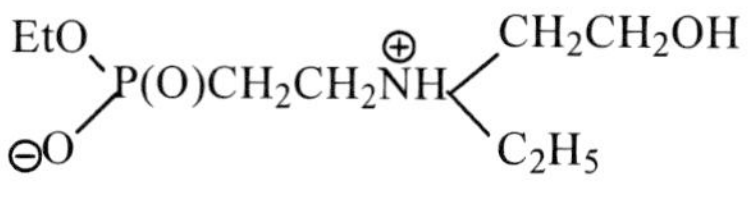

In the case of monoamines, a single product was formed. Thus, in the reaction of vinylphosphonate with butylamine, one of the primary amines, the addition product, i.e. 1-diethoxyphosphoryl-2-butylamino-ethane was only isolated.

$$(C_2H_5O)_2PCH=CH_2 + BuNH_2 \longrightarrow (C_2H_5O)_2PCH_2CH_2NHCH_2CH_2CH_2CH_3$$
$$\quad\overset{\|}{O} \qquad\qquad\qquad\qquad\qquad\qquad\qquad \overset{\|}{O}$$

The interaction between tetra-aza-macrocyclic compounds with NH-fragments and two equivalents of vinylphosphonate results in the formation of a new tetra-aza-macrocycle containing diethylphosphoryl fragments [Boetzel et al. 1995]:

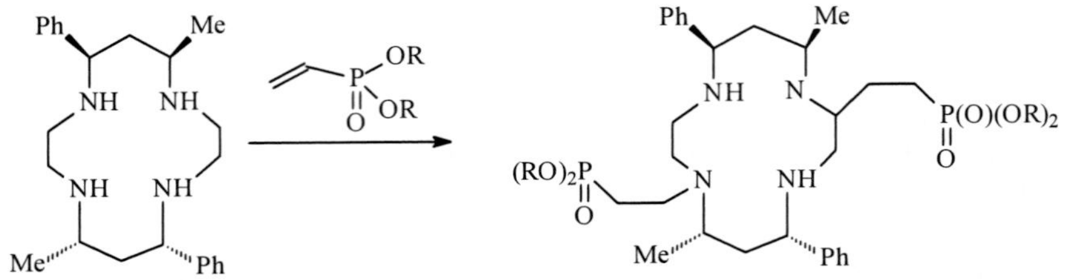

β-Aminophosphonates [87] can be synthesized from the corresponding acetoxyimino- or methoxyimino-2-arylphosphonates [86] by the reduction on Raney nickel catalyst followed by hydrolysis with hydrochloric acid to aminophosphonic acids [88] [Maier et al. 1995] and also from β-ketophosphonates [89] [Varlet et al. 1981].

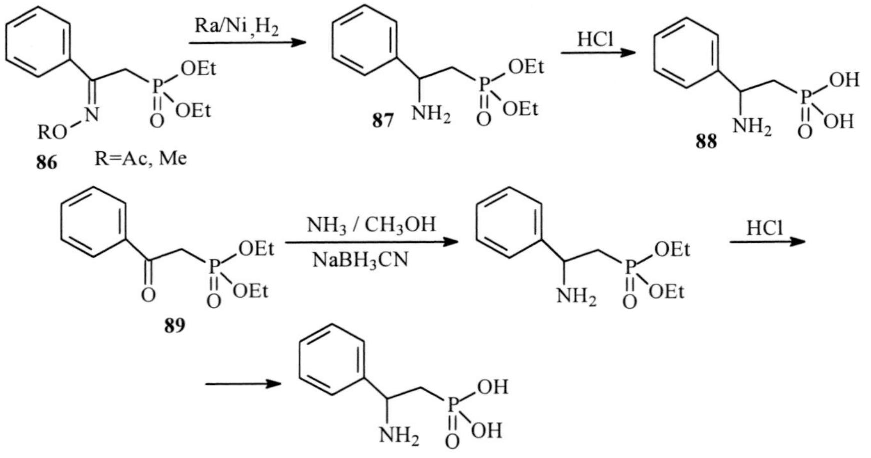

The synthesis of derivatives of both β-amino acids and β-aminophosphonates in the Arbuzov reaction with the derivative of the aspartic acid containing the β-amino acid fragment was reported. The amine group in this reaction was protected by p-toluenesulfonyl (Ts), a non-carbamate amino-protecting group [Teng 2010].

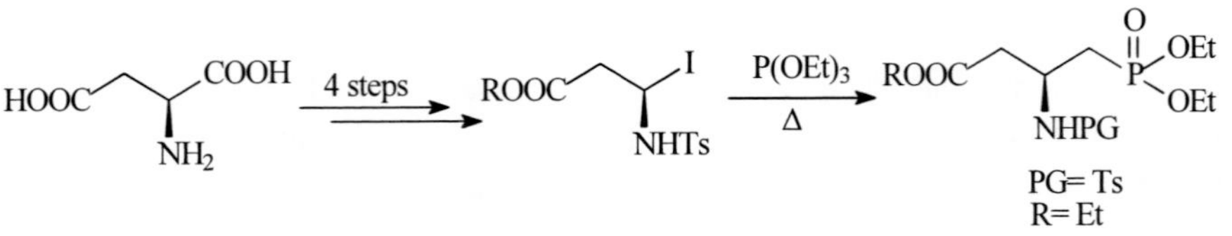

In the case of carbamate amino-protecting group, t-butoxycarbonyl (Boc), unexpectedly reacts with formation of 2-oxazolidinone [90]. The authors suggested that the carbamate group located in adjacent to the halogen competed with triethyl phosphite formed in Arbuzov reaction, and this led to the formation of O,O-diethyl-tert-butylphosphonate [91].

Nucleophilic addition of imidazole to vinylphosphonate accompanied the formation of β-imidazolylethylphosphonate, their monoester and ethylimidazole [Khusainova et al. 2007].

An interesting approach to the synthesis of β-aminophosphonates has been demonstrated in [Röschenthaler et al. 2006]. In some few stages, chiral esters of 2-amino-1,1-difluoroalkylphosphonate in R-configuration were obtained. The presence of three electron-acceptor substituents (two F atoms and one phosphoryl group) at α-carbon atom of the diethyl difluoromethylphosphonate made possible the formation of a carbanion by a strong base (e.g., lithium diisopropylamide). Addition of enantiomerically pure sulfinimine [92] to the carbanion and subsequent recrystallization yielded in a pure diastereomeric N-sulfinyl α,α-difluoro-β-aminophosphonate [93]. The product synthesized was N-desulfinylated by treatment with trifluoroacetic acid in EtOH. The resulting β-aminophosphonate [94] in the R-configuration was easily converted to the corresponding aminophosphonic acid [95] by hydrolysis in 10 N HCl, after treatment with the propylene oxide.

Nucleophilic addition to phosphorus substrates containing diene or alkyne groups leads to the synthesis of β-aminophosphonates containing multiple C=C bond in the β-position towards phosphorus. The addition of amines to allenylphosphonates in the absence of the catalysts was easily achieved for 1,2-double bond [Khusainova et al. 1987; Pudovik et al. 1966]. The interaction of secondary amines with phosphorylated propadienes produces unsaturated β-aminoalkylphosphonates. Thus, the esters of 3,3-disubstituted allenylphosphonic acids easily fuse amines to the 1,2-double bond activated by the electron-acceptor phosphoryl group with the formation of β-aminoalkylphosphonates [Khusainova et al. 1987; Pudovik et al. 1966]:

$$(RO)_2P(O)CH=C=C(CH_3)_2 + R_2NH \longrightarrow (RO)_2\underset{\underset{O}{\|}}{P}-CH_2-\underset{\underset{NR_2}{|}}{C}=C(CH_3)_2$$

In the study of interaction of diethyl ester of 3-methyl-1,2-butadienylphosphonic acid [96] with 2-aminoethanol, the formation of the 2,3-addition product of the amine group [97] was confirmed by X-ray analysis [Khusainova et al. 2005].

Probably, product of 1,2-addition initially underwent enamine-imino isomerization in the reaction conditions.

To determine whether the products obtained are individual compounds or related to the tautomeric equilibrium, the product of interaction of dimethylallenylphosphonate with ethanolamine was investigated by ^{31}P NMR spectroscopy at different temperatures (25-80 °C). The increasing amount of enamine product with increasing temperature and its reversible decrease while cooling indicated by ^{31}P NMR spectra confirms tautomeric equilibrium.

The formation of such a mixture difficult for separation similar in structure to adducts [98] and [99], was observed in the interaction of 3-methyl-1,2-butadienylphosphonate with butylamine.

Two adducts [100] and [101] with different positions of the double bond in the molecule were also obtained by the interaction of 2-(3'-methyl-1',2'-butadienyl)-1,3,2-dioxaphospholane with diethylamine.

$$\begin{array}{c}CH_2O \\ CH_2O\end{array}\!\!>\!\!P(O)CH\!=\!C\!=\!C\!\!<\!\!\begin{array}{c}CH_3 \\ CH_3\end{array} + NHEt_2 \longrightarrow \begin{array}{c}CH_2O \\ CH_2O\end{array}\!\!>\!\!P(O)CH_2\!-\!C\!=\!C\!\!<\!\!\begin{array}{c}CH_3 \\ CH_3\end{array} + \begin{array}{c}CH_2O \\ CH_2O\end{array}\!\!>\!\!P(O)CH\!=\!C\!-\!CH\!\!<\!\!\begin{array}{c}CH_3 \\ CH_3\end{array}$$

100 $N(CH_2CH_3)_2$ **101** $N(CH_2CH_3)_2$

The reactions with other secondary amines resulted in formation of a mixture of similar adducts. Thus, allenylphosphonates substituted at the terminal carbon with two methyl groups fuses to aminoethanol, primary and secondary amines by the 1,2-double bond of cumulene with a nitrogen fixed at sp-carbon. Furthermore, the initially formed adduct underwent various transformations depending on the nature of the nitrogen-containing reagent.

The interaction of secondary amines with 1-vinyl-3-methyl-1,2-butadienylphosphonates gives dienylphosphonates with trans-arrangement of methyl and phosphoryl groups. Their formation results probably from the addition of propadiene to the 1,2-double bond with prototrophic isomerization or due to 1,4-addition. The use of primary amines in these reactions led to the formation of tautomeric mixture of imines [102] and enamines [103] [Khusainova et al. 1987; Dangyan et al. 1981].

102 $P(O)(OR)_2$ ⇌   **103** $P(O)(OR)_2$

The addition of primary amines to allenylphosphonates and formation of a mixture of imine [104] and enamine [105] products was reported later on [Palacios et al. 1996].

104   ⇌   **105** $P(O)(OEt)_2$

Similarly, primary amines react with a mixture of diphenylphosphonylpropadienes with the formation of the imine and enamine substituted diphenylphosphine oxides. Their subsequent reduction resulted in the corresponding β-aminoalkyldiphenylphosphine oxides [106] [Palacios et al. 1994].

Dialkyl esters of 1-methoxy-2,3-butadienyl-2-phosphonic acid reacted with diethylamine to 3-diethylamino-1,3-butadienyl-2-phosphonates [Pudovik et al. 1966].

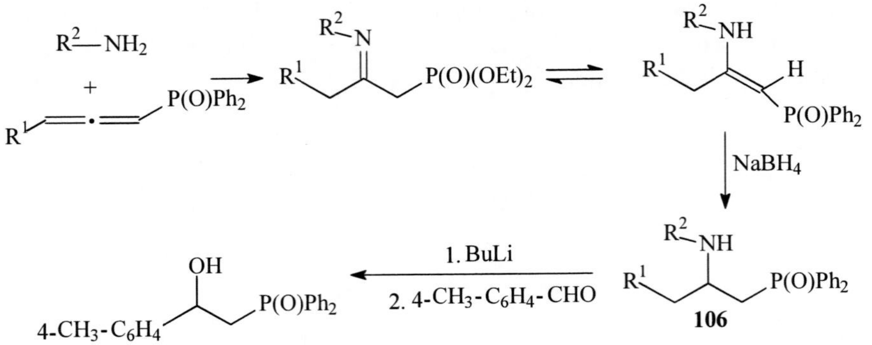

Based on the reaction of the dialkyl esters of 1-methoxy-2,3-alkadien-2-phosphonic acid with 2-aminopyridines, bifunctional nucleophilic reagents become available for reaction with the cyclic and exocyclic nitrogen atoms. This offered new potentialities for the synthesis of heterocyclic compounds [Brel' et al. 1990]. Thus, the reaction of propadienes with 2-amino-3-methylpyridine by heterocyclization resulted in formation of the C-phosphorylated pyrido[1,2,2-a]pyrimidines [107].

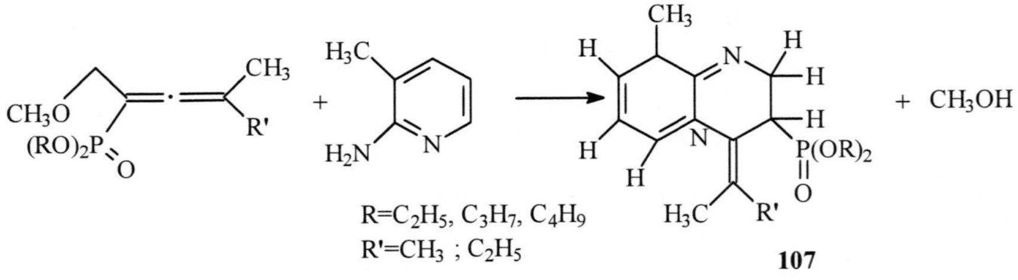

The compounds containing an ethyl group in the ethylene fragment as a substituent consist of a mixture of two geometric isomers in equal ratio. Variation of the substituents in the ester groups of the initial phosphonates does not exert significant effect on the reaction.

The interaction of allenylphosphonate with monosubstituted at the exocyclic nitrogen atom of 2-aminopyridine was considered to show its synthetic opportunities and establish the mechanism. In this case, the mixture of two compounds, i.e., allenyl- [108] and 1,3-alkadienylphosphonates [109], in the ratio near to 1:3 is formed.

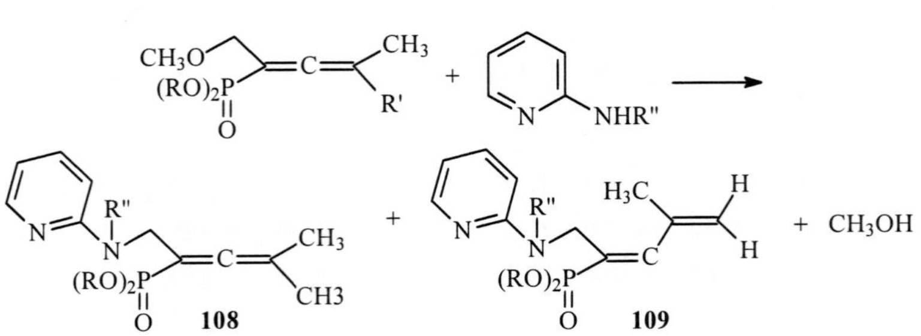

Based on experimental data, the authors proposed the following scheme of interaction of 2-aminopyridines with allenylphosphonates:

Probably, 2-aminopyridines react with allenylphosphonates similar to the secondary amides through the stage of the allene-1,3-diene isomerization [Brel' et al. 1990]. Nucleophilic attack of the cyclic nitrogen atom by the central atom of allene system results in the formation of C-N bond and, as a result, the disruption of pyridine ring conjugation and methanol formation. The resulting 1,3-alkadiene is unstable and readily undergoes intramolecular transformation. Thus, spontaneous intramolecular addition of H-N=C groups to the terminal double bond takes place for R=H. The presence of electron accepting phosphorus group, as well as a suitable geometry of the transition state of the cyclization greatly facilitate the reaction. For 2-aminopyridines alkylated at the exocyclic nitrogen atom (R = Et, i-Bu), the closure of the pyrimidine ring is impossible. However, the inclination of the intermediate phosphonate to form a more stable pyridine system leads to the intramolecular transformations toward allenylphosphonates or 1,3-alkadiene isomers. The rearrangements are probably promoted by the electron donating substituents of the exocyclic nitrogen atom.

Alcoholysis of amidophosphites [110] by propargyl alcohol at 80-100 °C leads to the formation of propargylphosphite [111] which immediately isomerizes to allenylphosphonate [112] and then to propinylphosphonate [113]. However, the reaction is not stopped at this stage. The leaving dialkylamine fuses to the triple bond of propinylphosphonate with the formation of β-aminopropenylphosphonate [114] [Khusainova et al. 1987].

Diethylamine and piperidine fuse with the 1,2-double bond of quaternary 3-monosubstituted allenylphosphonic salts. Interesting results were obtained for the interaction of phosphorylpropadienes [115] with hydrazines [116] [Khusainova et al. 1987].

$$(C_6H_5)_2P(O)CH{=}C{=}CH_2 + R^1NH{-}NH_2 \longrightarrow (C_6H_5)_2P(O)CH_2{-}\underset{\underset{CH_3}{|}}{C}{=}N{-}NHR^1 \xrightarrow{PCl_3}$$

$$\textbf{115} \qquad\qquad\qquad \textbf{116}$$

$$\xrightarrow{PCl_3}$$

The addition of diethylamine and piperidine to propinylphosphonates is performed already at ambient temperature in the absence of catalysts, but the yields of the adducts are low (10-15%). The reactions proceed more rapidly when heated and form the mixtures of 1-dialkylphosphon-2-aminopropenes [117] and 1-dialkylphosphon-2,2-diaminopropanes [118] with high yields. In the presence of a catalyst, no increase of the reaction product yields was observed [Pudovik et al. 1964].

$$R_2\overset{..}{N}H + CH_3C{\equiv}C{-}\underset{\underset{O}{\|}}{P}(OR')_2 \longrightarrow R_2NC(CH_3){=}CH\underset{\underset{O}{\|}}{P}(OR')_2 + (R_2N)_2C(CH_3){-}CH_2\underset{\underset{O}{\|}}{P}(OR')_2$$

$$\textbf{117} \qquad\qquad\qquad \textbf{118}$$

$$R=R'=C_2H_5$$
$$R'=C_2H_5; R_2=(CH_2)_5$$

However, propinylphosphonates were reported to be inert for amines addition [Sauveur et al. 1983].

The addition of secondary amines to alkynylphosphonates catalyzed by the salts of monovalent copper, proceeds regio- and stereospecifically with the formation of trans-2-dialkylaminoalkenylphosphonates [119]. Trans configuration was confirmed by the vicinal constants of spin-spin interaction in ^{13}C and ^{31}P NMR spectroscopy [Panarina et al. 2001]:

$$(RO)_2PC{\equiv}CX + R_2^1NH \xrightarrow{Cu(I)} \overset{(RO)_2P^{\nearrow O}}{\underset{H^{\diagup}}{}}C{=}C\overset{X}{\underset{NR_2^1}{}}$$

$$\textbf{119}$$

The low activity of propinylphosphonates against vinylphosphonates [Pudovik et al. 1964] in the reactions with amines is explained by the presence of the methyl group at the β-carbon atom which lowers the electrophilic properties of the triple bond as well as steric hindrance to the addition reaction.

APPLICATION OF α-AMINOPHOSPHONATES

Aminophosphoryl compounds are currently employed in various areas. Complexing agents and carriers are one of their most relevant applications. The presence of several active sites (phosphoryl and amino groups) in the structure of the compounds is responsible for their peculiar amphoterism, i.e. their participation in specific interactions with both proton donating and proton accepting reagents [Ovchinnikov et al 1998A; Ovchinnikov et al. 1998B]. While proton acceptors interact exclusively with the amino group of amino phosphonates, proton donors can bind to both the amino and the phosphoryl group. Moreover, the reactions mentioned are largely determined by sterical factors. In case of the sterically unloaded α-carbon atom, the phosphoryl and amino groups take part in binding. Even when the atom has a bulky substituent, the phosphoryl group is about unprotonated. Also, alkoxy fragments interact with the acidic substrates, but to a lesser degree. In general, α-aminophosphonates exhibit pronounced proton accepting ability.

Hence, the use of α-aminophosphonates to bind several different types of substrates is very promising. Several studies have been devoted to the complexing ability of amino phosphoryl compounds towards metals. The electron donating oxygen atoms of phosphoryl groups and nitrogen atom of amino groups act as coordination centers while the acidic group of aminophosphonic acid forms corresponding salts. Moreover, the introduction of additional binding functional groups (thiol, amine, etc.) may also enhance the complexing ability of aminophosphoryl compounds. Kiefer and co-authors exploited the ability of α-amino phosphonates to form complexes with metals to develop a laboratory model for removing heavy metal impurities from industrial wastewater [Kiefer et al. 2007]. The set up was based on commercially available chelating ion exchange resins (Purolite S 940 and S 950) and two experimental resins (Purolite D 3342 and D 3343), all with aminophosphonate functional groups. A mixture of nickel, zinc, cadmium and copper sulfates was used as a waste waters pollutant. Also, Finnish scientists studied the use of industrial columns with aminophosphonates for the extraction of zinc, cadmium, copper and nickel from wastewater in the metal-plating industry [Koivula et al. 2000]. Although these industrial complexing agents showed very good results for pure metal chlorides and ammonia complexes, the efficiency of chelating agents was greatly reduced for strong cyanide complexes. Among various complexing agents, including iminodiacetates, thiols, thioureas, sulfo groups, polyamines, etc., aminophosphonate columns gave the best results.

Studies on the influence of bulky anionic counterparts, i.e. citrate, lactate and malate, on the extraction of nickel and cobalt cations by aminophosphonate chelating ion-exchange resin, Purolite S950, showed that the ability of the resin to bind metal complexes with these acids depended on the size of the complex [Deepatana et al 2008]. It has been established that binding nickel lactate was more efficient against free nickel ion with nitrate as a counter ion. In general, the dependence is as follows: lactate > metal ion > malate > citrate. The uptake of metal by ion-exchange resins is most effective in dilute acid solutions.

S950

As mentioned earlier, aminophosphonates are effective complexing agents for Mn (III) [Wang et al. 2008], Cu (II), Ni (II), Cd (II), Zn (II), and Co (II) [Kiefer et al. 2001]. Ethylene diamine is also able to interact with metals with formation of five-membered ring via two nitrogen atoms. The introduction of the phosphonate fragments to the corresponding Schiff base by the Pudovik reaction followed by hydrolysis to aminophosphonic acids with hydrochloric acid resulted in formation of the effective metal chelator [Gałezowska et al. 2009]. The stability constants of complexes with Cu (II), Ni (II) and Zn (II) were determined by potentiometric titration, electron spectroscopy and EPR. The maximum ability of the complex formation was found for the copper cation, with ligand [122] as most effective (pM = - log[M] = 15.27). Other cations are bonded lesser. The pM for ligand [122] and zinc and nickel ions are 7.59 and 8.03, respectively. Ligand [122] is the most effective complexing agent for all the cations.

Bis-aminophosphonic derivatives of ethylenediamine have been proposed as protective groups in the synthesis of gold nanoparticles [Zhang et al. 2010]. It is known that gold nanoparticles tend to aggregate and precipitate. To overcome these limitations, stabilizers are used to prevent aggregation by repulsion of the charged groups, like acidic or ammonium groups precipitated on the nanoparticles surface. The selection of ethylenediamine-tetramethylene phosphonic acid (EDTMP) is explained by the fact that phosphonic acid being dibasic in nature has advantage over the carboxyl groups and can repel charged groups in a wider pH range. In addition, it makes the complexing agent highly hydrophilic. The nanoparticles obtained in the presence of such stabilizers are stable within the pH range 3 – 12 for up to three months.

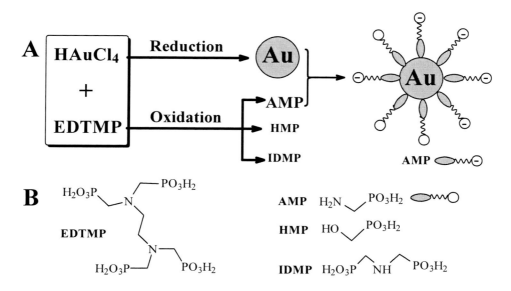

The ability of some tetraaminophosphonic derivatives of alkylenediamines to bind [153]Sm, ^{99m}Tc and [186]Re used as radiopharmaceuticals has been established [Banerjee et al. 2001); P. Panwar et al. 2007; Loussouarn et al. 2003].

New polydentate ligand was synthesized by the reaction of chloromethylphosphonic acid and ethylenediamine-N,N'-diacetic acid [Rajan et al.1969]. The ligand contains acetate and phosphonate groups able for metals binding. The study of its interaction with a number of alkaline earth and transition metals showed that $-PO_3^{2-}$ group has the highest coordinating ability among existing groups. It is followed by the COO^-, and the $PO(OH)O^-$ group is least able to metal coordination. The binding ability of these ligands towards metals is strongly pH dependent. The most effective binding was observed at pH higher than 8.

The presence of proton donating and proton accepting groups in α-aminophosphonic compounds allows using aminophosphonates for extraction of the acids. A carrier molecule should meet some requirements. First, the molecule must be able to get a stable configuration, form a cavity lined by polar groups, and correspond to the substrate stoichiometric requirements. Non-polar groups of the neutral carrier must form a lipophilic shell around the coordination sphere to ensure sufficient solubility of the ligand and complex in the membrane phase. Second, there is a need in the compromise between the stability of the complexes, which is responsible for selectivity of the complex formation, and the relatively high transfer rate providing the transport efficiency. Aminophosphonates meet the above requirements. Their simple synthesis offers wide possibilities for varying the structure and thus establishing optimal lipophilic-hydrophilic balance. As was mentioned earlier, α-amino phosphonates have two proton accepting groups (the phosphoryl P=O group and the nitrogen atom LEP), and a proton donating NH bond, which can be involved in specific interactions (hydrogen bonding) with the hydroxyl and carboxyl groups. The membrane extraction of dicarboxylic, hydroxy and amino acids has been studied [Antipin et al.1996A; Stoikov et al. 2004]. It was shown that N-substituted α-aminophosphonates [123-131] could transfer highly hydrophilic α-hydroxy acids, e.g., glycolic, mandelic and tartaric acids [Antipin et al. 1996A; Antipin et al. 1996B; Antipin et al. 1996C; Stoikov et al. 2000].

	123	124	125	126	127	128	129	130	131
R^1	amyl	amyl	2-ethyl-hexyl	2-ethyl-hexyl	2-ethyl-hexyl	decyl	2-ethyl-hexyl	2-ethyl-hexyl	ethyl
R^2					Me	Me	H	H	Me
R^3					Me	Me	Bu	H	Me

Thus, for glycolic acid as an example the relation between the kinetics of transportation through the liquid membrane and the structure of the carrier molecule was established [Antipin et al. 1998A]. Decreasing the number of alkyl substituents at the α-carbon atom in the carrier led to an increasing rate of the transport. The flux of glycolic acid through the membrane in the case of monoalkyl substituted α-carbon in aminophosphonates is considerably higher than that with carriers bearing dialkyl substituted α-carbon atoms.

O,O-Dipentyl-(N-benzyl)-aminocyclopentyl-phosphonate is able to transport a series of organic acids (d,l-valine, d,l-mandelic, glycolic, d,l-tartaric) through the membrane [Antipin, et al. 1996A]. The carrier exerts the highest influence on the rate of transport of d, l-valine which is increased by 2-3 orders of magnitude. For α-hydroxy acids, the carrier effect is much lesser and the rate of transport increases only two-fold. The authors attribute this to the varying stability of the complexes formed by α-aminophosphonates and the transported substances in the organic phase. In most cases, extraction of the substance from water into the organic phase limits the transport through the liquid impregnated membrane. However increasing concentration in the flow phase and corresponding increase in the extraction rate change limiting stage in most cases. This is mostly characteristic for lipophilic substrates easily extracted into the organic phase. In such cases, the process is limited by re-extraction from the organic phase into the receiving aqueous phase.

The complex of carrier and the α-amino acid was studied by the molecular modeling. A stable complex is achieved by the protonation of the phosphoryl group of the carrier and the ammonium group of amino acids. Also, hydrogen bonds between the amino group of the carrier and carboxyl group of the substrate, as well as non-bonding electron pair of the nitrogen atom and the NH_3^+ group are involved in the complex formation.

Subsequently, the structure proposed for the complexes of α-aminophosphonates and α-hydroxy acids (d, l-mandelic and glycolic acids as examples) was confirmed by various physicochemical methods, including X-ray diffraction [Antipin et al. 1998B]. The formation of the complexes of N-substituted α-aminophosphonates with α-hydroxy acids is supported by the proton transfer resulted in the formation of carboxylate and ammonium groups. Stability of the complex is due to electrostatic interaction of counter ions and the formation of hydrogen bonds, involving the phosphoryl, hydroxyl, ammonium and carboxylate groups.

Later on, calix[4]arene based receptors [132-135], containing α-aminophosphonate fragments were obtained [Stoikov et al. 2000]. Membrane extraction of aromatic α-amino acids, e.g., d,l-β-phenyl-α-alanine, d,l-dihydroxyphenylalanine, d,l-histidine, d,l-tyrosine, and d,l-tryptophan has been studied (Figure 1). The rate of the substrate transfer through the liquid organic membrane did not directly depend on the hydrophobicity (lgP) of these compounds. Tryptophan, the most lipophilic acid studied showed the lowest flux value.

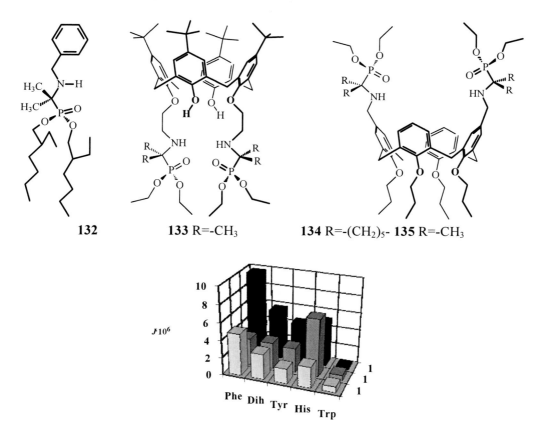

132   **133 R=-CH₃**   **134 R=-(CH₂)₅- 135 R=-CH₃**

Figure 1. Flux values (*J*) of a series of aromatic α-amino acids through liquid impregnated membranes at 25 °C, *J*10⁶, mol/(h·cm²).

The linear α-aminophosphonate [132] did not exhibit high selectivity. Maximum separation was achieved in the pair phenylalanine (Phe) - tryptophan (Trp) (J_{Phe} / J_{Trp} = 7.8) (Figure 1). In the case of calix[4]arenes [133] and [134] with α-aminophosphonate fragments at the lower ring, fluxes of most amino acids differ slightly except histidine (His). The most hydrophilic histidine unexpectedly showed the highest rate of transport through the lipophilic membrane. The flux ratio for phenylalanine and tryptophan was 4.9 and 7.5, and for histidine and tryptophan 10.5 and 9.9, respectively. Molecular recognition of the aromatic amino acid side chain can be provided by the lipophilic cavity of calix[4]arene [135] in *cone* conformation with two α-aminophosphonate fragments on the upper ring. For most substrates (d, l-phenylalanine, d, l-dihydroxyphenylalanine, d, l-histidine, d, l-tyrosine) the overall rate of transport through the membrane was higher than that obtained with linear α-amino phosphonates. The selectivity of phenylalanine transport against tryptophan was 40 [Stoikov et al. 2000].

The α-aminophosphonates are well known as effective carriers of aromatic α-amino acids in the membrane extraction. Attaching α-aminophosphonate fragments to the upper or lower rim of the macrocyclic platform increases the coefficient of selectivity. As expected, the nature of the alkyl substituents at the α-carbon atom has a significant influence on the ability of aminophosphonates to form complexes. The lowest transport rate is exhibited by carriers with cyclic substituents at the α-carbon atom, and decreasing the size of the ring from six- to five-membered resulted in decreasing the flux through the membrane [Antipin et al. 1998B]. This is due to the fact that the five-membered ring does not allow the receptor to attain the conformation required for effective binding. Also, the transport rate decreases with decreasing number of alkyl substituents at the α-carbon atom. This is explained by the decrease in the carrier lipophilicity. Thus, during the modeling of carriers for hydroxy- and amino acids based on aminophosphonates, the lipophilicity and steric hindrance of the carbon atom at the α-position should be considered.

It was shown recently that a series of α-aminophosphonates facilitated the transport of alanine across the phospholipid bilayered membranes [Danila et al. 2008]. By varying the substituents, the authors obtained products different in hydrophilic-hydrophobic balance and size. The phosphonates obtained showed moderate increase in trans-membrane transport capacity for alanine. Meanwhile, no direct relationship between the hydrophobicity and efficiency of transport was found. The authors suggested that the efficiency of transport simultaneously depended on several factors including availability of the carrier at the membrane interface, hydrophobicity of the carrier and alanine complex as well as mobility of the complex and free carrier.

$$R^1{-}NH_2 + \underset{R^2 \quad R^3}{\overset{O}{\|}} + \underset{H \quad O{-}R^4}{\overset{O}{\underset{\|}{P}}{-}O{-}R^4} \longrightarrow R^1{-}\underset{R^2 \quad R^3}{\overset{H}{\underset{N}{|}}}\underset{O{-}R^4}{\overset{O}{\underset{\|}{P}}{-}O{-}R^4}$$

$R^1 = C_6H_5;$	$R^2 = R^3 = CH_3;$	$R^4 = CH_3$
$R^1 = C_6H_5;$	$R^2 = R^3 = CH_3;$	$R^4 = C_4H_9$
$R^1 = C_6H_5;$	$R^2 = R^3 = CH_3;$	$R^4 = CH_2CH(CH_2CH_3)C_4H_9$
$R^1 = C_6H_5;$	$R^2 + R^3 = (CH_2)_5;$	$R^4 = CH_3$
$R^1 = C_6H_5;$	$R^2 + R^3 = (CH_2)_5;$	$R^4 = C_4H_9$
$R^1 = CH_2C_6H_5;$	$R^2 = R^3 = CH_3;$	$R^4 = CH_3$
$R^1 = CH_2C_6H_5;$	$R^2 + R^3 = (CH_2)_5;$	$R^4 = C_4H_9$

The ability of aminophosphonates to penetrate the membrane can be explored in medicine to deliver drugs into the cell. By attaching poly(oxyethylene H-phosphonates) to N-(4-dimethylaminobenzylidene)-p-toluidine or N-furfurylidene-p-toluidine. Bulgarian scientists have obtained biodegradable poly(oxyethylenaminophosphonate) [Kraicheva et al. 2010]. They were recommended for use as polymeric drug delivery substances. They are composed of non-toxic polyethylene glycol components and have potentially biologically active aminophosphonate parts. Binding of pharmaceutical drugs can be achieved by the coordination centers (P=O and NH groups) of the polymers. The cytotoxic effect of such aminophosphonates against some cancer cells was established. The 2-furyl-p-toluidino-bearing analogue with the longest polyoxyethylene chain is most cytotoxic. Shortening the chain led to decreasing cytotoxic activity of the compounds.

Besides drug delivery functions, pharmacophores are another promising application of aminophosphoryl compounds. The structural similarity between these organophosphorus compounds and amino acids is responsible for their effect on living systems. They inhibit some enzymes due to their binding. A new potent and selective inhibitor of human endothelin-converting enzyme-1 applicable for endothelin modulation was synthesized [De Lombaert et al. 2000].

Chinese scientists have isolated chiral quinazoline derivatives of α-aminophosphonate by semi-preparative chromatography [Zhang et al. 2010]. The combination of the quinazoline fragment exerting high antiviral and fungicidal activity with the aminophosphonate part led to the development of a drug which effectively inhibits the tobacco mosaic virus.

Structural similarity of aminophosphonates with aminoacids allows synthesizing so-called phosphono peptides [Mucha et al. 2010; Sieńczyk et al. 2011]. Thus, 1,4-phenylene-di(NL-alanylaminomethylphosphonate) tetraethyl [136] was synthesized from 1,4-phenylene-di(aminomethylphosphonate) [Młynarz et al. 2008]. The obtained peptide is able to form supramolecular complexes with amino acids (lysine and arginine) with a host-to-guest ratio of 1:1 and 1:2.

136

The ability of α-aminophosphonates to bind butyrylcholinesterase and carboxylesterase has been used in the enzymatic determination of these organophosphorus compounds [Evtyugin et al. 1999]. α-Aminophosphonates can inhibit the above enzyme reversibly via after protonation of the amino group and irreversibly by esterification of enzyme active site. However, no irreversible inhibition was observed. Aminophosphonates act as weak reversible inhibitors of cholinesterase and do not affect the carboxylesterase activity. This was explained by low reactivity of the aminophosphonates in the trans-esterification reaction of the enzyme active site. The proximity of the phosphoryl group decreases the basicity of the aminophosphonate. These results in a lesser prone to quaternization of the nitrogen atom. Moreover, the formation of hydrogen bonds between the amine proton and the phosphoryl group limits the availability of the phosphoryl oxygen during phosphorylation of cholinesterase.

The α-aminophosphonates are able also to inhibit dialkylglycine decarboxylase [Liu et al. 2002], D-alanine: D-alanine ligase, a known target for the antibacterial agent D-cycloserine [Duncan et al. 1988; Ellsworth et al. 1996], S-adenosyl-L-homocysteine hydrolase [Steere et al. 2002], UDP-galactopyranose mutase [Pan et al. 2007], cathepsin G [Sieńczyk et al. 2008], and trypsin-like enzymes [Sieńczyk et al. 2004].

The ability to bind enzymes is widely explored in the development of antibacterial drugs. An antibacterial activity against *Escherichia coli* and *Salmonella* has been established for aminophosphonates [3] containing aromatic rings substituted with nitro groups and halogens [Dake et al. 2011].

3

Carbonylaminophosphonates [Hu et al. 2008] and aminophosphonates containing the thiourea group [Chen et al. 2009] possess antiviral properties.

Antitumor activity is one of the most important properties of aminophosphonates. Currently, many works has been performed for identifying and predicting the carcinostatic action of organophosphorus compounds [Rezaei et al. 2009; Kraicheva et al. 2009]. Thus the reaction of chiral α-amino carboxamide derivatives with the racemic O,O'-dialkylisothiocyanato(phenyl)methylphosphonate gave the diastereomeric α-aminophosphonate analogues of peptides [137] which exhibited high antitumor activity against tumor cells PC3 (prostate cancer), Bcap37 (breast cancer) and BGC823 (stomach cancer) [Liu et al. 2010]. The authors established the relationship between the antitumor activity and the structure of the compounds. As a rule, D-diastereoisomers are more active than their L-analogues. The L-diastereomer containing F atom at 4-position of the aromatic ring in the α-aminocarboxamide derivative, substituted by the isopropyl group at the phosphorus atom significantly inhibited breast cancer cells. Its activity is similar to that of the widely used anticancer drug, adriamycin. The other compounds showed less significant results. The authors concluded that benzylamine derivatives substituted by electronegative group at the para-position should be used for perfect activity. Also, for the phosphoric part of the L- and D-diastereoisomer, diisopropyl ether and ethyl should be chosen respectively.

Anthracene derivatives of phosphonates [Kraicheva et al. 2011], their complexes with some metals [Tušek-Božić et al. 2008; Rezaei et al. 2009; Makarov et al. 2009] possess an antitumor activity.

Aminofluorenylphosphonates, analogous of fluorene carboxylic acid, a well-known plant growth regulator (morphactine) are of current interest [Gancarz et al. 1980]. Indeed, they possess herbicidal activity which largely depends on the substituent at the nitrogen and the alkyl radical of phosphorus [Wieczorek et al. 1987].

Calixarene derivative disubstituted at the upper rim by α-aminophosphonate groups [Kalchenko et al. 2003], showed good binding capacity towards the herbicides, i.e., 2,4-dichlorophenoxyacetic acid and atrazine. This was studied by ^{1}H NMR spectroscopy. The analogue of the receptor with no amino group bonded herbicides poorly. The calixarenes tetrasubstituted with phosphonate groups can interact with the herbicides studied. This behavior is explained by the interaction of calixarenes with guests facilitated by the π-π interactions between the aromatic fragments of the guest and host, hydrophobic effects and electrostatic interactions. The low stability constant between 2,4-dichlorophenoxyacetic acid and tetra acids can be due to the predominance of the repulsions of four negatively charged phosphoryl groups of the receptor and the carboxyl group of the substrate over the other interactions. The high stability of the complexes with bis-aminophosphonic acids is due to the increased molecular cavity of the receptor. It is formed by two phosphoryl-N-tolylaminomethyl substituents. In general, the efficiency of host-guest interaction depends on the calixarene preorganization during the complexation. In contrast to the conformationally mobile analogues with four propoxy groups at the lower rim, the bis-aminophosphonic derivative of calixarene substituted at the lower rim by two propoxy groups forms intramolecular bond with two free phenolic groups. This results in a molecule rigidly fixed in the flattened-*cone* configuration. As a result of such a configuration, the complex of aminophosphonic derivatives with guests is stabilized by π-π interactions between 2,4-dichlorophenoxyacetic acid and benzene rings of calixarenes. The complexes of all studied receptors with atrazine are significantly more stable. Apart from hydrophobic and π-π interactions, they are stabilized by electrostatic interactions between the positively charged ammonium group of the substrate with the negatively charged phosphoryl groups of the acids.

The useful properties of α-aminophosphonates are not exhausted by their biological activity. In particular, the authors [Malmgren et al. 2008] proposed the use of chiral aminophosphonate [138] and its salt [139] (diethyl (2R)-tetrahydropyrro-2-ylphosphonate) as a catalyst for the asymmetric Michael reaction. This catalyst proved to be very effective in the addition reaction of nitroalkanes with α, β-unsaturated ketones. The hydrate salt of this α-aminophosphonate is also effective as the aminophosphonate itself at least in terms of selectivity. The increase in selectivity of the reaction comparable with that of the widely used pyrrolidine-based catalysts which do not contain phosphorus, is due to the large volume of the phosphonate group.

138 X = no
139 X = H$_2$O

APPLICATION OF β-AMINOPHOSPHONATES

The study of the extraction properties of β-aminophosphonates is of great interest in the search for new, highly effective analytical and transport reagents. Great variations in the nature of substituents at the reaction centers; phosphorus and nitrogen atoms, of the aminoalkylphosphoryl skeleton of these compounds offer wide opportunity in the study of the influence of structural factors on extraction and other important properties.

However, in order to study the mechanisms of liquid and membrane extraction, to develop aminophosphonate purification technologies, and also to predict their biological activity, it is very important to obtain quantitative data on their behavior in two-phase systems, water - organic solvent. Also, acid-base properties of aminophosphoryl compounds affect various aspects of their practical application as extraction reagents, ionophores, etc. The acid-base properties of water-soluble β-aminophosphonates have been studied by potentiometric titration in aqueous medium (ionic strength μ= 0.05) and in aqueous 2-propanol (75:25 vol., μ = 0.25 and 0.05) [Cherkasov et al. 2005].

First of all, it should be noted that although all the studied β-aminophosphoryl compounds are less basic than the corresponding non-phosphorylated amines, they are more basic than α-aminophosphonates (see Table 1). Moreover, the environment of the phosphorus atom has a little influence on the pK$_a$ value.

The previously observed decrease in basicity of α-aminophosphonates against corresponding aliphatic amine as their precursors [Zakharov et al. 2004] was attributed to the strong acceptor effect of the phosphoryl group. The introduction of an additional methylene group between the atoms of nitrogen and phosphorus weakens the acceptor effect of the phosphoryl fragment leading to increased basicity of the β-phosphorylated amines by about 2.5 units of pK$_a$. Meanwhile, lower basicity of the latter compounds against amines by 2 - 3 pK$_a$ units was observed.

Table 1. Decrease in basicity of amines following their phosphorylation

Amine	pK$_a$	α-AP [a]	pK$_a$ (ΔpK$_a$)	β-AP [a]	pK$_a$ (ΔpK$_a$)
(C$_2$H$_5$)$_2$NH	10.93	(C$_2$H$_5$)$_2$NX	6.61(4.32)	(C$_2$H$_5$)$_2$NCH$_2$X	8.54(2.39)
NH	8.36	NX	3.89(4.47)	NCH$_2$X	5.67(2.69)

[a] X = (C$_2$H$_5$O)$_2$P(O)CH$_2$.

The investigation of the distribution of aminophosphoryl compounds between water and organic phases is of theoretical and practical interest because of their potential application in extraction where losses of extractant and extractable material in aqueous phase are undesirable and also in the technological processes of the synthesis, isolation and purification of aminophosphonates.

Distribution constants of the synthesized β-aminoethylphosphonates (Table 2) were determined by two-phase potentiometric titration in water - organic solvent systems (chloroform, carbon tetrachloride, toluene, octane, n-octanol, o-xylene, nitrobenzene).

Table 2. Distribution constants of some diethyl-□-aminoethylphosphonates between water and chloroform, carbon tetrachloride, o-xylene and toluene, 298±0.2 K

Compound	Distribution constants $lgP_0\pm0.05$			
	$CHCl_3$	CCl_4	$C_6H_4(CH_3)_2$	$C_6H_5CH_3$
$(EtO)_2P(O)CH_2CH_2N(Et)_2$	1.72	0.56	0.55	0.64
$(EtO)_2P(O)CH_2CH_2N$ ⌇⌇O	1.28	0.33	0.41	0.44

Introducing an oxygen atom into the amine fragment led to an increase in the hydrophilicity of the compound which was manifested by the decrease in the distribution constant. During transition from non-polar to polar solvents, an increase in distribution constant was observed because of the polarity of the aminophosphonates themselves.

Like their α-analogues, β-aminophosphonates can form complexes with metals [Maier 1971]. The phosphonates obtained by the Michaelis-Becker reaction of potassium phosphite and tris (2-chloroethylamine) were hydrolyzed with hydrochloric acid to corresponding acids possessed weak complexing properties towards polyvalent metals. In contrast to the α-analogues, the acids obtained showed very weak chelating ability towards calcium ion. The authors explained that by moving the P=O group away from the chelating center resulted in decreased binding ability. The esters of this acid exhibited weak insecticidal activity. Later on, a complex of β-aminophosphonic acids with Co(II) was obtained [Gemmill et al. 2005].

The application of β-aminophosphonates [140] as dental adhesives to enamel and dentin is very promising [Klee et al. 2009]. They were acylated with (meth)acrylolyl chloride followed by methanolysis of the phosphonic acid ethyl ester with trimethylsilyl bromide, before being used as adhesive agents.

As was mentioned earlier, α-aminophosphonates catalyze the Michael reaction [Malmgren et al. 2008]. β-Aminophosphoryl compounds have been also successfully used for this purpose [Widianti et al. 2010]. Japanese scientists obtained cyclic β-aminophosphonates [141-143] containing a β-homoproline fragment and studied its effect on the asymmetric proline-catalyzed Michael reaction. The phosphonate group is rather bulky against carboxyl fragment and the phosphonic acid is more acidic than appropriate carboxylic acid. Using cyclic β-aminophosphonic acid monoester [143] as a catalyst favors the asymmetric Michael addition of ketones to trans-β-nitrostyrenes with high diastereoselectivity (syn:anti up to 95:5), and enantioselectivity (up to 92% *ee*). The β-aminophosphonic acid monoester [143] is most promising catalyst.

Anticancer agents have been discovered among the β-aminophosphoryl compounds [Makarov et al. 2009]. Some compounds have high hypotensive and α-adrenolytic activity [Reznik et al. 1999].

CONCLUSION

In this review, data on the synthesis of α- and β-aminophosphonates have been analyzed and summarized. Currently, extensive experimental data on the synthesis and application of these compounds has been obtained. Approaches to the synthesis of various functional derivatives of α- and β-aminophosphonates, and their application as insecticides, fungicides, plasticizers and stabilizers for polymers, additives for flame retardant materials, extractants, catalysts, pharmaceuticals, etc. were presented. Aminophosphonates, organophosphorus analogs of natural amino acids are of great interest. Although phosphonates containing the amine group in the β-position are less studied, recent studies suggest they prospects as bioactive substances and receptor compounds. Not only biological activity but also effective extraction and membrane transportation was found for various substrates (metal ions, organic and inorganic acids, etc.).

ACKNOWLEDGMENTS

The financial support of the Russian Foundation for Basic Research (09-03-00426, 10-03-92661-NSF) and the Federal Program "Research and scientific-pedagogical personnel of innovative Russia" for 2009-2013 (№ 16.740.11.0472 on 13 May 2011) is kindly acknowledged.

REFERENCES

[1]   Agawane, S. M. and Nagarkar, J. M. (2011). Nano ceria catalyzed synthesis of α-aminophosphonates under ultrasonication Tetrahedron Lett., 52, 3499–3504.

[2]   Ambica, Kumar, S., Taneja, S.C., Hundal, M.S. and Kapoor, K.K. (2008). One-pot synthesis of α-aminophosphonates catalyzed by antimony trichloride adsorbed on alumina Tetrahedron Lett., 49, 2208–2212.

[3]   (A) Antipin, I. S., Stoikov, I. I., Garifzyanov, A. P. and Konovalov, A. I. (1996). Membrane Extraction of Organic Compounds. I. α-Amino Phosphonates as Carriers for α-Hydroxy- and α-Aminoacids Russian Journ. Gen. Chem., 66, 391-394.

[4]   (B) Antipin, I. S., Stoikov, I. I., Garifzyanov, A. P. and Konovalov, A. I. (1996). (-)-Diamyl 1-(N-L-bornylamino)-1-methylethylphosphonate as a stereoselective carrier for the membrane transport of α-hydroxy and α-amino acids Doklady Chemistry, 347, 90-92.

[5]   (C) Antipin, I. S., Stoikov, I. I., Garifzyanov, A. P. and Konovalov, A. I. (1996). Chiral alpha-aminophosphonates: synthesis and transport properties Phosphorus, Sulfur and Silicon, 111, 117.

[6]   (A) Antipin, I. S., Stoikov, I. I., Repeikov, S. A. and Konovalov, A. I. (1998). Membrane extraction of organic compounds 2. * Transport of glycolic acid induced by α-aminophosphonates: Kinetic study Russ. Chem. Bul., Int. Ed., 47, 1697-1701.

[7]   (B) Antipin, I. S., Stoikov, I. I., Repeikov, S. A., Yarkova, E. G., Gubaidullin, A. T., Litvinov, I. A. and Konovalov, A. I. (1998). Structure of Complexes of N-Substituted α-Amino Phosphonates with α-Hydroxy Acids in Solutions and in the Solid Phase Russ.Journ. Gen. Chem., 68, 1455-1461.

[8]   Antipin, I.S., Stoikov, I.I. and Konovalov, A.I. (1999). α-Aminophosphonates: effective carriers for the membrane transport of biorelevant species Phosphorus, Sulfur and Silicon, 144, 347-350.

[9]   Bailly, T. and Burgada, R. (1994). Etude par RMN de l'addition des fonctions -NH,-OH et P_V-H sur l'ethenylidène bis phosphonate de diéthyle. Synthèse de gem bis phosphonates fonctionnalises Phosphorus, Sulfur and Silicon, 86, 217-228.

[10]   Banerjee, S., Samuel, G., Kothari, K., Unni, P. R., Sarma, H. D. and Pillai M. R. A. (2001). Tc-99m and Re-186 complexes of tetraphosphonate ligands and their biodistribution pattern in animal models Nuclear Medicine and Biology, 28, 205–213.

[11]   Bartlett, P. A., Hanson, J. E. and Giannousis, P. P. (1990). Potent Inhibition of Pepsin and Penicillopepsin by Phosphorus-Containing Peptide Analogues J. Org. Chem., 55, 6268-6274.

[12] Berlin, K. D., Roy, N. K., Claunch, R. T. and Bude, D. (1968). A Novel Route to α-Aminoalkylphosphonic Acids and Dialkyl α-Aminoalkylphosphonate Hydrochlorides *J. Am. Chem.* Soc., 4494-4495.

[13] Boduszek, B. (1996). The acidic cleavage of pyridylmethyl(amino)phosphonates. Formation of the corresponding amines *Tetrahedron*, *52*, 12483-12494.

[14] Boetzel, R., Failla, S., Finocchiaro P. and Hägele, G. (1995). The phosphorylation of 5,12-diphenyl-7,14-dimethyl-1,4,8,11-tetraazacyclotetradecane. An NMR and molecular modelling study of the parent cycle and the reaction product *Phosphorus, Sulfur and Silicon*, *104*, 71-80.

[15] Bongini, A., Camerini, R., Hofman, S. and Panunzio, M. (1994). Synthesis of (1S,2S)-phosphothreonine via N-trimethylsilylimine of (S)-lactic aldehyde *Tetrahedron Lett.*, *35*, 8045-8048.

[16] Bordwell, F.G. (1988). Equilibrium Acidities in Dimethyl Sulfoxide Solution *Acc. Chem. Res.*, *21*, 456-463.

[17] Brel', V. K. and Abramkin, E. V. (1990). Funkcional'no zameschennye allenphosphonaty i produkty ih prevrascheniy. Soobscenie 3. Vzaimodejstvie phosphorsoderzhaschih 1-methoxy-2,3-alkadienov s 2-aminopyridinami *Izv. AN SSSR Ser. Khim.*, *175*, 1880-1881.

[18] Chai, B.J. and Muggee, F.D. (1980). Method of Preparing Phosphonates from Nitriles, *U.S. Patent 4,239,695.*

[19] Chen, M.-H., Chen, Zh., Song, B.-A., Bhadury, P. S., Yang, S., Cai, X.-J., Hu, De-Yu, Xue, W. and Zeng, S. (2009). Synthesis and Antiviral Activities of Chiral Thiourea Derivatives Containing an α-Aminophosphonate Moiety *J. Agric. Food Chem.*, *57*, 1383–1388.

[20] Cheng, L., Goodwin, C.A., Scully, M.F., Kakkar, V.V. and Claeson, G. (1991). Substrate-related phosphonopeptides, a new class of thrombin inhibitors *Tetrahedron Lett.*, *32*, 7333-7336.

[21] Cherkasov, R. A. and Galkin, V. I. (1998). The Kabachnik–Fields reaction: synthetic potential and the problem of the mechanism *Russ. Chem. Rev.*, *67*, 857-882.

[22] Cherkasov, R. A., Galkin, V. I., Khusainova, N. G., Mostovaya, O. A., Garifzyanov, A. R., Nuriazdanova, G. Kh., Krasnova, N. S. and Berdnikov E. A. (2005). Synthesis of β-aminophosphonates and study of their acid-base properties and phase distribution in water-organic solvent systems *Russ. Journ. Org. Chem.*, *41*, 1481-1484.

[23] Dake, S. A., Raut, D. S., Kharat, K. R., Mhaske, R. S., Deshmukh, S. U. and Pawar R. P. (2011). Ionic liquid promoted synthesis, antibacterial and in vitro antiproliferative activity of novel α-aminophosphonate derivatives *Bioorganic & Medicinal Chemistry Letters*, *21*, 2527–2532.

[24] Dangyan, Yu. M., Panosyan, G. A., Voskanyan, M. G. and Badanyan, Sh. O. (1981). Reakcija nepredel'nyh soyedineniy. Prisoedineniye aminov k vinylallenovym phosphonatam *Zhourn. Obsch. Khim.*, *51*, 767-775.

[25] Danila, D. C., Wang, X., Hubble, H., Antipin, I. S. and Pinkhassik, E. (2008). Increasing permeability of phospholipid bilayer membranes to alanine with synthetic α-aminophosphonate carriers *Bioorganic & Medicinal Chemistry Lett.*, *18*, 2320–2323.

[26] De Lombaert, S., Blanchard, L., Stamford, L.B., Tan, J., Wallace, E. M., Satoh, Y., Fitt, J., Hoyer, D., Simonsbergen, D., Moliterni, J., Marcopoulos, N., Savage, P., Chou, M., Trapani, A. J., Jeng and A. Y. (2000). Potent and Selective Non-Peptidic Inhibitors of Endothelin-Converting Enzyme-1 with Sustained Duration of Action *J. Med. Chem.*, *43*, 488-504.

[27] Deepatana, A. and Valix M. (2008). Steric hindrance effect on adsorption of metal–organic complexes onto aminophosphonate chelating resin *Desalination*, *218*, 297–303.

[28] Duncan, K. and Walsh, C. T. (1988). ATP-Dependent Inactivation and Slow Binding Inhibition of *Salmonella typhimurium* D-Alanine:D-Alanine Ligase (ADP) by (Aminoalkyl)phosphinate and Aminophosphonate Analogues of D- Alanine *Biochemistry*, *27*, 3709-3714.

[29] Ellsworth, B. A., Tom, N. J. and Bartlett, P. A. (1996). Synthesis and evaluation of inhibitors of bacterial D-alanine:D-alanine ligases *Chemistry & Biology*, *3*, 37-44.

[30] Evtyugin, G. A., Stoikova, E. E., Stoikov, I. I., Budnikov, G. K., Antipin, I. S. and Konovalov, A. I. (1999). Enzymatic determination of α-aminophosphonates with butyryl cholinesterase and carboxylesterase *Journ. Analytical Chem.*, *54*, 283-289.

[31] Fields, E. K. (1952). The Synthesis of Esters of Substituted Amino Phosphonic Acids *J. Am. Chem. Soc.*, *74*, 1528 – 1531.

[32] Finkelstein, J. (1946). The preparation of β-aminoethanephosphonic acid *J. Am. Chem. Soc.*, *68*, 2397-2398.

[33] Gałezowska, J., Kafarski, P., Kozłowski, H., Młynarz, P., Nurchi, V. M. and Pivetta, T. (2009). N,N'-Ethylenediaminobis(benzylphosphonic acids) as a potent class of chelators for metal ions *Inorganica Chimica Acta*, *362*, 707–713.

[34] Galleotti, N., Coste, J., Bedos, P. and Jouin, P. (1996). A straightforward synthesis of α-amino phosphonate monoesters using BroP or TPyClU *Tetrahedron Lett.*, *37*, 3997-3998.

[35] Gancarz, R. and Wieczorek, J.S. (1980). Synthesis of Phosphonic Analogues of Morphactines *Journal f. prakt. Chemie*, *322*, 213-222.

[36] Gemmill, W. R., Smith, M. D. and Reisner, B. A. (2005). A tetrahedrally coordinated cobalt(II) aminophosphonate containing one-dimensional channels *Journal of Solid State Chemistry*, *178*, 2658–2662.

[37] Genêt, J.P., Uziel, J., Port, M., Touzin, A.M., Roland, S., Thorimbert, S. and Tanier, S. (1992). A practical synthesis of α-aminophosphonic acids *Tetrahedron Lett.*, *33*, 77-80.

[38] Groth, U., Lehmann, L., Richter, L. and Schöllkopf, U. (1993). Synthesis of diastereomerically pure 1-aminocyclopropylphosphonic acids *Liebigs Ann. Chem.*, 427-431.

[39] Gubnitskaya, E.S. and Peresypkina, L.P. (1989). Efiry N-zameschennoy β-aminoethylphosphonovoy kisloty *Zhourn. Obsch. Khim.*, *59*, 556 – 564 *(in Russian)*.

[40] Gulea-Purcarescu, M., About-Jaudet, E., Collignon, N., Saquet, M., Masson, S. (1996). Sigmatropic [2,3]-wittig rearrangement of α-allylic-heterosubstituted methylphosphonates. Part 2: Rearrangement in the nitrogen series *Tetrahedron*, *52*, 2075-2086.

[41] Hatani, M., Goerlich, J. R., Schmutzler, R., Groger, H. and Martens, J. (1996). The totally protected hydroxyl containing α-amino phosphonic esters and α-amino phosphinoxides as well as their carbamoyl derivatives *Synth. Commun.*, *26*, 3685-3698.

[42] Hosseini-Sarvari, M. (2008). TiO2 as a new and reusable catalyst for one-pot three-component syntheses of α-aminophosphonates in solvent-free conditions *Tetrahedron*, *64*, 5459–5466.

[43] Hu, De-Yu, Wan, Q.-Q., Yang, S., Song, B.-A., Bhadury, P. S., Jin, L.-H., Yan, K., Liu, F., Chen, Zh. and Xue, W. (2008). Synthesis and Antiviral Activities of Amide Derivatives Containing the α-Aminophosphonate Moiety *J. Agric. Food Chem.*, *56*, 998–1001.

[44] Huber, J. W. and Middlebrooks, M. (1977) Synthesis of Aminoalkanephosphonic Acids from Ureidoalkanephosphonates *Synthesis*, 883-884.

[45] Jin, L., Song, B., Zhang, G., Xu, R., Zhang, S., Gao, X., Hu, D. and Yang, S. (2006). Synthesis, X-ray crystallographic analysis, and antitumor activity of N-(benzothiazole-2-yl)-1-(fluorophenyl)-O,O-dialkyl-α-aminophosphonates *Bioorganic & Medicinal Chemistry Letters*, *16*, 1537–1543.

[46] Kabachnik, M. I. and Medved', T. Ya. (1952) Novyj metod syntheza α-aminophosphinovyh kislot // Dokl. AN SSSR. т. 83. № 5. с. 689-692.

[47] Kabachnik, M.I. (1964). Conjugation in non-coplanar systems involving a tetrahedral phosphorus atom *Tetrahedron*, *20*, 655-669.

[48] Kaboudin, B. and Sorbiun, M. (2007). β-Cyclodextrin as an efficient catalyst for the one-pot synthesis of 1-aminophosphonic esters in water *Tetrahedron Lett.*, *48*, 9015–9017.

[49] Kafarski, P. and Lejczak, B. (1991). Biological activity of aminophosphonic acids *Phosphorus, Sulfur, and Silicon*, *63*, 193-215.

[50] Kalchenko, O. I., Solovyov, A. V., Cherenok, S. A., Starodub, N. F. and Kalchenko, V. I. (2003). Complexation of Calix[4arenephosphonous Acids with 2,4-Dichlorophenoxyacetic Acid and Atrazine in Water *Journ. of Inclusion Phenomena and Macrocyclic Chemistry*, *46*, 19-25.

[51] Kankorat, T., Neda, I., Jones, P. G. and Schmutzler, R. (1996). Darstellung von peptoiden mit der organoaminomethyl-dimethylphosphinoxid-gruppierung *Phosphorus, Sulfur and Silicon*, *112*, 247-259.

[52] Keglevich, G., Fehervari, A. and Csontos, I. (2011). A study on the Kabachnik-Fields reaction of benzaldehyde, propylamine and diethyl phosphite by in situ Fourier Transform IR Spectroscopy. *Heteroatom Chemistry*, *22*, 599-604.

[53] Khailova, N. A., Shaimardanova, A. A., Saakyan, G. M., Zyablikova, T. A., Azancheev, N. M., Krivolapov, D. B., Gubaidullin, A. T., Litvinov, I. A., Musin, R. Z., Chmutova, G. A., Pudovik, M. A. and Pudovik, A.N. (2003). Reactions of α-aminoalkylphosphonates with iso(thio) cyanatophosphates(phosphonates, phosphinates). Synthesis of 1,3,4- diazaphospholidines and 1,3,4-oxaza(thiaza)phospholines // *Russ. Journ. Gen. Chem.*, *73*, 1213-1226.

[54] Khusainova, N. G., Mostovaya, O. A., Berdnikov, E. A., Litvinov, I. A., Krivolapov, D. B. and Cherkasov, R. A. (2005). Reactions of allenylphosphonates with 2-aminoethanol and amines *Russ. Journ. Org. Chem.*, *41*, 1260-1264.

[55] Khusainova, N. G. and Pudovik, A.N. (1987). Phosphorylated Allenes. Methods of Synthesis and Properties *Russ. Chem. Rev.*, *56*, 564–578.

[56] Khusainova, N. G., Berdnikov, E. A., Mostovaya, O. A., Rybakov, S. M. and Cherkasov, R. A. (2007). Reactions of Allenyl- and Vinylphosphonates with Imidazole *Russ. Journ. Org. Chem.*, *43*, 1703–1705.

[57] Khusainova, N., Mostovaya, O., Berdnikov, E., Rybakov, S. and Cherkasov, R. (2009). Interaction of vinylphosphonates with 1,2-diaminoethane and ethanolamine // *Phosphorus, Sulfur, and Silicon*, *184*, 865-871.

[58] Kiefer, R. and Höll, W. H. (2001). Sorption of Heavy Metals onto Selective Ion-Exchange Resins with Aminophosphonate Functional Groups *Ind. Eng. Chem. Res.*, *40*, 4570-4576.

[59] Kiefer, R., Kalinitchev, A. I. and Höll, W. H. (2007). Column performance of ion exchange resins with aminophosphonate functional groups for elimination of heavy metals *Reactive & Functional Polymers*, *67*, 1421–1432.

[60] Kiss, N.Z., Kaszas, A., Drahos, L., Mucsi, Z. and Keglevich, G. (2012). A neighbouring group effect leading to enhanced nucleophilic substitution of amines at the hindered α-carbon atom of an α-hydroxyphosphonate *Tetrahedron Lett.*, *53*, 207–209.

[61] Klee, J. E. and Lehmann U. (2009). *N*-alkyl-*N*-(phosphonoethyl) substituted (meth)acrylamides – new adhesive monomers for self-etching self-priming one part dental adhesive *Beilstein Journal of Organic Chemistry*, *5,* doi:10.3762/bjoc.5.72.

[62] Koivula, R., Lehto, J., Pajo, L., Gale, T. and Leinonen H. (2000). Purification of metal plating rinse waters with chelating ion exchangers *Hydrometallurgy*, *56*, 93–108.

[63] Kosolapoff, G. M. (1947). The synthesis of amino-substituted phosphonic acides. *J. Am. Chem. Soc.*, *69*, 2112-2113.

[64] Kraicheva, I., Bogomilova, A., Tsacheva, I., Momekov, G. and Troev K. (2009). Synthesis, NMR characterization and in vitro antitumor evaluation of new aminophosphonic acid diesters *European Journal of Medicinal Chemistry*, *44*, 3363–3367.

[65] Kraicheva, I., Bogomilova, A., Tsacheva, I., Momekov, G., Momekova, D. and Troev, K. (2010). Synthesis, NMR characterization and in vitro cytotoxicity evaluation of new poly(oxyethylene aminophosphonate)s *European Journal of Medicinal Chemistry*, *45*, 6039-6044.

[66] Kraicheva, I., Tsacheva, I., Vodenicharova, E., Tashev, E., Tosheva, T., Kril, A., Topashka-Ancheva, M., Iliev, I., Gerasimova, Ts. and Troev, K. (2012). Synthesis, antiproliferative activity and genotoxicity of novel anthracene-containing aminophosphonates and a new anthracene-derived Schiff base *Bioorg. Med. Chem.*, *20*, 117-124.

[67] Kudrimoti, S. and Bommena, V. R. (2005). (Bromodimethyl)sulfonium bromide: an inexpensive reagent for the solvent-free, one-pot synthesis of α-aminophosphonates // *Tetrahedron Lett.*, *46*, 1209-1210.

[68] Kudzin, Z. H. and Kotinski, A. (1980). Synthesis of O,O-Dialkyl 1-Aminoalkanephosphonates *Synthesis*, 1028-1032.

[69] Kudzin, Z. H. and Stec, W. J. (1978). Synthesis of 1-Aminoalkanephosphonates via Thioureidoalkanephosphonates *Synthesis*, 469-472.

[70] Kukhar', V. P., Svistunova, N. Yu., Solodenko, V.A. and Soloshonok, V.A. (1993). Asymmetric synthesis of fluorine- and phosphorus-containing analogues of aminoacids, *Russ. Chem. Rev.*, *62*, 261–278.

[71] Liboska, R., Picha, J., Hančlová, I., Buděšinský, M., Šanda, M. and Jiráček, J. (2008). Synthesis of methionine- and norleucine-derived phosphinopeptides *Tetrahedron Lett.*, *49*, 5629–5631.

[72] Liu, J.-Z., Song, B.-A., Fan, H.-T., Bhadury, P. S., Wan, W.-T., Yang, S., Xu, W., Wu, J., Jin, L.-H., Wei, X., Hu, De-Yu and S. Zeng (2010). Synthesis and in vitro study of pseudo-peptide thioureas containing α-aminophosphonate moiety as potential antitumor agents *European Journal of Medicinal Chemistry*, *45*, 5108-5112.

[73] Liu, W., Rogers, C. J., Fisher, A. J. and Toney, M. D. (2002). Aminophosphonate inhibitors of dialkylglycine decarboxylase: structural basis for slow binding inhibition *Biochemistry*, *41*, 12320-12328.

[74] Loussouarn, A., Ouadi, A., Morandeau, L., Remaud, P., Giles, R., Gestin, J.-F. and Webb, J. (2003). Synthesis of new semi-rigid chelating agents for samarium-153 *Tetrahedron Lett.*, *44*, 3539–3541.

[75] Maier, L. (1971). Organic Phosphorus Compounds. 45. Preparation and properties of nitrilotri(ethylenophosphonates) and the corresponding acid. *Phosphorus*, *1*, 67-69.

[76] Maier, L. and Diel, P. J. (1995). Organic Phosphorus Compounds. 105. Synthesis and properties of 2-amino-2-arylethylephosphonic acids and derivatives *Phosphorus, Silicon and Sulfur*, *107*, 245-255.

[77] Makarov, M. V., Rybalkina, E. Yu., Röschenthaler, G.-V., Short, K. W., Timofeeva, T.V. and Odinets, I. L. (2009). Design, cytotoxic and fluorescent properties of novel N-phosphorylalkyl substituted E,E-3,5-bis(arylidene)piperid-4-ones *European Journal of Medicinal Chemistry*, *44*, 2135–2144.

[78] Malmgren, M., Granander, J. and Amedjkouh, M. (2008). Asymmetric conjugate addition of nitroalkanes to enones with a chiral α-aminophosphonate catalyst *Tetrahedron: Asymmetry*, *19*, 1934–1940.

[79] Märkl, G. and Merkl, B. (1981). Optisch aktive β(amino)ethyl-phosphonsäureester, β(amino)ethyl-phenylphosphinsäureester, β(amino)ethyl-diphenylphosphinoxide und β(amino)ethyl-diphenylphosphine *Tetrahedron Lett.*, *22*, 4459 – 4462.

[80] Matveev, S. V., Bel'skii, F. I., Matveeva, A. G., Gukasova, A. Yu., Polikarpov, Yu. M. and Kabachnik, M. I. (1998). N-substituted 2-aminoethylidenediphosphonic acids as complexones *Russ. Chem. Bull., Int. Ed.*, *47*, 1736-1740.

[81] Matveeva, E. V., Petrovskii, P. V. and Odinets I. L. (2008). Efficient synthesis of racemic β-aminophosphonates via aza-Michael reaction in water *Tetrahedron Lett.*, *49*, 6129–6133.

[82] McNulty, J., Dasa, P. and Gosciniak, D. (2008). An improved synthesis of α-phosphonoenamines based on a modified Peterson olefination *Tetrahedron Lett.*, *49*, 281–285.

[83] Młynarz, P., Olbert-Majkut, A., Śliwińska, S., Schroeder, G., Banrkowski, B. and Kafarski, P. (2008). 1,4-Phenylene-di(N-L-alanylaminomethylphosphonate) a new diaminophosphonate peptide receptor for lysine and arginine *Journal of Molecular Structure*, *873*, 173–180.

[84] Młynarz, P., Rydzewska, A. and Pok1adek, Z. (2011). Preparation of a novel group of hybrid compounds N-benzyl aminoboronbenzylphosphonic and N,N'-ethylenedi (aminoboronbenzylphosphonic) acids *Journal of Organometallic Chemistry*, *696*, 457-460.

[85] Mucha, A., Drag, M., Dalton, J. P. and Kafarski, P. (2010). Metallo-aminopeptidase inhibitors *Biochimie*, *92*, 1509-1529.

[86] Mucha, A., Kafarski, P., Plenat, F. and Cristan, H. J. (1995). Preparation of benzyl N-benzyloxycarbonylaminophosphonates and –aminophosphonites – the scope and limitations of O-benzyl-N,N'-dicyclohexyloisourea method *Phosphorus, Sulfur, and Silicon*, *105*, 187-193.

[87] Mykhaylychenko, S. S., Pikun, N. V. and Shermolovich, Y. G. (2011). Reaction of N,N-disubstituted perfluoroalkanethioamides with trialkyl phosphites. A new method for the synthesis of polyfluorinated α-aminophosphonates *Tetrahedron Lett.*, *52*, 4788–4791.

[88] Oleksyszyn, J. (1980). 1-N-Alkylaminoalkanephosphonic and 1-N-Alkylaminoalkylphenylphosphinic Acids *Synthesis*, 722-724.

[89] Oleksyszyn, J., Tyka, R. and Mastalerz, M. (1977). Guanidinophosphonic Acids *Synthesis*, 571-572.

[90] Oleksyszyn, J., Tyka, R. and Mastalerz, P. (1978). Direct Synthesis of 1-Aminoalkanephosphonic and 1-Aminoalkanephosphinic Acids from Phosphorus Trichloride or Dichlorophosphines *Synthesis*, 479-480.

[91] Ovchinnikov, V. V., Cherezov, S. V., Cherkasov, R. A. and Pudovik, A. N. (1985). Reakcionnaya sposobnost' cyclicheskih I acyclicheskih hydrophosphoryl'nyh soedineniy v reakcijah electrophil'nogo prisoedinenija k ketenacetalyam i enaminam *Zhourn. Obsch. Khim.*, *55*, 1244-1253 *(in Russian)*.

[92] (A) Ovchinnikov, V. V., Sagadeev, E. V., Lapteva, L. I., Khasieva, L. R., Alikberov, M. Z., Sitnikova, E. Yu., Antipin, I. S., Stoikov, I. I. and Konovalov A. I. (1998). Thermochemistry of heteroatomic compounds. X. The thermochemistry of solution and salvation of substituted alkylphosphonic derivatives *Journ. Of Thermal Analysis*, *54*, 305 – 309.

[93] (B) Ovchinnikov, V. V., Sagdeev, E. V., Stoikov, I. I., Safina, Yu. G. and Sopin, V. F. (1998). Thermochemistry of α-Aminophosphonic Acid Derivatives *Russ. Journ. Gen. Chem.*, *68*, 1488-1492.

[94] Palacios, F., Aparacio, D. and Garcia, J. (1994). An Efficient and General Strategy for The Synthesis of Secondary E-Allylamines from Phosphorylated Allenes *SYNLETT*. 260-262.

[95] Palacios, F., Aparico, D., De Los Santos, J. M., Garcia, J. and Rodriguez, E. (1996). Synthetic applications of β-functionalized phosphorus compounds. An effective strategy for the preparation of acyclic and heterocyclic compounds derived from amines and hydrazones *Phosphorus, Sulfur and Silicon*, *109-110*, 401-404.

[96] Palacios, F., Gil, M. J., de Marigorta, E. M. and Rodriguez, M. (1999). Synthesis of 3-phosphorylated 2-aza-1,3-dienes from imines derived from bisphosphonates *Tetrahedron Lett.*, *40*, 2411-2414.

[97] Pan, W., Ansiaux, C. and Vincent, S. P. (2007). Synthesis of acyclic galactitol- and lyxitol-aminophosphonates as inhibitors of UDP-galactopyranose mutase *Tetrahedron Lett.*, *48*, 4353–4356.

[98] Panarina, A. E., Dogadina, A. V., Zakharov, V. I. and Ionin B.I. (2001). Addition of secondary amines to alkynylphosphonates *Tetrahedron Lett.*, *42*, 4365-4368.

[99] Panwar, P., Singh, S., Kumar, N., Rawat, H. and Mishra, A. K. (2007). Synthesis, characterization, and in vivo skeletal localization of a new 99mTc-based multidentate phosphonate chelate: 5-Amino-1,3-bis(ethylamine-(N,N dimethyl diphosphonic acid) acetamido) benzene *Bioorganic & Medicinal Chemistry*, *15*, 1138–1145.

[100] Pousset, C. and Larchevêque, M. (2002). An efficient synthesis of α- and β-aminophosphonic esters from α-amino acids *Tetrahedron Lett.*, *43*, 5257–5260.

[101] Pudovik, A. N. (1952) Novyj metod syntheza efirov aminophosphinovyh kislot // *Dokl. AN SSSR*, *83*, 865-868 *(in Russian)*.

[102] Pudovik, A. N. and Denisova, G. M. (1953). Syntez i svojstva vinylphosphinovyh efirov. Reakcii phosphonethylirovaniya, prisoedineniya dialkylphosphoristyh kislot, ammiaka i aminov k ethylovomu efiru vinylphosphinovoy kisloty *Zhourn. Obsch. Khim.*, *23*, 263-267 *(in Russian)*.

[103] Pudovik, A. N. and Khusainova, N. G. (1966). Prisoedinenie spirtov, aminov, dialkylphosphoristyh kislot k efiram γ,γ-dimethylallenylphosphinovoy kisloty *Zhourn. Obsch. Khim.*, *36*, 1236-1240.

[104] Pudovik, A. N., Khusainova, N. G. and Ageeva, A. B. (1964). O reakcijah nucleophil'nyh reagentov s efirami propinylphosphinovoy kisloty *Zhourn. Obsch. Khim.*, *34*, 3938-3942.

[105] Pudovik, A.N., Saakyan, G.M., Khairullin, V.K. and Pudovik, M.A. (1997). Synthesis and Properties of N-Silylated α-Amino Phosphonates *Russ. Journ. Gen. Chem.*, *67*, 1878-1880.

[106] Rajan, K. S., Murase, I. and Martel, A. E. (1969). New Multidentate Ligands. VII. Ethylenediamine-N,N'-diacetic-N,N'-di (methylenephosphonic) Acid *J. Am. Chem. Soc.*, 4408 – 4411.

[107] Rassukana, Y.V., Onys'ko, P.P., Kolotylo, M.V., Sinitsa, A.D., Łyzwa, P. and Mikołajczyk, M. (2009). A new strategy for asymmetric synthesis of aminophosphonic acid derivatives: the first enantioselective catalytic reduction. of C-phosphorylated imines *Tetrahedron Lett.*, *50*, 288–290.

[108] Reddy, M.V., Dindulkar, S.D. and Jeong, Y.T. (2011). BF_3_SiO_2-catalyzed one-pot synthesis of α-aminophosphonates in ionic liquid and neat conditions *Tetrahedron Lett.*, *52*, 4764–4767.

[109] Rezaei, Z., Firouzabadi, H., Iranpoor, N., Ghaderi, A., Jafari, M. R., Jafari, A.A. and Zare, H. R. (2009). Design and one-pot synthesis of α-aminophosphonates and bis(α-aminophosphonates) by iron(III) chloride and cytotoxic activity *European Journal of Medicinal Chemistry*, *44*, 4266–4275.

[110] Reznik, V. S., Akamsin, V. D., Galyametdinova, L. V., Fattakhov, S. G. and Ivanov, B. E. (1999). Two-fragment α-adrenolytics 1. Addition of β-aroxyethylamines and N-arylpiperazines to dialkyl vinylphosphonates *Russ. Chem. Bull., Int. Ed.*, *48*, 979-983.

[111] Röschenthaler, G.-V. Kukhar, V. P., Belik, M. Yu., Mazurenko, K. I. and Sorochinsky, A. E. (2006). Diastereoselective addition of diethyl difluoromethylphosphonate to enantiopure sulfinimines: synthesis of α,α-difluoro-β-aminophosphonates, phosphonic acids, and phosphonamidic acids *Tetrahedron*, *62*, 9902–9910.

[112] Rudzinska, E., Berlicki, Ł., Mucha, A. and Kafarski, P. (2007). Chiral discrimination of ethyl and phenyl N-benzyloxycarbonylaminophosphonates by cyclodextrins *Tetrahedron: Asymmetry*, *18*, 1579–1584.

[113] Rudzinska, E., Dzygiel, P., Wieczorek, P. and Kafarski, P. (2002). Separation of aromatic aminophosphonic acid enantiomers by capillary electrophoresis with the application of cyclodextrins *Journal of Chromatography A*, *979*, 115–122.

[114] Safina, Yu. G. and Cherkasov, R. A. (1992). Kineticheskoe izuchenije reakciy 2-hydro-4,5-dimethyl-2-oxo-1,3,2-dioxaphospholana s enaminoefirami *Zhourn. Obsch. Khim.*, 1992. *62*, 945-946 *(in Russian)*

[115] Safina, Yu. G., Malkova, G. Sh., Cherkasov, R. A. and Ovchinnikov V. V. (1990). Reakcii cyclicheskih nepolnyh efirov phosphoristoy kisloty s enaminami *Zhourn. Obsch. Khim.*, *60*, 221-222 *(in Russian)*.

[116] Sauveur, F., Collignon, N., Guy, A. and Savignac, Ph. (1983). Acces a l'acide amino-2 propylphosphonique optiquement actif *Phosphorus and Sulfur*, *14*, 341-346.

[117] Seebach, D., Charczuk, R., Gerber, C., Renaud, P., Berner, H. and Schneider, H. (1989). Elektrochemische Decarboxylierung von L.-Threonin- und Oligopeptid-Derivaten unter Bildung von *N*-Acyl-N, O-acetalen: Herstellung von Oligopeptiden mit Carboxamid-oder Phosphonat-C-Terminus *Helv. Chim. Acta*, *72*, 401-425.

[118] Sieńczyk, M. and Oleksyszyn, J. (2004). A convenient synthesis of new α-aminoalkylphosphonates, aromatic analogues of arginine as inhibitors of trypsin-like enzymes *Tetrahedron Lett.*, *45*, 7251–7254.

[119] Sieńczyk, M., Kliszczak, M. and Oleksyszyn, J. (2006). Synthesis of isocyanide derivatives of α-aminoalkylphosphonate diphenyl esters *Tetrahedron Lett.*, *47*, 4209–4211.

[120] Sieńczyk, M., Lesner, A., Wysocka, M., Łęgowska, A., Pietrusewicz, E., Rolka, K. and Oleksyszyn, J. (2008). New potent cathepsin G phosphonate inhibitors *Bioorganic & Medicinal Chemistry*, *16*, 8863–8867.

[121] Sieńczyk, M., Podgórski, D., Błazejewska, A., Kulbacka, J., Saczko, J. and Oleksyszyn, J. (2011). Phosphonic pseudopeptides as human neutrophil elastase inhibitors—a combinatorial approach *Bioorganic & Medicinal Chemistry*, *19*, 1277–1284.

[122] Sobhani, S., Safaei, E., Asadi, M. and Jalili, F. (2008). An eco-friendly procedure for the efficient synthesis of dialkyl α-aminophosphonates in aqueous media *Journal of Organometallic Chemistry*, *693*, 3313–3317.

[123] Song, B., Yang, S., Hong, Y., Zhang, G., Jin, L. and Hu, D. (2005). Synthesis and bioactivity of fluorine compounds containing isoxazolylamino and phosphonate groups *Journal of Fluorine Chemistry*,*126*, 1419–1424.

[124] Song, B.-A., Zhang, G.-P., Yang, S., Hu, D.-Y. and Jin, L.-H. (2006). Synthesis of N-(4-bromo-2-trifluoromethylphenyl)-1-(2-fluorophenyl)-O,O-dialkyl-α-aminophosphonates under ultrasonic irradiation *Ultrasonics Sonochemistry*, *13*, 139–142.

[125] Steere, J. A., Sampson, P. B. and Honek, J. F. (2002). Synthesis of an α-Aminophosphonate Nucleoside as an Inhibitor of S-Adenosyl-L-Homocysteine Hydrolase *Bioorganic & Medicinal Chemistry Letters*, *12*, 457–460.

[126] Stoikov, I. I., Antipin, I. S. and Konovalov, A. I. (2010). Sinteticheskie receptory. Osnovy dizaina, koncepcii, metody konstruirovaniya na osnove (thia)calix[4]arenov *Verlag: LAP LAMBERT Academic Publishing*, 266 *(in Russian)*.

[127] Stoikov, I. I., Fitseva, N. A., Akhmetzyanova, L. R., Gafioullina, L. I., Antipin, I. S., Zheltukhin, V. F., Devyaterikova, A. I., Alfonsov, V. A. and Konovalov, A. I. (2004). Membrane transport of dicarboxylic and α_hydroxy carboxylic acids induced by α-amino phosphonates *Russ. Chem. Bull., Int. Ed.*, *53*, 1577—1583.

[128] Stoikov, I. I., Repejkov, S. A., Antipin, I. S. and Konovalov, A. I. (2000). Lipophilic aminophosphonates and their calix[4]arene derivatives: synthesis and membrane transport of biorelevant species *Heteroatom Chem.*, *11*, 518-527.

[129] Swamy, K. C. K., Kumaraswamy, S., Kumar, K. S. and Muthiah, C. (2005). Cyclic chlorophosphites as scaffolds for the one-pot synthesis of α-aminophosphonates under solvent-free conditions *Tetrahedron Lett.*, *46*, 3347–3351.

[130] Tang, J., Wang, L., Wang, W., Zhang, L., Wu, S. and Mao, D. (2011). A facile synthesis of α-aminophosphonates catalyzed by ytterbium perfluorooctanoate under solvent-free conditions *Journal of Fluorine Chemistry*, *132*, 102–106.

[131] Teng, H. B. (2010). The design and synthesis of a novel organophosphorus compound containing the structure of both β-amino acid and β-aminophosphonate *Chinese Chemical Letters*, *21*, 810–812.

[132] Tillu, V.H., Dumbre, D.K., Wakharkar, R.D. and Choudhary, V.R. (2011). One-pot three-component Kabachnik–Fields synthesis of α-aminophosphonates using H-beta zeolite catalyst *Tetrahedron Lett.*, *52*, 863–866.

[133] Tušek-Božić, L., Juribašić, M., Traldi, P., Scarcia, V. and Furlani, A. (2008). Synthesis, characterization and antitumor activity of palladium(II) complexes of monoethyl 8-quinolylmethylphosphonate *Polyhedron*, *27*, 1317–1328.

[134] Varlet, J. M. and Collignon, N. (1981). Animation reductrice des β-cetophosphonates: preparation d'acides aminoalkylphosphoniques *Tetrahedron*, 37, 3713-3721.

[135] Wang, H., Li, X., Wu, F. and Wan, B. (2012). Direct oxidative phosphonylation of amines under metal-free conditions *Tetrahedron Lett.*, *53*, 681-683.

[136] Wang, Y. and Stone A. T. (2008). Phosphonate- and Carboxylate-Based Chelating Agents that Solubilize (Hydr)oxide-Bound Mn III *Environ. Sci. Technol.*, *42*, 4397–4403.

[137] Widianti, T., Hiraga, Y., Kojima, S. and Abe, M. (2010). Novel cyclic β-aminophosphonate derivatives as efficient organocatalysts for the asymmetric Michael addition reactions of ketones to nitrostyrenes *Tetrahedron: Asymmetry*, *21*, 1861–1868.

[138] Wieczorek, J. S., Boduszek, B., Wielkopolski, W. A. and Gancarz, R. (1987). Herbicidal 9-aminofluorene-9-phosphonates *Journal f. prakt. Chemie*, *329*, 165-170.

[139] Yokomatsu, T., Yoshida, Y., Nakabayashi, N. and Shibuya, S. (1994). Simple and Efficient Method for Preparation of Conformationally Constrained Aminomethylene gem-Diphosphonate Derivatives *via* Beckmann Rearrangement *J. Org. Chem.*, *59*, 7562-7564.

[140] Zakharov, S. V., Nuriazdanova, G. Kh., Garifzyanov, A. R., Galkin, V. I. and Cherkasov, R. A. (2004). Synthesis and acid-base properties of α-aminophosphoryl compounds *Russ. Journ. Gen. Chem.*, *74*, 873-881.

[141] Zhang, F., Zhou, Y., Chen, Y., Shi, Z., Tang, Y. and Lu, T. (2010). Facile controlled preparation of phosphonic acid-functionalized gold nanoparticles *Journal of Colloid and Interface Science*, *351*, 421–426.

[142] Zhang, X.Y., Qu, Y.Y. and Fan, X.S. (2010). An efficient and green preparation of 5-aminophosphonate substituted pyrimidine nucleosides under solvent-free conditions *Chinese Chemical Letters, 21*, 1191–1194.

[143] Zhang, Y., Bai, S., Song, B., Bhadury, P. S., Hu, D., Yang, S., Zhang, X., Fan, H. and Lu, P. (2010). Enantioseparation and plant virucidal bioactivity of new quinazoline derivatives with α-aminophosphonate moiety *Journal of Chromatography B, 878*, 1285–1289.

[144] Zygmunt, J. (1985). Aziridine-2-phosphonic acid, the valuable synthon for synthesis of 1-amino-2-functionalized ethanephosphonic acids *Tetrahedron, 41*, 4979-4982.

[145] Zymanczyk-Duda, E., Lejczak, B. and Kafarski, P. (1996). Esterification of phosphonic and phosphinic acid analogues of glutamic and aspartic acids with ethyl orthoformate – scope and limitations of the method *Phosphorus, Sulfur and Silicon, 112*, 47-55.

In: Phosphorus: Properties, Health Effects and the Environment   ISBN: 978-1-62081-399-7
Editors: Ming Yue Chen and Da-Xia Yang   © 2012 Nova Science Publishers, Inc.

Chapter 2

THE ROLE OF PHOSPHORUS LIGANDS IN THE HOMO- AND CO-POLYMERIZATION OF VINYL MONOMERS

Giovanni Ricci[1], Anna Sommazzi[2], Giuseppe Leone[1], Aldo Boglia[1] and Francesco Masi[3]

[1]CNR - Istituto per lo Studio delle Macromolecole, via E. Bassini 15, Milano, Italy
[2]Eni S.p.A., Research Center of Non-Conventional Energies
Istituto Eni Donegani, Novara, Italy
[3]Polimeri Europa, San Donato Milanese, Italy

ABSTRACT

A breakthrough in the field of olefin, cycloolefin and diolefin homo- and copolymerization was, at the beginning of the '90s, the discovery, by both academic and industrial groups, of a new generation of catalysts based on transition metal and lanthanide complexes with a wide range of ligands having N, P, O or other donor atoms. The use of these novel systems permitted to obtain novel polymer structures with unique properties other than those existing, even in the well-studied field of vinyl monomer homo- and copolymerization. Among the wide range of ligands used, phosphines played a relevant role; it is well known, in fact, that phosphine steric and electronic properties strongly depend on the type of substituents on the phosphorus atoms, and that changing substituents can cause marked changes in behavior of the free ligands and of their transition metal complexes.

Among the major discoveries, we can mention:

(i)   perfectly alternating olefin/carbon monoxide copolymers obtained with catalysts based on palladium(II) complexes with bidentate chelating phosphorus ligands;

(ii) polybutadienes and polyisoprenes having different microstructure, obtained with catalysts based on cobalt and chromium complexes with mono and bidentate phosphines;

(iii) stereoregular polynorbornenes obtained with catalysts based on bidentate phosphine chromium complexes.

This paper provides an overview on recent progress in the homo- and copolymerization of vinyl monomers with catalysts based on transition metal complexes with phosphorus ligands.

1. INTRODUCTION

The history of coordinative homo- and copolymerization of olefins, cycloolefins and conjugated diolefins covers more than six decades, from the beginning in the early 1950s until today [1-13]. The first systems used were obtained by combining an early transition metal (*e.g.*, titanium, vanadium) compound (*e.g.*, chloride, alcoholate) with an aluminium-alkyl (*e.g.*, AlEt$_3$, AlEt$_2$Cl), in presence or not of an active support (*e.g.*, MgCl$_2$). With the discovery of methylaluminoxane as alkylating agent, at the beginning of 1980s, a novel generation of Ziegler-Natta catalysts, based on group 4 metallocene compounds, were introduced [14,15]. These novel systems were found to be extremely active, homogeneous and with a single site structure, allowing to develop new polyolefin materials and to improve our knowledge on the olefin and diolefin polymerization mechanism. A breakthrough in the field of olefin polymerization occurred at the beginning of 1990s, with the discovery of new catalyst systems based on transition metal complexes with various ligands having N, P, O or other donor atoms [16-18]. These systems permitted to prepare polymers with different structures and unique properties with respect to the existing ones, even in the well-studied field of olefin and diolefin homo- and copolymerization. Among the wide range of ligands used, phosphine ligands, mono- and bidentate, aliphatic and aromatic, played a relevant role, mainly due to the fact that their steric and electronic properties strongly depend on the type of substitution on the phosphorus atom. As major discoveries attributable to the use of catalysts based on phosphine transition metal complexes, we can mention: *(i)* synthesis of perfectly alternating olefin/carbon monoxide copolymers with catalysts based on palladium(II) complexes with bidentate chelating phosphorus ligands; *(ii)* synthesis of polybutadienes having a controlled microstructure (*cis*-1,4; 1,2, iso- and syndiotactic; mixed *cis*-1,4/1,2 with variable 1,2 content) with catalysts based on phosphine cobalt complexes, depending on the type of phosphine ligand coordinated to the cobalt atom; *(iii)* synthesis of 1,2 polybutadienes, isotactic and syndiotactic, with catalysts based on Cr(II) bidentate phosphine complexes; *(iv)* synthesis of crystalline and amorphous polynorbornenes with chromium and cobalt catalysts, respectively.

2. OLEFIN-CARBON MONOXIDE COPOLYMERIZATION

Alkenes and carbon monoxide are copolymerized in the presence of Group VIII-transition metal catalysts to give materials with a perfectly alternating structure (Figure 1).

Catalytic olefin/CO copolymerization has found wide interest because carbon monoxide is an exceptionally cheap starting material and the obtained polyketones are a family of high-performance thermoplastic polymers. The polar ketone groups in the polymer backbone of these materials give rise to a strong attraction between polymer chains, which increases the material melting point. Such materials also show other attractive properties like photodegradability, good chemical resistance to acids, bases and solvents, impermeability to hydrocarbons, ease of functionalization, good mechanical properties. Shell Chemical commercially launched such a thermoplastic polymer with the name of *Carilon* in the U.S. in 1996, but discontinued it in 2000, due to commercial failure. *Carilon* was made with a palladium(II) catalyst from ethylene and carbon monoxide. A small fraction of the ethylene was generally replaced with propylene to reduce the melting point (255 °C for *Carilon*). In 2002, Shell Oil Company donated his patents, related to CARILON® polyketones, to SRI International, a nonprofit research institute.

The first copolymerization was made in 1941 by Farben-fabriken Bayer under rush conditions [19]. Later, the copolymerization was studied by Reppe and Mangini [20] by using a nickel based catalyst ($K_2Ni(CN)_4$) in water and obtaining oligomers mainly. Considerable efforts were directed towards the development of catalysts derived from Group VIII transition metal complexes, capable of producing linear, perfectly alternating copolymers, with high productivity. Several metal compounds were examined such as $Ni(Bu_4N)_2(CN)_4$, $Ni(CN)_4^{2-}$/acid (acid = H_3PO_4, H_2SO_3, CF_3COOH, p-$CH_3C_6H_4SO_3H$, BF_3) [21,22], nickel complexes based upon phosphorus-oxygen chelate ligands (*e.g.*, $Ni[Ph_2PCH=C(Ph)O](PEt_3)Ph)$ [23], rhodium carbonyl complexes [24], Rh(I) catalysts ($RhCl(CO)(PPh_3)_2$, $HRh(CO)(PPh_3)_3$) [25], bis(tertiary phosphine) palladium chloride complexes [26], but with unsatisfactory results in terms of reaction conditions required, productivity, polymer molecular weights. A list of early catalysts used for CO/ethylene copolymerization was reviewed by Zhao and Chien [27].

Among the different metals, Pd(II) seemed the most promising, so the academic and industrial research was focused on this metal.

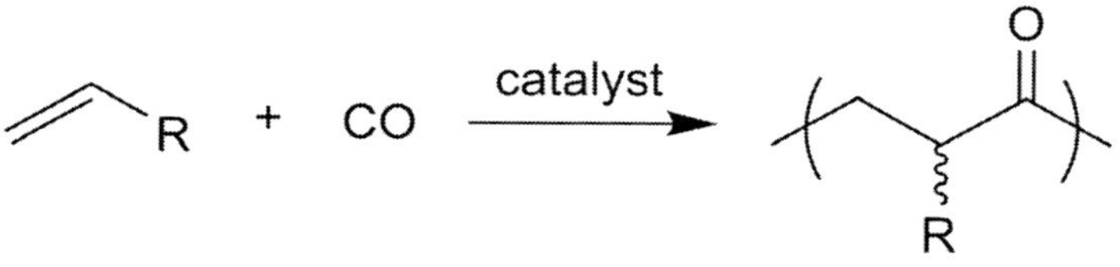

Figure 1. Alternating CO/α-olefin copolymerization.

2.1. Palladium(II)-Based Catalytic Systems

The chronological development of the main catalysts for the synthesis of polyketones is shown in Table 1.

Sen and co-workers first showed the importance of phosphorus ligand and counter ion in the catalytic complex. In fact, while the cationic Pd(II) compound $[Pd(CH_3CN)_4][BF_4]_2$ and the neutral $Pd(PPh_3)_2Cl_2$ were inactive, certain tertiary phosphine-modified Pd(II) complexes of the type $[Pd(PR_3)_n(MeCN)_{4-n}]$ $(BF_4)_2$ (n =1-3), containing both a stabilizing phosphorus ligand and a weakly coordinating tetrafluoroborate anion, produced, in dichloromethane, polyketone under mild conditions even if with results not entirely satisfactory (rather low activity) [34,35]. While the presence of the stabilizing ligand PPh_3 is necessary in order to observe some catalytic activity, an excess of ligand ($PPh_3/Pd \geq 4$) suppresses the catalytic activity, probably due the blockage of the coordination sites [34,35,38].

A considerable improvement of the prior art was accomplished when a new class of catalytic systems was discovered and patented by Shell, constituting a technological breakthrough concerning molecular weight and productivity. This great advance in the use of palladium based catalyst systems for the production of perfectly alternating copolymers of carbon monoxide with α-olefins occurred when Drent and coworkers (Shell) discovered that the replacement of monodentate ligands by bidentate ligands, in particular 1,3-bis(diphenylphosphine)propane (dppp), gives rise to high copolymerization rates and long catalysts lifetime [39-41].

The discovery of this new family derived from a study on the alcoxycarbonylation of ethylene to methylpropionate.

$$H_2C{=}CH_2 + CO + CH_3OH \xrightarrow{\text{[Pd]}} CH_3CH_2COOCH_3$$

The catalysts were based on palladium(II) compounds, bearing monodentate phosphine ligands (i.e., PPh_3), and, when used in methanol, produced a relatively high fraction of methyl propionate. The replacement of the monodentate phosphine by bidentate phosphine ligand (dppp) led to the production of a perfectly alternating CO/ethylene copolymer with 100% selectivity.

Table 1. Chronological development of C_2/CO copolymerization catalyst precursors

Year	Catalyst System	Polymerization Conditions	Activity (g C_2-CO/g metal × h)	Ref.
1948	$K_2Ni(CN)_4$	T = 150°C, P = 150 atm, time = 14 h	0.8	[20]
1970	$Pd(CN)_2$	T = 100°C, P_{CO} = 27 atm, P_{C2} = 27 atm	6.7	[28]
1970	$Pd(CN)_2/Hg(OAc)_2$	T= 125°C, P_{CO} = 27 atm, P_{C2} = 27 atm	6.5	[28]
1972	$Pd(PPh_3)_4$	T = 120°C, P_{CO} = 10 atm, P_{C2} = 58 atm	14.7	[29]
1972	$PdCl_2/PPh_3$, $(PPh_3)_2PdCl_2$	T = 95°C, P_{CO} = 10 atm, P_{C2} = 58 atm	35	[30]
1974	$HPd(CN)_3/PPh_3$	T = 115°C, P_{CO} = 10 atm, P_{C2} = 58 atm	4.7	[31]
1975	$Pd(CN)_2/acid$	T = 50-200°C, P = 200 atm	-	[32]
1976	$Ni(Bu_4N)_2(CN)_4/Ni(CN)_4^{2-}/acid$	T = 115°C, P = 70 atm, time = 66 h	19.7	[33]
1982	$[Pd(PPh_3)_n(CH_3CN)_{4-n})][BF_4]_2$	T = 25°C, P = 48 atm	3.0	[34,35]
1984	$Pd(CH_3COO)_2/dppp/acid$	T = 135°C, P = 60 atm	6000	[36]
1991	$[Pd(dpppp)(bipy)][PF_6]_2$	T = 115°C, P = 70 atm	8500	[37]
1992	$[Pd(dppp)(CH_3CN)_2](BF_4)_2/MeOH$	T = 50°C, P = 40.8 atm	775	[27]

The discovery of the combined importance of bidentate ligands and weakly coordinating counteranions opened the way for obtaining high activity catalysts for efficient synthesis of perfectly alternating polyketones. The factors that control the strictly alternating copolymer chain have been studied in detail since the discovery of the first Shell Pd(II) catalysts [36,41]. Sen was the first demonstrating that double carbonylation is thermodynamically unfavourable and suggesting that the higher affinity of Pd(II) towards CO compared to ethylene prevents multiple ethylene insertions, even at very low concentration of CO [34].

The palladium catalytic systems can be formed either as *in situ* systems, by mixing the various reagents, either as preformed complexes for isolation of neutral monochelated Pd(II) complexes of the type $Pd(L-L)(RCOO)_2$, ($R = CH_3$, CF_3) or for isolation of dicationic bis(chelate) Pd(II) complexes of formula $[Pd(L-L)(L'-L')][X]_2$ ($X = PF_6^-$, BF_4^-, CH_3COO^-, CF_3COO^-).

The *in situ* formed catalyst family is based on a ternary system: *(1)* a palladium salt of a (preferably) carboxy acid, like $[Pd(CH_3COO)_2]$ or $[Pd(CF_3COO)_2]$; *(2)* a phosphorus bidentate ligand like 1,3-bis(diarylphosphino)propane (Pd/ligand = 1 mol/mol); *(3)* a strong acid, preferably an organic acid, with a pKa value of approximately 2. Optionally an oxidant, like 1,4-benzoquinone, is added in many catalytic systems to improve the activity, probably to avoid the palladium reduction [42]. Methanol is typically used as a reaction medium, showing the stability of these catalysts in protic media. Usually, the reaction is carried out in a stirred reactor, preferably at 70-150°C, and at a total pressure of monomers of 50 – 60 bars. High molecular weight polyketone is formed at high rates (6000g C_2-CO/gPd·h) in mild reaction conditions (135°C, 60 bar) [36,41].

Moreover the palladium catalysts are active in the copolymerization or terpolymerization of alkenes other than ethylene (*i.e.*, propylene, styrene). The catalytic systems allow the polymer modification by random addition of other olefin comonomers. For example, adding also propylene to reaction gas mixture, an alternating ethylene/propylene/CO terpolymer is achieved and the propylene units are randomly distributed along the chain [43]. Propylene is predominantly incorporated in the 1-2 or 2-1 modes, while only small amounts follow the 1-3 mode [41].

Several parameters can influence the polymerization: reaction conditions, solvent, catalyst components like type of ligand, acid and oxidant, the use of preformed catalysts or catalysts prepared *in situ*. The use of phosphine catalysts prepared *in situ* may be hazardous. In fact, depending on the chelating phosphine, the preparation of the catalyst precursor *in situ* may give much lower activity than that obtained when a preformed Pd(II) complex is used.

The choice of ligand and counteranion is very important. In fact, the most efficient catalysts should have two common characteristics: a neutral ligand able of suitable bidentate coordination and an anion having a weak or non-coordinating attitude towards the metal center, in order to be displaced from the coordinating sphere by an incoming nucleofile molecule [37,41,44].

2.2. Influence of the Structure of the Diphosphine Ligands

Since the discovery by Shell of the efficacy of 1,3-bis(diphenylphosphino)propane (dppp) palladium catalysts in the alternating α-olefins/CO copolymerization [36,41], many different types of phosphine ligands have been synthesized and employed in the palladium catalysts preparation. Variation of the bidentate ligand leads to important changes in reaction rate and in the molecular weight of the obtained polyketone. The influence of the structure of the diphosphine ligands on the corresponding palladium catalysts activity was first studied by Drent and coworkers [41].

Among the chelating diphosphines of the type $Ph_2P(CH_2)_nPPh_2$, significant changes in the reaction rate and in copolymer molecular weight are obtained by varying the number of carbon atoms separating the diphenylphosphino groups.

Drent and coworkers have shown that the copolymerization catalytic activity of palladium(II) complexes with diphosphines of the type $Ar_2P(CH_2)_nPAr_2$ (n = 1-6) depends on the chain length and the aryl group (Ar). The effect of the chain length of the disphosphine $Ph_2P(CH_2)_nPPh_2$ (n = 1-6) on polymerization activity is summarized in Table 2 [41].

The rate is negligible for $Ph_2P(CH_2)PPh_2$ (n = 1), increases with $Ph_2P(CH_2)_2PPh_2$ (n = 2) up to the maximum with $Ph_2P(CH_2)_3PPh_2$ (n = 3). A further increase in chain length leads to a progressive decrease in rate activity. The molecular weight of copolymer obtained shows the same variation: it increases significantly for $Ph_2P(CH_2)_2PPh_2$, reaching a maximum for $Ph_2P(CH_2)_3PPh_2$ (dppp) and then decreasing for n = 4 and 5. While $Ph_2P(CH_2)_5PPh_2$ gives mainly oligomers, $Ph_2P(CH_2)_3PPh_2$ produces high molecular weight copolymer. According to several authors the Pd(diphosphine) chelate ring size is the main factor determining the catalyst activity. The influence of the chelate ring size on catalyst activity might be explained in terms of bite angle effects [45].

Table 2. Effect of the chain length of ligand $Ph_2P(CH_2)_nPPh_2$ on the reaction rate and molecular weight in C_2/CO copolymerization[a] [41]

Ligand	$H(CH_2CH_2CO)_nOCH_3$ $(n)^{b)}$	Productivity (g polymer/g Pd×h)
$Ph_2P(CH_2)PPh_2$	2	1
$Ph_2P(CH_2)_2PPh_2$	100	1000
$Ph_2P(CH_2)_3PPh_2$	180	6000
$Ph_2P(CH_2)_4PPh_2$	45	2300
$Ph_2P(CH_2)_5PPh_2$	6	1800
$Ph_2P(CH_2)_6PPh_2$	2	5

[a] Reaction carried out with $Pd(MeCN)_2(O_3STol)_2$ (0.1 mmol), in MeOH (150 mL), C_2H_4/CO = 1, Temperature = 84 °C, Pressure = 45 atm. [b] Average degree of polymerization (n) determined by end-group analysis from ^{13}C-NMR spectra.

The bidentate ligand $Ph_2P(CH_2)_3PPh_2$ with three CH_2 spacers ensures the correct geometry within the catalytic complex (see Figure 2).

Polymers with average molecular weights greater than those obtained with the complexes carrying unsubstituted ligands, are achieved by using special phosphines, such as diarylphosphines, having one or more polar substituents on aryl groups (for instance the complex 1,3-bis[di(2-methoxy-phenyl)phosphine]propane containing *ortho*-methoxy substituents) or by using tetrakisphosphines [46-50]. These phosphines are particularly suitable for the preparation of ethylene/propylene/CO terpolymers. In fact dppp are unsuited for the preparation of terpolymers with a high molecular weight at an acceptable reaction rate.

The effect of the dppp ligand substituents on co- and terpolymerization is reported in Table 3.

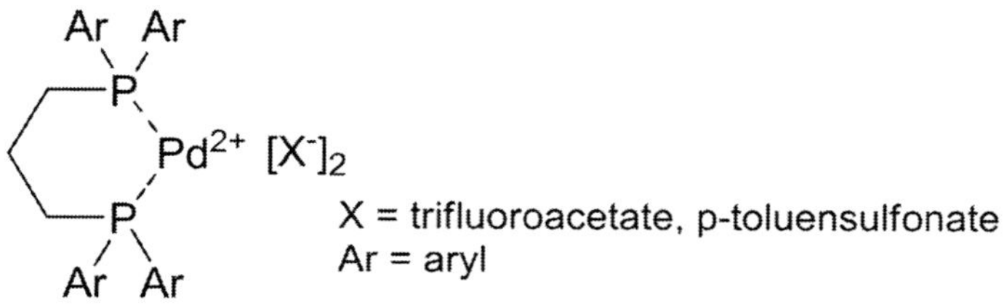

Figure 2. High productivity palladium(II) catalyst systems.

Table 3. Effect of the dppp ligand substituents on co- and terpolymerization [a] [50]

| Run | Ligand | | C_3 | $T^{c)}$ | Productivity | $LVN^{d)}$ |
	Type	mmol	(ml)	(°C)	(g polymer/g Pd × h)	(dl/g)
1	dppp	0.010	–	85	6000	0.8
2	dmpp	0.012	–	90	2300	1.7
3	dmppo	0.005	–	90	9500	1.8
4	dppp	0.010	24	87	5300	0.4
5	dmppo	0.011	24	80	3400	2.1
6[b]	dmppo	0.005	24	80	11100	2.6

dppp:1,3-bis(diphenylphosphino)propane, dmpp: 1,3-bis[di(2-methoxydiphenyl)phosphine]propane, dmppo:1,8-bis[di(2-methoxydiphenyl)phosphine]-2,7-bis[di(2-methoxyphenyl)phosphinomethyl] octane.

[a] Polymerization conditions: $Pd(OCOCH_3)_2$ = 0.01 mmol, CF_3COOH = 0.2 mmol, MeOH = 200 mL, P = 55 bar. [b] $Pd(OCOCH_3)_2$ = 0.009 mmol. [c] polymerization temperature. [d] intrinsic viscosity measured in *m*-cresol at 60°C.

For the diphosphines forming a four-memberd chelate ring (Figure 3) the presence of bulky *ortho* substituents on the aryl groups leads to an increase in the ethylene-propylene-carbon monoxide terpolymerization activity [51].

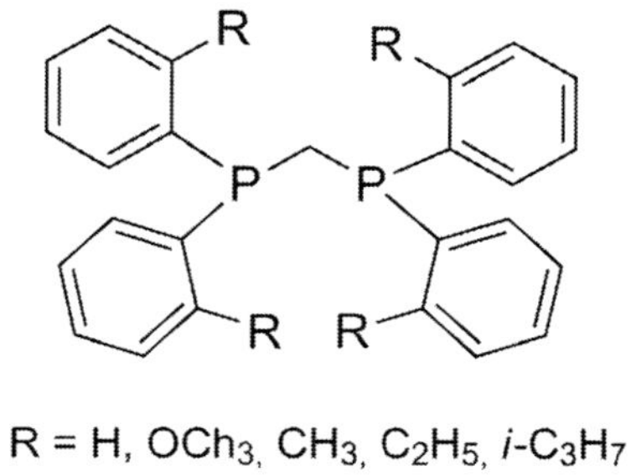

R = H, OCh3, CH3, C2H5, *i*-C3H7

Figure 3. Four-membered chelate forming ligands (dppm).

Table 4. Effect of the substituents on phenyl in ligands of the type Ar₂PCH₂PAr₂ [51]

Run	Ligand R	Activity[a] (g polymer/g Pd×h)	M_W	MWD
1	H	-[b]	58000	2.4
2	OCH$_3$	1029	81000	2.6
3	CH$_3$	2185	71000	1.7
4	C$_2$H$_5$	2776	98000	2.0
5	i-C$_3$H$_7$	9396	278000	2.6

[a] Polymerization conditions: [Pd(OAc)$_2$(ligand)] (0,01 mmol), promoter B(C$_6$F$_5$)$_3$ (0,2 mmol),C$_2$H$_4$/CO 50 barg, C$_3$H$_6$ 20 g, solvent CH$_2$Cl$_2$, temperature 70 °C, time 3h. [b]negligible, does not show activity in the copolymerization of ethylene and CO in the presence of propylene using B(C$_6$F$_5$)$_3$.

Later investigations have demonstrated that the catalytic activity and the selectivity of Ar$_2$P(CHX)$_n$PAr$_2$ ligands (Figure 4) depend not only on the number of carbon atoms bridging the two phosphorus (chelate ring size) but also on other parameters like, in some cases, the bridge rigidity of the diphosphine and the substituents of the arene on the phosphorus atoms (steric hindrance at the Pd center).

The influence of backbone rigidity on the catalytic activity is evident for the series of ligands reported in Figure 4, which form with the palladium atom a five-membered chelate ring. In comparison with the analogous diphenylphosphinoethane (dppe), the catalyst activity is increased by increasing the rigidity of the backbone (Table 5) [52].

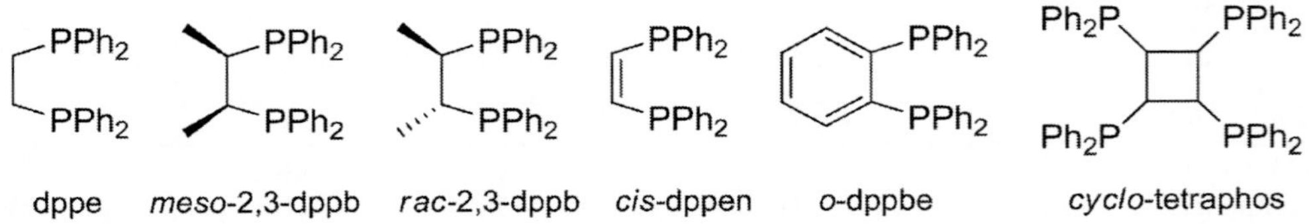

Figure 4. Sterically rigid diphosphine ligands: 1,2-bis(diphenylphosphino)etane (dppe); *meso*-2,3-bis diphenylphosphino)butane (*meso*-2,3-dppb); *rac*-2,3-bis(diphenylphosphino)butane (*rac*-2,3-dppb); *cis*-bis(diphenylphosphino)ethene (*cis*-dppen); *o*-bis(diphenylphosphino)benzene (*o*-dppbe); *cis,trans,cis*-1,2,3,4-tetrakis(diphenylphosphino)cyclobutane (*cyclo*-tetraphos).

Table 5. Ethylene/CO copolymerization catalyzed by preformed palladium catalysts Pd[P-P](CH₃CO₂)₂[a] [52]

P-P ligand	Productivity (g C$_2$-CO/g Pd× h)
dppe	1000
cis-dppen	5500
o-dppbe	6400
rac-dppb	8800
meso-dppb	11100
cyclo-tetraphos	6400

[a] Conditions Pd(P-P)(CH$_3$COO)$_2$(0.01 mmol), methanol (100mL), 1,4-benzoquinone. (0.8 mmol), TsOH (0.2 mmol), C2/CO (300psi), T (85°C), time 3 h.

Several dppp-like ligands which form with the palladium atom six-membered chelate ring have been studied in ethylene (ethylene/propylene)/CO alternating copolymerization [53].

It has been found that the introduction of certain substituents on the carbon backbone of dppp can produce beneficial effects on the catalytic activity.

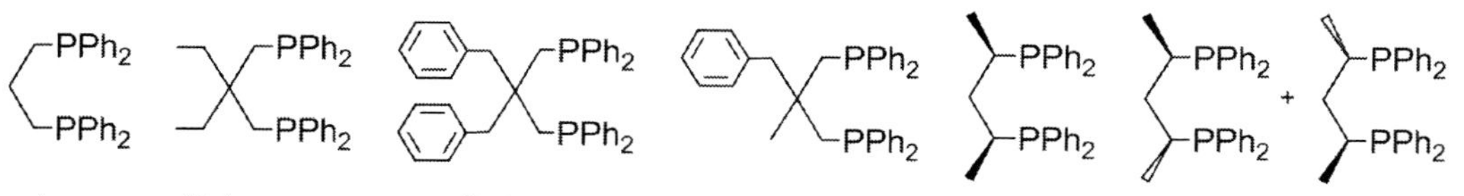

Figure 5. dppp-like ligands: 1,3-bis(diphenylphosphine)propane (dppp); 2-diethyl-1,3-bis(diphenylphosphine)propane (Etdppp); 2-dibenzyl-1,3-bis(diphenylphosphine)propane (Bzdppp); 2-benzyl-2-methyl-1,3-bis(diphenylphosphine)propane (BzMedppp); *meso*-2,4-bis(diphenylphosphine)pentane (*meso*-bdpp); *rac*-2,4-bis(diphenylphosphine)pentane (*rac*-bdpp).

The catalyst activity depends on a complex network of steric and electronic effects. The dppp-like ligands (Figure 5), bearing different substituents on the carbon backbone, used as palladium trifluoroacetate complexes in the same reaction conditions, show different activity (Table 6). The introduction of alkyl substituents in the 2-position of the carbon chain of dppp decreases the productivity (Table 6, runs 1 and 2). Instead the activity increases and, in some cases, also significantly, when substituents are introduced in both 1-positions. In particular the *meso*-bdpp ligand (Table 6, run 5) shows the highest activity. ^{31}P NMR studies on these ligands indicate that the *meso*-bdpp and *rac*-bdpp exhibit the most downfield-shifted resonances, suggesting that the palladium in the corresponding complexes is the least electron-rich [53].

Table 6. Alternating C_2/CO copolymerization catalyzed by trifluoroacetate palladium complexes with dppp-like ligands [53]

Run	Ligand	Productivity (kg C_2-Co/g Pd × h)
1	dppp	5.2
2	Etdppp	4.1
3	Bzdppp	5.9
4	BzMedppp	5.2
5	*meso*-bdpp	7.7
6	*rac*-bdpp	5.6

Polymerization conditions: $Pd(P-P)(CO_2CF_3)_2$, (0.01 mmol), methanol (100 mL), 1,4-benzoquinone (0.8 mmol), TFA (0.2 mmol), initial P_{C2} (300 psi),), initial P_{CO} (300 psi), T (85°C), time 3 h.

Dicationic bis(chelate) complexes of formula $[Pd(L-L)(L'-L')][X]_2$ (L-L = nitrogen bidentate ligand such as 2,2'-bipyridine (bipy) or 1,10 phenanthroline (phen); L'-L' = phosphorus bidentate ligand such as dppp; X = PF_6^-, CF_3COO^-, CH_3COO^-) are reported to be more efficient than monochelated dppp-Pd(II) systems [37,54]. Ethylene-carbon monoxide copolymerization with these catalysts allows to recognise some important features of these catalytic systems:

(i) the anion should be non-esterificable, non-coordinating, and hexafluorophosphate represents the best choice;

(ii) the active species is very likely a monochelated one, therefore an equilibrium involving the dissociation of at least one of the two chelating ligands has to occur in solution (Figure 6). ^{1}H NMR and ^{31}P NMR spectra of the complexes indicate that the environment of the palladium centre in solution can be either the same as in the solid state or different, depending on the solvent. While in CD_2Cl_2 the coordination sphere remains intact, partial dissociation of the nitrogen ligand is observed in coordinating solvents. NMR studies in $(CD_3)_2SO$ evidence the presence of a dissociation equilibrium of the nitrogen donor ligand from the bischelate mixed–ligand complex, yielding a monochelated phosphorated species, which is very likely the active species:

$$[Pd(dppp)(N-N)][PF_6]_2 \leftrightarrows [Pd(dppp)(solv)_2][PF_6]_2 + N-N \ (solv = DMSO).$$

The dissociation degree depends on the nature of the nitrogen ligand. For complexes with bipy and dmbipy (4,4'-dimethyl-2,2'-bipyridine), 20% and 10% of dissociation can be estimated, respectively. In the case of complexes with phenanthroline the percentage of dissociation is lower.

(iii) once dissociated the nitrogen ligand can bind to protons, buffering their concentration and influencing the molecular weight of the polymer;

(iv) dppp is the ancillary ligand which shows the highest catalytic activity in the CO-aliphatic olefin co- and terpolymerization reactions.

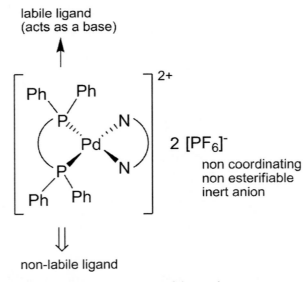

Figure 6. Schematic drawing of the different components of the catalyst precursor.

Table 7. Effect of the ligand in the catalyst precursor in ethylene/CO copolymerization[a] [54]

Run	Complex (mmol)	Activity (kg polymer/g Pd)	LVN[b] (dl/g)
1	[Pd(dppp)(bipy)][PF$_6$]$_2$	42.3	1.52
2	[Pd(dppp)(bipy)][PF$_6$]$_2$*	23.0	1.66
3	[Pd(dppp)(bipy)][BF$_4$]$_2$	2.6	n.d.
4	[Pd(dppp)(bipy)][BF$_4$]$_2$*	1.3	n.d.
5	[Pd(dppp)(dmbipy)][PF$_6$]$_2$	18.2	1.7
6	[Pd(dppp)(phen)][PF$_6$]$_2$	11.2	2.13
7	[Pd(dppp)(tmphen)][PF$_6$]$_2$	3.9	1.2
8	[Pd(dppp)(dppp)][PF$_6$O]$_2$	3.5	n.d.
9	[Pd(dppp)CF$_3$COO]$_2$	17.1	0.74
10	[Pd(dppp)CH$_3$COO]$_2$	0.08	n.d
11	Pd(CH$_3$COO)$_2$ + dppp + CF$_3$COOH	21.5	1.03

[a]Reaction conditions: Pd = 0.1 mmol; solvent (methanol) = 1200 mL; oxidant = 1,4-benzoquinone, Ox/Pd = 8 mol/mol; P$_{tot}$ = 56 atm: T = 80°C; time = 5 h. [b] Limiting viscosity number calculated in *m*-cresol at 60°C. *without oxidant. dmbipy: 4,4'-dimethyl-2,2'-bipyridine; tmphen: 3,4,7,8-tetramethyl-1,10-phenantroline.

The ligand influence on the catalytic activity is reported in Table 7.

The nature of the nitrogen ligands influences the catalytic activity as reported in Table 7.

A remarkable decrease in the copolymer yield is observed with the increase of coordinating ability of the nitrogen-donor ligand. The highest activity is obtained with 2,2'-bipyridine. Mixed ligands complexes of the type [Pd(dppp)(N-N)][PF$_6$]$_2$ show an activity higher than the corresponding symmetrical bischelated species [Pd(dppp)(dppp)][PF$_6$]$_2$, because dissociation of one of the two molecules of diphosphine is expected to be rather difficult, with consequent reduction of the concentration of monochelated active species. The mixed complex is also more active than the corresponding monochelated derivatives [Pd(dppp)CF$_3$COO]$_2$ and [Pd(dppp)CH$_3$COO]$_2$.

It is interesting to note that the non-perfect alternating copolymerization of ethylene with carbon monoxide has been uniquely obtained by palladium(II) precursors with anionic P-O ligands (Figure 7) [55].

The research of alternative conditions and most environmentally friendly and cheapest solvents in catalytic reactions has led to the study of new palladium systems for the production of polyketones by aqueous catalysis. The type of ligand offers the possibility to adapt the solubility of the catalyst for different media. Various water-soluble phosphines have been designed to give palladium complexes with good tolerance to water. First Sen [56], and, a few years later, Sheldon [57], have studied C$_2$/CO copolymerization in water with catalytic systems prepared *in situ* using a cationic Pd(II) compound ([Pd(NCCH$_3$)$_4$][BF$_4$]$_2$) with water-soluble bidentate phosphine based ligands such as those showed in Figure 8.

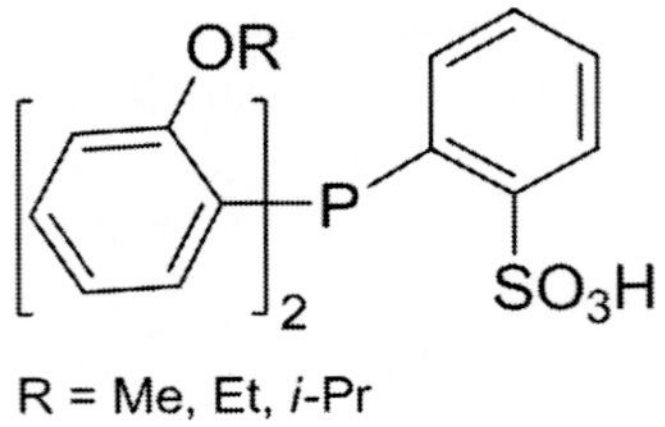

R = Me, Et, i-Pr

I

Figure 7. P-O Ligands.

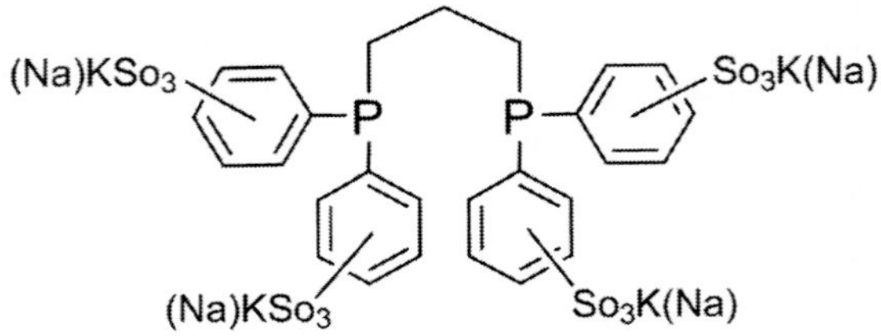

Figure 8. (dppp-SO$_3$K) Sen ligand (II), (dppp-SO3Na) Sheldon ligand (III).

The productivity obtained by Sen by using dppp-SO$_3$K ligand was quite low (470 g C$_2$/CO copolymers/g Pd in 22 h); better productivity was reported by Sheldon employing a dppp-SO$_3$Na ligand and with the co-addition of p-toluensulphonic acid in the catalytic system (4 kg C$_2$/CO copolymers/g Pd).

Other palladium complexes with water-soluble ligands, carring sulfonates or hydroxylates moieties (Figure 9), are reported to be efficient copolymerization catalysts [58,59].

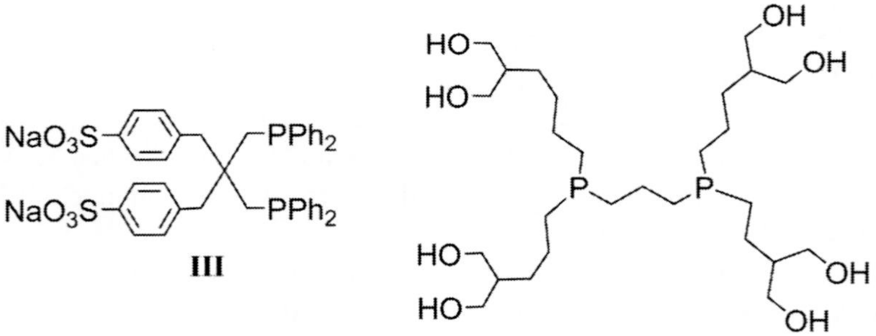

Figure 9. Water-soluble ligands, carrying sulfonates or hydroxylates moieties.

The ligand (NaO$_3$S(C$_6$H$_4$)CH$_2$)$_2$C(CH$_2$PPh$_2$)$_2$ has been designed preserving the carbon backbone of dppp ligand, used in methanol catalysis, but the polar sulfonate groups are located far away the phosphorus donors, minimizing therefore the negative charge and the steric hindrance in the proximity of phosphorus atoms, which are able to coordinate the palladium as well the corresponding atoms in well known non-water-soluble ligand (dppp). The palladium complex V (Figure 10) is easily prepared by reaction of the ligand with [Pd(CO$_2$CF$_3$)$_2$] in methanol.

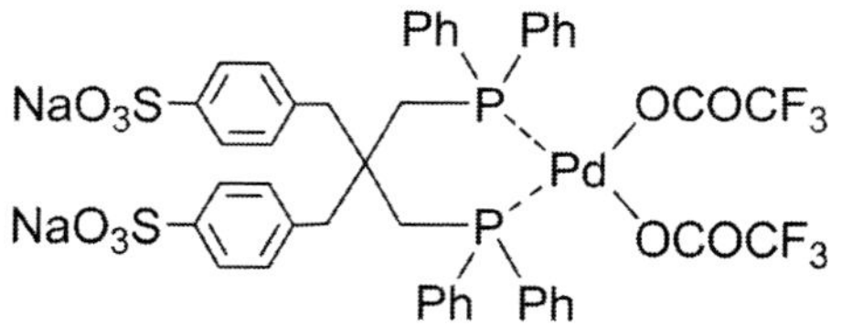

Ph   Ph

NaO$_3$S—⟨benzene ring⟩—CH$_2$—C—P—Pd—OCOCF$_3$

NaO$_3$S—⟨benzene ring⟩—CH$_2$—P—Pd—OCOCF$_3$

Ph   Ph

V

Figure 10. Palladium complex structure with water-soluble ligand (**III**).

Under comparable conditions, the activity of the palladium complex (**V**) is similar to that of the industrial Pd(II) 1,3-bis(diphenylphosphino)propane catalysts in MeOH, only using a much higher concentration of protic acid [58].

3. STEREOSPECIFIC POLYMERIZATION OF 1,3-DIENES

1,3-Dienes can give several types of polymers having different structure: *trans*-1,4; *cis*-1,4; 1,2 and, in case of asymmetric monomers (*e.g.*, isoprene), 3,4 (Figure 11a). Moreover, isotactic or syndiotactic isomers can be obtained in the case of *cis*-1,4 and *trans*-1,4 polymers when an asymmetric carbon is present in the polymer chain (*e.g.*, polymers from 1,3-pentadiene) (Figure 11b). Stereoregular 1,2- or 3,4-polydienes may also exhibit iso- or syndiotacticity and, depending on the structure of the monomer, the double bond in the side chain may present a *trans* or a *cis* configuration (Figure 11c).

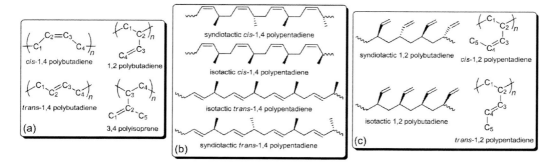

Figure 11. Polydienes microstructures.

The above stereoregular diene polymers can be obtained only through the stereospecific polymerization, which, differently from other polymerization methods (*i.e.*, radical and ionic polymerization), is characterized by *i*) high chemoselectivity, *i.e.* it can give polymers having only one type of monomeric unit (1,4; 1,2 or 3,4) and *ii*) high stereoselectivity, *i.e.* it can give polymers with a very high configurational order when steric isomeric sites are present on the monomeric unit (*e.g.*, an internal double bond, an asymmetric carbon).

The polymerization of 1,3-dienes with Ziegler-Natta catalysts [8] began in 1954, just after the first results obtained in the α-olefin polymerization. The first catalysts used were obtained by combining TiCl$_4$ or TiCl$_3$ with aluminium-alkyls, the catalyst systems already used for the polymerization of ethylene and propylene. The first stereoregular polydiene synthesized was a polyisoprene with a structure very similar to that of natural rubber [60], and it was immediately followed by a polyisoprene with a structure very close to that of gutta-percha [61]. Successively, several other catalytic systems, obtained by combining transition metal (*e.g.*, Ti, V, Cr, Fe, Co, Ni) compounds or lanthanide (*e.g.*, Nd, Pr) compounds with suitable alkylating agents (*e.g.*, AlEt$_3$, AlEt$_2$Cl), were proposed and examined, leading to a breakthrough in the field of conjugated diolefin polymerization [8-11]. Four stereoregular polymers were obtained from 1,3-butadiene, having a *trans*-1,4, *cis*-1,4, isotactic 1,2 and syndiotactic 1,2 structures, respectively; several other stereoregular polymers were obtained from terminal substituted butadienes (CH$_2$=CH–CH=CHR; R = alkyl group) and disubstituted butadienes [*e.g.* CH$_2$=C(Me)–C(Me)=CH$_2$; CH$_2$=CH–CH=CMe$_2$; CH$_2$=C(Me)CH=CH(Me); CH(Me)=CH–CH=CH(Me)]. More detailed information on catalysts and polymers can be found on some already published reviews on this topic [8-11].

With the discovery of methylaluminoxane as alkylating agent, at the beginning of the '80s [62,63], novel catalytic systems were introduced in the field of conjugated diolefin polymerization [64-70]. These novel catalysts were in some cases more active and stereospecific than those previously known and based on common aluminium-alkyls. Specifically, MAO permitted to use, as catalyst precursors, cyclopentadienyl transition metal compounds (*e.g.*, CpTiCl$_3$, Cp$_2$TiCl$_2$, CpVCl$_2$) [71-76], obtaining extremely active catalytic systems able to polymerize also monomers such as (Z)-1,3-pentadiene [77-79] and 4-methyl-1,3-pentadiene [71,73-76,80], which were not polymerized with the common Ziegler-Natta catalysts.

A further improvement in the polymerization of 1,3-dienes was recently achieved by using catalysts based on transition metal (mainly cobalt and chromium) complexes with phosphorus ligands in combination with MAO. These systems were extremely active and allowed to modulate the polydiene microstructure (*cis*-1,4; 1,2; mixed *cis*-1,4/1,2 structure with variable 1,2 content) by varying the type of ligand and metal [12,13,81-90]. The same catalysts were also able to give novel highly stereoregular polymers from different types of substituted butadienes (*e.g.*, isoprene, 1,3-pentadiene, 1,3-hexadiene, 3-methyl-1,3-pentadiene) [91-97]. Furthermore, their ability to polymerize different types of 1,3-dienes allowed to support some of the hypotheses previously formulated on the diene polymerization mechanism [8,74,75,12,98-122] and to highlight some novel aspects of the mechanism, such as the influence of the catalyst structure (*i.e.*, type of ligand on the metal) and of the monomer structure on the polymerization stereoselectivity.

3.1. Polymerization of 1,3-Dienes with Cobalt Catalysts

Several catalytic systems based on transition metals and lanthanides were investigated for the polymerization of 1,3-dienes [8,9-11]. The systems based on cobalt proved perhaps the most versatile ones, since, by varying the catalytic formulation, they were able to give, showing high catalytic activity and stereospecificity, all the possible polybutadiene stereoisomers: cis-1,4 polybutadiene, 1,2 polybutadiene, polybutadiene with a mixed cis-1,4 / 1,2 structure, trans-1,4 polybutadiene. The most common cobalt catalysts used in the polymerization of 1,3-butadiene are summarized in Table 8.

Table 8. Polymerization of butadiene with cobalt-based catalysts

Catalyst	Polybutadiene microstructure	Ref.
$Co(acac)_2$-$AlEt_2Cl$-H_2O	*cis*-1,4 (~97%)	[123]
$CoCl_2$-MAO	*cis*-1,4 (~97%)	[84]
$Co(acac)_3$-MAO	*cis*-1,4 (~97%)	[124]
$Co(acac)_3$-$AlEt_3$-H_2O	equibinary *cis*-1,4/1,2 polybutadiene	[125]
$Co(acac)_3$-$AlEt_3$-H_2O-CS_2	syndiotactic 1,2 polybutadiene	[126-129]
$(\eta^5$-$C_8H_{13})(\eta^4$-$C_4H_6)Co$ at -30°C	syndiotactic 1,2 polybutadiene	[130]
$(\eta^5$-$C_8H_{13})(\eta^4$-$C_4H_6)Co/CS_2$	syndiotactic 1,2 polybutadiene	[126-129]
$AlEt_2Cl$-$Co(acac)_2$-NMe_3 (or NEt_3)	*trans*-1,4 polybutadiene (~95%)	[131]

Very recently some novel catalyst systems based on cobalt phosphine complexes were introduced. An interesting aspect of these catalysts was that the phosphine seemed to have a strong influence on the catalyst stereospecificity. This fact prompted the researchers to systematically explore the polymerization of butadiene with catalysts based on cobalt complexes with different phosphine ligands [84-86,132-137]; it is well known in fact that steric and electronic properties of phosphines strongly depend on the type of substituents on the phosphorus atom [45,138-140].

It turned out that the use of defined cobalt complexes with commercial phosphines in combination with methylaluminoxane (MAO) allowed to manage polybutadiene microstructure. Moreover, these catalysts worked very well at room temperature, in aliphatic solvents, and were very active at rather low Al/Co molar ratio.

Several cobalt complexes with mono- and bidentate phosphines, aliphatic and aromatic, were synthesized and characterized (Figure 12); for some of them single crystals were obtained and the crystalline molecular structure was determined (Figure 13) [84-86,136].

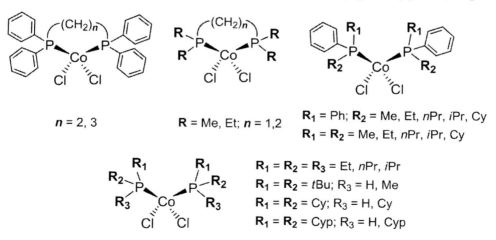

Figure 12. Cobalt phosphine complexes.

All the cobalt phospine complexes synthesized were used as catalyst precursors for the polymerization of 1,3-butadiene, obtaining polymers having different microstructure (*cis*-1,4; 1,2; mixed *cis*-1,4/1,2 with variable 1,2 content) depending on the type of phosphine on the cobalt atom (Table 9) [12,13,84,86,135,137].

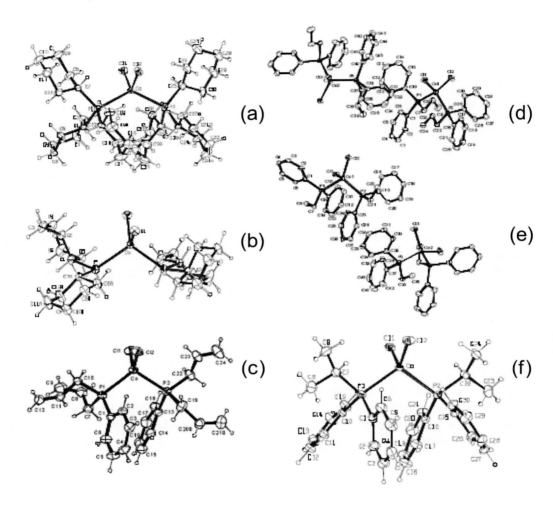

Figure 13. X-Ray Crystal molecular structure of (a) $CoCl_2(PCy_3)_2$; (b) $CoCl_2(PCy_2H)_2$; (c) $CoCl_2(P(C_3H_5)_2Ph)_2$; (d) $CoCl_2(PEtPh_2)_2$; (e) $CoCl_2(P^nPrPh_2)_2$; (f) $CoCl_2(P^iPrPh_2)_2$.

In the polymerization of 1,3-butadiene with aliphatic cobalt phosphine complexes, high *cis*-1,4 or predominantly *cis*-1,4 polymers were obtained with catalysts using more hindered ligands (*e.g.*, P^tBu_3; P^iPr_3; P^tBu_2Me; PCy_3; $PCyp_3$), while polybutadienes with a mixed *cis*-1,4/1,2 structure or predominantly 1,2 structure were obtained in the case of less hindered ligands (PCy_2H; P^tBu_2H;PEt_3; P^nPr_3) [12,13,84,135]. The *cis* content seems indeed to increase with increasing the ligand bulkiness.

Table 9. Polymerization of butadiene with catalysts based on aliphatic phosphine cobalt complexes [a]

Run	catalyst	polymerization				polymer		
	Co-complex	θ [b] (deg)	time (min)	conv (%)	cis-1,4 [c] (%)	1,2 [c] (%)	M_w [d] (g/mol)	M_w/M_n [d]
1	$CoCl_2(PEt_3)_2$	132	30	74.8	39.9	60.1		
2	$CoCl_2(P^nPr_3)_2$	132	35	85.5	38.2	61.8		
3	$CoCl_2(PCy_2H)_2$	143	30	70.8	51.0	49.0	280000	1.9
4	$CoCl_2(P^tBu_2H)_2$	150	35	60.4	59.0	41.0	275000	2.0
5	$CoCl_2(P^tBu_2Me)_2$	161	40	59	94.0	6.0	260000	1.8
6	$CoCl_2(PCyp_3)_2$	—	39	56.4	73.6	26.4	245000	2.0
7	$CoCl_2(PCy_3)_2$	170	32	44.4	77.4	22.6	250000	2.1
8	$CoCl_2(P^iPr_3)_2$	160	20	57.4	94.5	5.5	340000	2.3
9[g]	$CoCl_2(P^iPr_3)_2$	160	25	50.2	92.8	7.2	330000	2.9
10	$CoCl_2(P^tBu)_3$	182	22	73.0	96.0	4.0	360000	2.0
11[g]	$CoCl_2(P^tBu)_3$	182	25	67.5	94.0	6.0	320000	2.6
12	$CoCl_2$	—	52	68.6	95.4	4.6	815000	2.2

[a] Polymerization conditions: butadiene, 2 mL; toluene (heptane in runs 9 and 11), 16 mL; MAO, Al/Co = 1000; moles of Co, 5×10^{-6}; temperature, +20 °C. [b] Phosphine cone angle, as reported by Tolman [140]. [c] Determined by 1H NMR. *Trans*-1,4 units are almost negligible, as indicated by the fact that in the IR spectra of the polymers no band at 967 cm^{-1} was detected. [d] Molecular weight and molecular weight distribution determined by GPC.

It is worthwhile to note that the high *cis*-1,4 polymers obtained with catalysts using hindered phosphines (*e.g.*, P^{t}Bu$_3$, P^{i}Pr$_3$, P^{t}Bu$_2$Me) are branched, while the high *cis*-1,4 polymers from CoCl$_2$-MAO are linear [12,13,135]. This different behavior seems to indicate that the two systems, although giving polymers having the same microstructure, are in some way different, and that the phosphine ligand is not displaced from the cobalt atom during the polymerization (Figure 14). The above suggestion is also supported by the fact that in the polymers having a mixed *cis*-1,4/1,2 structure, the *cis*-1,4 and 1,2 units are randomly distributed along the polymer chain, and consequently do not originate from different active sites.

High *cis*-1,4 polymers (around 95%) were also obtained with CoCl$_2$[R$_2$P(CH$_2$)$_n$PR$_2$]/MAO (R = Me, Et, Ph; n = 1, 2), independently on the cobalt complex used (Table 10) [12,13,135].

If the active site structure in the polymerization of butadiene with cobalt phospine complexes based catalysts is that shown in Figure 14, with the butenyl group of the growing chain η^3-bonded, and the incoming butadiene monomer *cis*-η^4-bonded, only one phosphorus atom can coordinate to the cobalt atom because otherwise, with two phosphorus atoms coordinated, we would have an electron in excess with respect to the rare gas (18e) rule. It follows that in the active site formed in the polymerization of 1,3-butadiene with catalysts based on bidentate phosphine cobalt complexes, the bidentate phosphine likely remains coordinated to the cobalt atom with only one phosphorus atom (Figure 14b) [12,13].

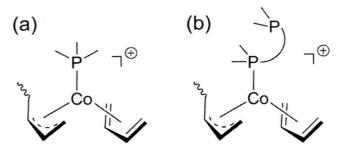

Figure 14. Possible active site structures in the polymerization of 1,3-butadiene with cobalt phosphine complexes-based catalysts (only the *exo-exo* structure is shown): (a) monodentate phosphines; (b) bidentate phosphines.

Table 10. Polymerization of 1,3-butadiene with catalyst based on bidentate phosphine cobalt complexes [a]

Co-complex	polymerization[a]		*cis*-1,4[b]	M_w[c]	polymer	
	time (min)	conv (%)	(%)	(g/mol)	M_w/M_n[c]	g[d]
CoCl$_2$	47	74	95.4	615000	2.2	1.00
CoCl$_2$(dmpm)	86	32	95.0	463000	2.7	0.80
CoCl$_2$(dmpe)	91	55	95.2	237000	2.6	0.82
CoCl$_2$(depe)	76	63	94.1	249000	2.0	0.79
CoCl$_2$(dppe)	125	48	96.1	147000	2.3	0.86
CoCl$_2$(dppp)	100	50	96.3	155000	2.4	0.87

[a] Polymerization conditions: butadiene, 5 mL; toluene, total volume, 40 mL; MAO, Al/Co = 1000; moles of Co, 1×10^{-5}; temperature, +20°C. [b] Determined by ^{1}H NMR. The remaining units are 1,2. [c] Molecular weight and molecular weight distribution determined by GPC analysis. [d] g is a branching index, calculated by GPC/MALLS analysis.

The systems CoCl$_2$(PRPh$_2$)$_2$/MAO (R = methyl, *normal*-propyl, ethyl, allyl, *iso*-propyl, cyclohexyl) were found to be extremely active in the polymerization of butadiene (Table 11); complete conversions were reached in a few minutes [12,13,85,86,137]. The polymers obtained are essentially 1,2, in the range 70÷88 %, and the 1,2 content varies with varying the type of complex and the polymerization conditions. The polymer tacticity strongly depends on the type of complex, *i.e.* the type of phosphine bonded to the cobalt atom. The syndiotactic index (expressed as percentage of syndiotactic triads *rr*) of the polymers, determined by their

^{13}C NMR spectra (Figure 15), increases with increasing the hindrance of the phosphorus ligand, *i.e.* the steric demand of the alkyl group bonded to the phosphorus atom.

The 1,2 polybutadienes obtained with the cobalt systems using less hindered ligands (*e.g.*, PMePh$_2$; PEtPh$_2$; P^{n}PrPh$_2$) (Table 11, runs 1-3) are amorphous and no melting point could be detected; the T$_g$ values of these polymers were found to be in the range -10 ÷ -15°C. The polymers obtained with systems using more hindered ligands (*e.g.*, P^{i}PrPh$_2$ and PCyPh$_2$) (Table 11, runs 5 and 6) are crystalline by X-ray with a melting point around 110-120°C, depending on the polymerization conditions. They exhibit T$_g$ values in the range 3÷5°C and crystallization enthalpies ranging from −10 to −20 J/g (DSC data).

Table 11. Polymerization of butadiene with CoCl$_2$(PR$_n$Ph$_{3-n}$)$_2$/MAO (R = Me, Et, ^{n}Pr, allyl, ^{i}Pr, Cy; n = 1,2) [a]

Run	Co-complex	polymerization		polymer microstructure [b]			T$_m$ [c] (°C)
		time	conv	cis-1,4	1,2	rr:mr:mm	
		(min)	(%)	(%)	(%)	(molar fraction)	
1	CoCl$_2$(PMePh$_2$)$_2$	5	64.7	23.9	76.1	24/52/24	—
2	CoCl$_2$(PEtPh$_2$)$_2$	5	93.7	22.3	77.7	42/45/13	—
3	CoCl$_2$(P^{n}PrPh$_2$)$_2$	5	100	21.3	78.7	44/43/13	—
4	CoCl$_2$[P(allyl)Ph$_2$]$_2$	5	76	19.8	80.2	41/44/15	—
5	CoCl$_2$(P^{i}PrPh$_2$)$_2$	5	100	14.6	85.4	74/26/0	126
6	CoCl$_2$(PCyPh$_2$)$_2$	5	75.0	15.5	84.5	69/27/4	109
7	CoCl$_2$(PMe$_2$Ph)$_2$	5	39.8	27.0	73.0	15/51/34	—
8	CoCl$_2$(PEt$_2$Ph)$_2$	5	55.4	24.7	75.3	19/49/32	—
9	CoCl$_2$[P(allyl)$_2$Ph]$_2$	5	40.1	26.0	74.0	22/49/29	—
10	CoCl$_2$(PCy$_2$Ph)$_2$	5	55.1	20.6	79.4	44/41/15	—

[a] Polymerization conditions: butadiene, 2 mL; toluene, total volume 16 mL; MAO, Al/Co = 100; 5×10^{-6} moles of Co; polymerization temperature, +20°C. The molecular weight and molecular weight distribution of the amorphous 1,2 polybutadienes are in the range 250–300000 g/mol and 2–2.5, respectively. The predominantly syndiotactic 1,2 polybutadienes (runs 4-10) were not soluble in the GPC conditions used. [b] Determined by ^{1}H and ^{13}C NMR analysis; trans-1,4 units were found to be negligible, as indicated by the extremely low intensity of the band at 967 cm^{-1} in the IR spectra of the polymers. [c] melting temperature, determined by DSC.

The polymerizaton of butadiene with the systems CoCl$_2$(PR$_2$Ph)$_2$/MAO (Table 11, runs 7-10) was also examined [12,13,85,137]. Essentially 1,2 polymers were obtained also in this case but the syndiotactic index of the polymers, at the same polymerization conditions, was in general slightly lower with respect to that of the 1,2 polybutadienes obtained with CoCl$_2$(PRPh$_2$)$_2$ / MAO.

Table 12. Polymerization of 1,3-dienes with the systems CoCl₂(PRPh₂)₂/MAO (R= *normal*-propyl, *iso*-propyl) [a)]

Monomer[b)]	Co-complex	Polymerization					Polymer		
		time (min)	conv (%)	1,2[c)] (%)	rr[d)] (%)	mm[d)] (%)	M_w[e)] (g/mol)	M_w/M_n[e)]	T_m[f)] (°C)
EP	CoCl₂(P^{i}PrPh₂)₂	180	78.0	~99	72		220000	1.7	132
EP	CoCl₂(P^{n}PrPh₂)₂	30	97.2	~99	45		101000	1.4	n.d.
H	CoCl₂(PP^{i}PrPh₂)₂	300	49.9	~99	63		74000	1.9	95
H	CoCl₂(P^{n}PrPh₂)₂	300	50.4	~99	38		65000	1.7	n.d.
3MP	CoCl₂(PP^{i}PrPh₂)₂	7200	79.1	~99		≥60	62000	1.6	79
3MP	CoCl₂(P^{n}PrPh₂)₂	7200	78.0	~99		≥90	81000	1.2	101

[a)] Polymerization conditions: monomer, 2 mL; toluene, total volume 16 mL; Co, 1×10^{-5} moles; MAO, Al/Co = 100; +20°C. [b)] EP = E-1,3-pentadiene; H = 1,3-hexadiene; 3MP = 3-methyl-1,3-pentadiene. [c)] percentage of 1,2 units, determined by NMR analysis (the remaining units are essentially *cis*-1,4, being *trans*-1,4 units almost negligible). [d)] Triads molar ratio, determined by NMR analysis; complementary percentages are mainly due to mr triads. [e)] Molecular weight and molecular weight distribution, determined by GPC analysis. [f)] Determined by DSC analysis.

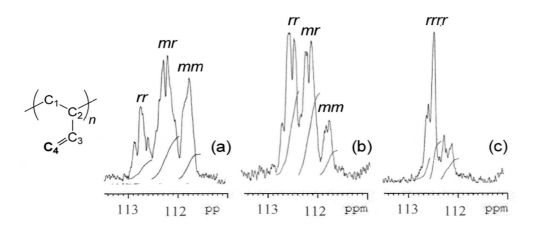

Figure 15. ^{13}C NMR spectra (olefinic region, C4 signal; C₂D₂Cl₄, HMDS as internal standard, 103°C) of 1,2 polybutadienes obtained with (a) CoCl₂(PMePh₂)₂/MAO (Table 4, run 1); (b) CoCl₂(P^{n}PrPh₂)₂/MAO (Table 4, run 3); (c) CoCl₂(PCyPh₂)₂/MAO (Table 4, run 6).

The systems CoCl₂(PRPh₂)₂/MAO were also used for the polymerization of substituted butadienes such as 1,3-pentadiene, 1,3-hexadiene and 3-methyl-1,3-pentadiene (Table 12) [85,12,13,92,95].

The systems CoCl₂(PRPh₂)₂/MAO (R = methyl, ethyl, *normal*-propyl, *iso*-propyl, cyclohexyl) gave 1,2-polymers from all the above monomers (Figure 16). As occurred in the polymerization of 1,3-butadiene, the polymers from 1,3-pentadiene and 1,3-hexadiene were predominantly syndiotactic when R = *iso*-propyl or cyclohexyl, while they had an atactic structure, with predominance of syndiotactic sequences, when R = methyl, ethyl or *normal*-propyl. The polymers from 3-methyl-1,3-pentadiene were also crystalline, but exhibited an opposite tacticity, isotactic instead of syndiotactic. In particular $CoCl_2(P''PrPh_2)_2/MAO$, giving the "less syndiotactic" polybutadienes, polypentadienes, and polyhexadienes, gave the "most isotactic" poly(3-methylpentadiene)s; *vice versa*, $CoCl_2(P'PrPh_2)_2/MAO$, giving the "most syndiotactic" polybutadiene, polypentadiene, and polyhexadiene, gave the "less isotactic" poly(3-methyl-1,3-pentadiene).

Very recently the polymerization of isoprene with $CoCl_2(PRPh_2)_2/MAO$ (R = alkyl group) was also examined [97]. Unexpectedly a polymer having a rather unusual equibinary, alternating *cis*-1,4/3,4 structure, was obtained.

The formation of polymers having different tacticity from the same monomer with different cobalt phosphine complexes based catalysts, and the different behavior exhibited by 3-methyl-1,3-pentadiene with respect to the other monomers had some mechanistic implications, and allowed us, as illustrated in the paragraph reported below, to validate once more the diene polymerization mechanism previously proposed.

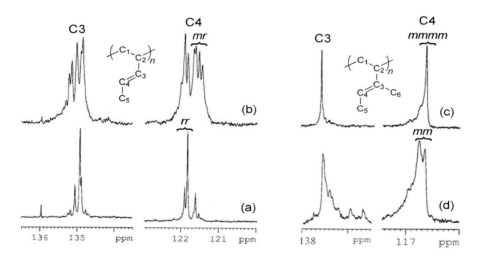

Figure 16. ^{13}C NMR spectra (olefinic region) of (a) *(E)*-1,2 polypentadiene obtained with $CoCl_2(P'PrPh_2)_2/MAO$; (b) *(E)*-1,2 polypentadiene obtained with $CoCl_2(P''PrPh_2)_2/MAO$; (c) *(E)*-1,2 poly(3-methyl-1,3-pentadiene) obtained with $CoCl_2(P'PrPh_2)_2/MAO$; (d) *(E)*-1,2 poly(3-methyl-1,3-pentadiene) obtained with $CoCl_2(P''PrPh_2)_2/MAO$ ($C_2D_2Cl_4$, HMDS as internal standard, 103°C).

3.2. Polymerization of 1,3-Dienes with Chromium Catalysts

Chromium catalysts, differently from other transition metals such as Ti or Co, were not extensively studied; nevertheless, they play a relevant role in the field of 1,3-diene polymerization, being among the first systems used for the preparation of 1,2 polybutadiene [141]. 1,2 Polybutadiene is a polymer of industrial interest, and can exist in three different isomeric forms: isotactic, syndiotactic and atactic. Specifically, the syndiotactic polymer is used in the production of films (packaging breathing items for fruits, vegetables and seafood), footwear soles, tubes and hoses; the atactic polymer is used in the rubber and tire industry

[142-144]. The importance of chromium catalysts in the field of butadiene polymerization is pointed out by the fact that, up to now, 1,2 isotactic polybutadiene was obtained only with chromium systems. Specifically, this polybutadiene isomer was obtained several years ago by Porri using catalysts prepared from aluminium trialkyls and soluble Cr compounds [141]. These apparently homogeneous catalysts gave either syndiotactic or isotactic polymers, or a mixture of them, depending in particular on the Al/Cr molar ratio. At low Al/Cr ratios predominantly syndiotactic polymers were obtained, while upon increasing the Al/Cr ratio, the amount of isotactic polymer gradually increased.

The above systems were however characterized by not exceptional catalytic activity and stereospecificity, in the sense that large amount of catalyst had to be used to obtain acceptable polymer yield, and that the proportion of the crystalline product, with respect to the crude polymer, was generally low.

Recently more active and stereospecific catalysts for the polymerization of 1,3-dienes (butadiene in particular) were obtained by combining chromium bidentate-phosphine complexes with MAO [13,81,83,87,88,90].

The bidentate phosphine chromium(II) complexes (Figure 17) were prepared by reacting $CrCl_2(THF)$ with various bidentate phosphines (Table 13), using toluene or diethyl ether as solvent [83,87,145-147].

Table 13. Bidentate phosphines used for the chromium complexes syntheses

bis(dimethylphosphino)methane	*dmpm*	1,2-bis(dicyclohexylphosphino) ethane	*dcpe*
1,2-bis(dimethylphosphino)ethane	*dmpe*	bis(diphenylphosphino)methane	*dppm*
1,2-bis(diethylphosphino)ethane	*depe*	1,2-bis(diphenylphosphino) ethane	*dppe*
1,3-bis(diethylphosphino)propane	*depp*	1,3-bis(diphenylphosphino) propane	*dppp*
bis(dicyclohexylphosphino)methane	*dcpm*	bis(diphenylphosphino)amine	*dppa*

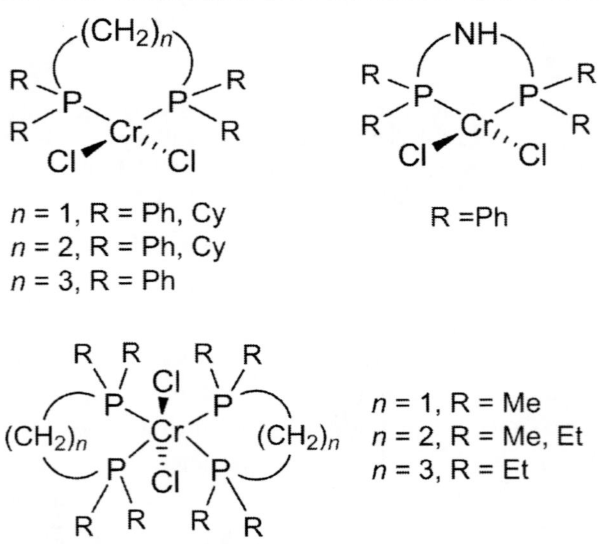

Figure 17. Cr(II) complexes with bidentate phosphines.

The crystal structures of some of the complexes prepared (Figure 18) [83], together with the elemental analyses of all the products obtained, clearly indicated that two ligands were bonded to the chromium atom in case of *dmpm, dmpe, depe,* and *depp,* while only one bidentate phosphine was bonded in case of *dcpm, dcpe, dppm, dppe, dppp* and *dppa* (Figure 17). This different behaviour was mainly attributed to the different steric hindrance of the ligands [45,138-140], which, as shown below, was found to strongly affect the catalytic activity and stereospecificity of the corresponding chromium complex.

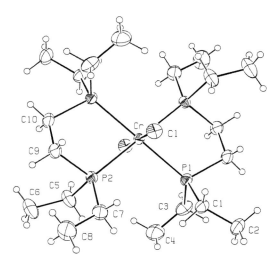

Figure 18. ORTEP plot of $CrCl_2(depe)_2$ with atom numbering scheme. Displacement ellipsoids are drawn at the 30% probability.

The above phosphine chromium complexes were used in combination with MAO for the polymerization of 1,3-butadiene (Table 14).

They were found to be, in some cases, extremely active, giving essentially 1,2 polybutadienes (1,2 content >85%) having different tacticity (syndiotactic or predominantly isotactic) depending on the phosphine ligand bonded to the chromium atom [81,83,87]. A correlation between stereoselectivity and phosphine ligand bulkiness was suggested, based on the fact that, as it is well known, steric and electronic effects of phosphorus ligands strongly depend on the type of substituents on phosphorus atom [45,138-140]. Essentially isotactic 1,2 polybutadienes were obtained with catalysts having minimally hindered phosphines (*e.g.,* $CrCl_2(dmpm)_2$-MAO; $CrCl_2(dppm)$-MAO), while highly syndiotactic 1,2 polymers were obtained using catalysts with more hindered ligands (*e.g.,* $CrCl_2(dmpe)_2$-MAO; $CrCl_2(depe)_2$-MAO; $CrCl_2(dppa)$-MAO) (Figure 19).

With much more hindered phosphines (*e.g.,* $CrCl_2(depp)_2$-MAO; $CrCl_2(dppp)$-MAO; $CrCl_2(dcpe)$-MAO), predominantly 1,2 syndiotactic polymers were still obtained, but with a lower 1,2 content (70-80%), meaning that the type of ligand has also some influence on chemoselectivity. The catalyst activity too was found to be strongly influenced by the type of phosphine ligand. In general quite good monomer conversions were reached in a relatively short polymerization time. Nevertheless, catalyst activity was particularly high for catalysts using less hindered phosphines (*e.g., dmpm* and *dppm;* only one CH_2 group bridging the two phosphorus atoms). The maximum activity was exhibited by the $CrCl_2(dppa)$-MAO system;

this fact was tentatively interpreted by admitting that the presence of a potential donor nitrogen atom in the bridge between the two phosphorus atoms could in some way affect the electronic properties of the complex [45,138-140].

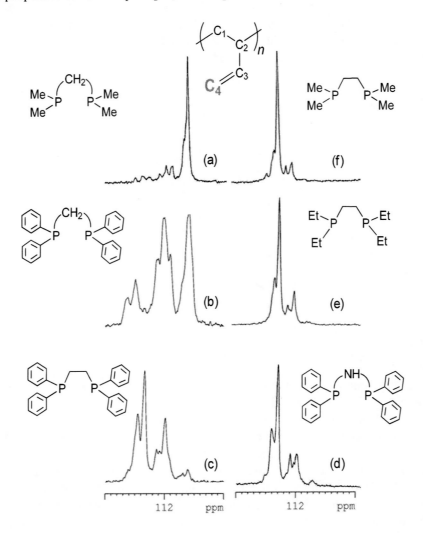

Figure 19. ^{13}C NMR spectra ($C_2D_2Cl_4$; HMDS as internal standard; 103°C; olefinic region, C4 signal) of 1,2 polybutadienes obtained with (a) $CrCl_2$ (dmpm)$_2$-MAO; (b) $CrCl_2$(dppm)-MAO; (c) $CrCl_2$(dppe)-MAO; (d) $CrCl_2$(dppa)-MAO; (e) $CrCl_2$(depe)$_2$-MAO; (f) $CrCl_2$(dmpe)$_2$-MAO.

The system $CrCl_2$(dmpe)$_2$-MAO was also used for the polymerization of substituted butadienes such as isoprene, (E)-1,3-pentadiene and (Z)-1,3-pentadiene (Table 15) [13,81,83,87,88,90].

Isoprene polymerizes much more slowly than butadiene to give an essentially 3,4 polymer (≥90%), which was found to be amorphous by X-ray. The low stereoregularity of the polymer is clearly evident from the multiplicity exhibited by the olefinic carbons in the ^{13}C NMR spectrum (Figure 20).

Table 14. Polymerization of 1,3-butadiene with chromium(II) catalysts

Cr-complex	Polymerization[a]			Polymer	
	time (min)	yield (%)	1,2[b] (molar %)	rr/mr/mm[c] (molar ratio)	m.p.[d] (°C)
CrCl$_2$(dmpm)$_2$	30	80.2	89	16/13/71	—
CrCl$_2$(dmpe)$_2$	60	39.5	95	83/17/0	152
CrCl$_2$(depe)$_2$	60	76.0	89	72/26/2	106
CrCl$_2$(depp)$_2$	160	31.1	84.8	67/30/3	104
CrCl$_2$(dcpe)	1110	5.9	66.0		—
CrCl$_2$(dppm)	20	55.7	89	18/48/34	—
CrCl$_2$(dppe)	1020	15.3	88	61/34/5	95
CrCl$_2$(dppp)	1440	17.6	80	64/32/4	100
CrCl$_2$(dppa)	5	37.5	90	66/30/4	105

[a] Polymerization conditions: butadiene, 2 mL; toluene, total volume 16 mL; MAO, Al/Cr = 1000; Cr, 1×10^{-5} mol; polymerization temperature, +20°C. [b] Determined by NMR analysis; the remaining units are essentially *cis*-1,4. [c] Molar ratio of 1,2 syndiotactic/atactic/isotactic triads, determined by ^{13}C NMR analysis. [d] Melting point determined by DSC analysis.

A predominantly *cis*-1,4 polymer having an isotactic structure was obtained from *(E)*-1,3-pentadiene, while an exclusively *cis*-1,4 polymer, amorphous by X-ray, was obtained from *(Z)*-1,3-pentadiene (Table 15) [81].

Table 15. Polymerization of substituted butadienes with CrCl$_2$(dmpe)$_2$-MAO[a]

Monomer[b]	Polymerization[a]		Polymer Microstructure[c]	
	Time (h)	Yield (%)	*cis*-1,4 (%)	1,2 (%)
I	100	69	10	90[d]
EP	1.5	75.6	84	16
ZP	0.5	84.5	≥99	

[a] Polymerization conditions: monomer, 1 mL; toluene, total volume 8 mL; CrCl$_2$(dmpe)$_2$, $3\cdot10^{-5}$ moles; MAO, Al/Cr = 100; polymerization temperaure+20°C. [b] I = isoprene; EP, (E)-1,3-pentadiene; ZP, (Z)-1,3-pentadiene. [c] Determined by ^{1}H NMR analysis. [d] 3,4 Units.

3.3. Mechanistic Considerations

The results obtained in the polymerization of 1,3-dienes with the above reported catalysts based on cobalt and chromium phosphine complexes, turned out to be extremely interesting and useful also from a mechanistic point of view, since they permitted to confirm and support the diene polymerization mechanism previously proposed [8,12,13,89,90,98,102-107], putting in evidence the relevant role played by catalyst (*i.e.*, type of ligand bonded to metal atom) [85,86,148] and monomer structures [95] in determining the polymerization chemo-

and stereoselectivity. Before discussing these results, it would be useful to sum up what it is known about the diene polymerization mechanism. For a deeper and more detailed information on such a mechanism, a careful reading of the various papers by Porri and other authors is strongly recommended [8, 102-107].

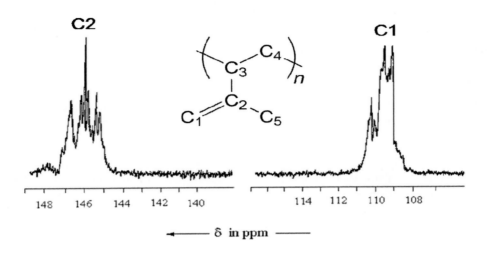

Figure 20. ^{13}C NMR spectrum (olefinic region) of 3,4 atactic polyisoprene obtained with CrCl$_2$(dmpe)$_2$-MAO system [C$_2$D$_2$Cl$_4$, 103°C, HMDS as internal standard].

It is well known that, in the polymerization of 1,3-dienes, the growing polymer chain is bonded to the metal atom (Mt) through an allylic bond formed by insertion of the monomer into the carbon-metal bond of the catalyst system (Figure 21); it is worthwhile to note that the Mt-butenyl group is a chiral group.

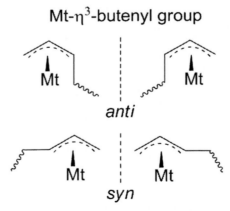

Figure 21. Bonds between the growing polymer chain and the transition metal of the catalyst in 1,3-diene polymerization.

According to the polymerization mechanism proposed by Porri, the allylic unit can exist in two forms (*anti* and *syn*) (Figure 21) both exhibiting two reactive positions: C1 and C3 (Figure 22). When the new entering monomer reacts at C1, a 1,4 unit is formed (*cis* if the allylic unit is in the *anti* form, *trans* if the allylic unit is in the *syn* form), whereas a 1,2 unit is obtained if the incoming monomer reacts at C3 (Figure 22).

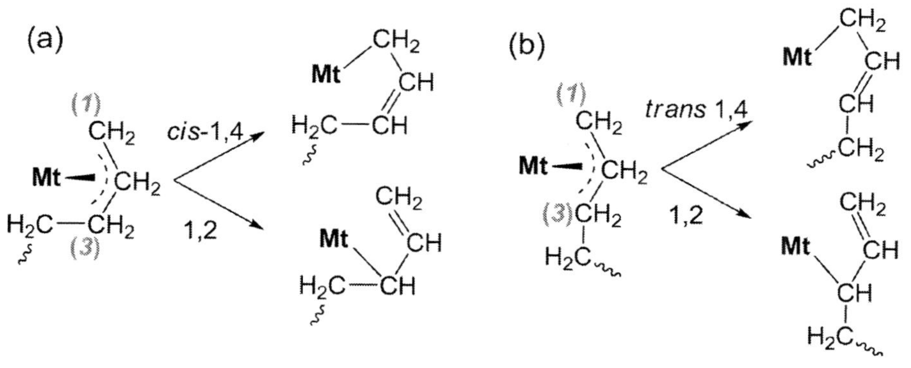

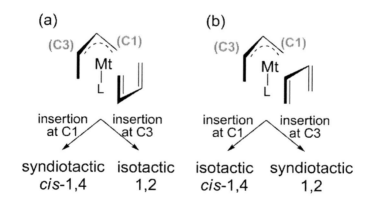

Figure 22. Formation of 1,4 *vs* 1,2 monomeric units from (a) anti and (b) syn Mt-butenyl group.

Furthermore, the new monomer can orient in two different ways with respect to the allylic unit of the polymer growing chain, as in Figure 23a (*exo-endo*) or as in Figure 23b (*exo-exo*) (for simplicity we have reported only the case of the *anti* unit, but the same is valid in the case of the *syn* unit).

Figure 23. Possible orientations [(a) *exo-endo* and (b) *exo-exo*] of the new incoming monomer with respect to the last-inserted unit (L is a generic ligand) and formation of *cis*-1,4 and 1,2-polymers having a syndiotactic or an isotactic structure.

From a situation as in Figure 23a, *cis*-1,4 syndiotactic or 1,2 isotactic units are formed if the monomer reacts at C1 or C3, respectively; from a situation as in Figure 23b, we have instead the formation of *cis*-1,4 isotactic units if the monomer reacts at C1, and of 1,2 syndiotactic units if the monomer reacts at C3.

By admitting the validity of the above mentioned polymerization mechanism, it appears plausible hypothesize that it is possible to control the polymerization chemoselectivity (*i.e.*, formation of 1,4 or 1,2 units) and the stereoselectivity (formation of isotactic or syndiotactic polymers) simply varying the catalyst and the monomer structures. We will see in the following that these hypotheses have been supported and confirmed by the results obtained in the polymerization of various 1,3-dienes (*e.g.*; butadiene, isoprene, 1,3-pentadiene, 1,3-

hexadiene and 3-methyl-1,3-pentadiene) with the catalysts based on cobalt and chromium phosphine complexes.

3.3.1. Chemoselectivity: Influence of the Cobalt Complex Structure

The results obtained in the polymerization of butadiene with $CoCl_2(PR_3)_2$/MAO systems (R = alkyl or cycloalkyl group) allowed us to point out the fundamental role played by the ligand nature in determining polymerization chemoselectivity. We obtained polymers ranging from a predominantly 1,2 structure to an essentially cis-1,4 structure, depending on the bulkiness of the phosphine ligand. If we consider an active site structure (shown in Figure 14), with only one phosphine bonded to the cobalt atom, it appears evident that small variations in the reciprocal orientation of incoming monomer and butadienyl group, due to the nature of the ligand on the cobalt atom, may favour the insertion of the monomer at C1 or C3 of the allylic group (Figure 24).

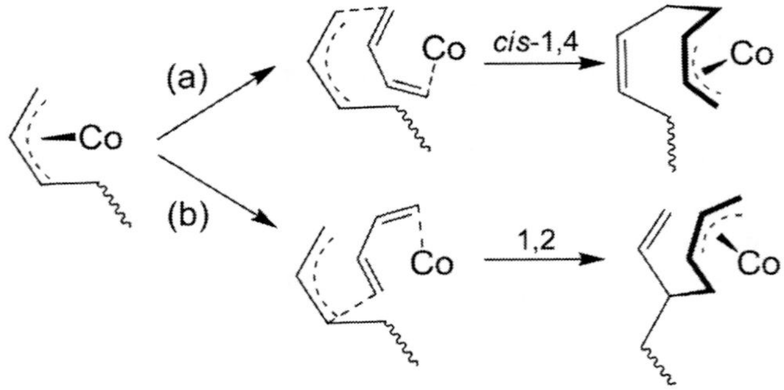

Figure 24. Scheme of formation of 1,4 units *vs.* 1,2 units.

Thus, hindered ligands seem to favour the insertion of the monomer at C1, while less hindered ligands favour insertion at C3 of the allylic unit.

3.3.2. Chemoselectivity: Influence of the Monomer Structure

It has been shown in previous papers that chemoselectivity may depend on the monomer structure (*i.e.*, presence of substituents on the different carbons) [106,149,150]. For example, in the polymerization of 1,3-dienes with $CpTiCl_3$/MAO [106,149] we obtained polymers with different microstructure from different monomers and a clear relationship was found between the polymer microstructure and the presence of alkyl substituents on the C1 and C3 positions of the allylic units. The insertion of the new incoming monomer preferentially occurs at the less substituted reactive carbons C1 and C3. This indication is now supported and validated by the results obtained in the polymerization of 1,3-dienes with the systems $CoCl_2(PRPh_2)_2$/MAO. Exclusively 1,2 units were observed in the polymers obtained from 1,3-pentadiene, 1,3-hexadiene and 3-methyl-1,3-pentadiene, while polymers containing a certain amount of cis-1,4 units were obtained from butadiene (15-20%) and isoprene (~45%) [85,86]. If we consider the allylic units formed during the polymerization of the above monomers (Figure 25), it appears clear that in the case of pentadiene, hexadiene and 3-methylpentadiene, the C1 position, due to the presence of an alkyl substituent, is more hindered and consequently less reactive with respect to the same position in the allylic unit formed in the case of butadiene or isoprene.

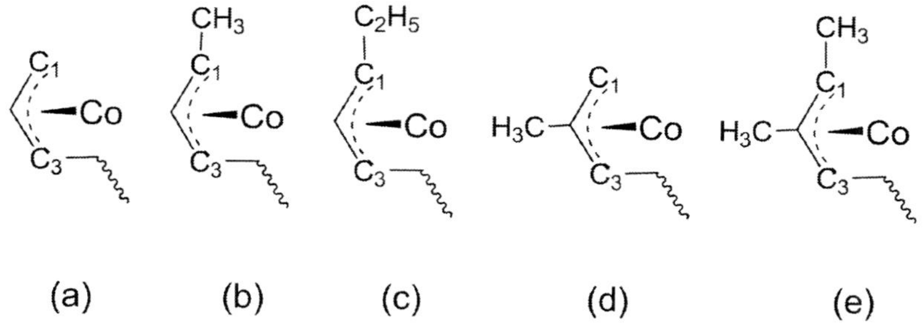

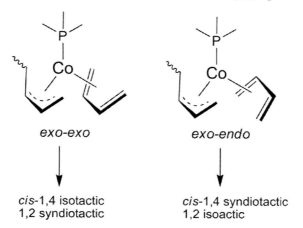

Figure 25. Possible allylic units in the polymerization of (a) butadiene; (b) 1,3-pentadiene; (c) 1,3-hexadiene; (d) isoprene; (e) 3-methyl-1,3-pentadiene.

It follows that the formation of 1,4 units (insertion of the new monomer at C1) is more probable in the polymerization of butadiene and isoprene than in the polymerization of 1,3-pentadiene, 1,3-hexadiene and 3-methyl-1,3-pentadiene.

3.3.3. Stereoselectivity: Influence of the Cobalt Complex Structure

The polymerization of butadiene with the systems $CoCl_2(PRPh_2)_2/MAO$ (R = alkyl or cycloalkyl group) (see Table 12) gave 1,2 polymers [86] with different tacticity depending on the type of ligand (*i.e.*, type of alkyl group R bonded to the phosphorus atom and consequently steric hindrance of the ligand). Highly syndiotactic polybutadienes were obtained with $CoCl_2(P^iPrPh_2)_2/MAO$ and $CoCl_2(PCyPh_2)_2/MAO$ in which hindered alkyl groups are present on the P atoms. Atactic polymers with predominance of isotactic sequences were obtained with $CoCl_2(PRPh_2)_2/MAO$ in which the steric demand of the alkyl group R (methyl, ethyl or *n*-propyl) is lower. The formation of polybutadienes having different type and/or degree of stereoregularity was interpreted on the basis of the previously reported diene polymerization mechanism [8,102-107]. The type of phosphorus ligand (*i.e.*, its steric hindrance) may influence the reciprocal orientation (*exo-exo* or *exo-endo*) of the butadienyl group and of the incoming monomer, thus determining the formation of iso- or syndiotactic polymers (*i.e.*, the polymerization stereoselectivity) (Figure 26).

Figure 26. Possible reciprocal orientation of allylic unit and new entering monomer.

3.3.4. Stereoselectivity: Influence of the Chromium Complex Structure

The fact that $CrCl_2(dmpm)_2$-MAO and $CrCl_2(dppm)$-MAO gave predominantly isotactic 1,2 polybutadienes, while catalysts based on $CrCl_2(dmpe)_2$, $CrCl_2(dppe)$, $CrCl_2(depe)_2$ and $CrCl_2(dppp)$ gave predominantly syndiotactic 1,2 polybutadienes, can be interpreted according to the previously suggested diene polymerization mechanism [8,102-107], confirming indeed its validity.

The catalytic site in the polymerization of butadiene with chromium systems is most likely that shown in Figure 27. The incoming monomer and the butadienyl unit can assume two different orientations (*exo-exo* and *exo-endo*). By insertion of the incoming monomer at C3 of the butadienyl group, a 1,2 polybutadiene is obtained in both cases, isotactic from an *exo-endo* orientation, syndiotactic from an *exo-exo* orientation. An *exo-endo* orientation is favored when no ligand or a low hindered ligand is bonded to the chromium atom, while an *exo-exo* orientation is favored when a bulky ligand is coordinated to the metal atom. This is the reason why predominantly isotactic polybutadienes were obtained when L = *dmpm* or *dppm*, and syndiotactic polybutadienes with the other catalytic systems using more bulky ligands. Nevertheless, the same systems giving syndiotactic polybutadienes (*e.g.*, $CrCl_2(dmpe)_2$-MAO) gave an atactic 3,4 polyisoprene (with predominance of isotactic sequences), meaning that the monomer structure too has a strong influence on the polymerization stereoselectivity. Most likely the lack of stereoregularity in case of isoprene polymers is due to the steric interaction between the incoming monomer and the butadienyl group of the growing chain, determined by the presence of a methyl group on the isoprene unit. The above steric interaction may favor the formation of an *exo-endo* situation, in addition to the *exo-exo* one, resulting in the formation of syndiotactic dyads together with isotactic dyads.

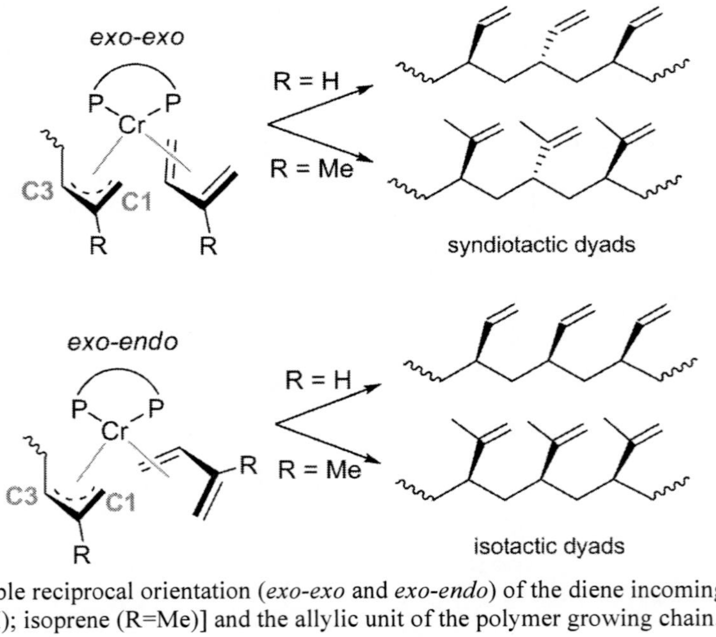

Figure 27. Possible reciprocal orientation (*exo-exo* and *exo-endo*) of the diene incoming monomer [butadiene (R=H); isoprene (R=Me)] and the allylic unit of the polymer growing chain.

3.3.5. Stereoselectivity: Influence of the Monomer Structure

According to the diene polymerization mechanism previously proposed, the reciprocal orientation (*exo-exo* or *exo-endo*) of the butadienyl group and of the incoming monomer should be in principle affected by the monomer structure (*i.e.*, presence of substituents on the different carbons of the monomer and consequently of the butadienyl group).

The results obtained in the polymerization of butadiene, 1,3-pentadiene, 1,3-hexadiene, and 3-methyl-1,3-pentadiene with $CoCl_2(P''PrPh_2)_2$/MAO and $CoCl_2(P'PrPh_2)_2$/MAO (see Tables 5 and 7) permitted us to confirm the validity of this hypothesis.

The analysis of the results reported above suggests the following remark. Using the same catalyst, polymers obtained from 3-methyl-1,3-pentadiene have an essentially isotactic structure (the isotactic degree depending on the type of cobalt complex, specifically increasing with decreasing the steric hindrance of the phosphine ligand bonded to the cobalt atom); polymers from butadiene, E-1,3-pentadiene and 1,3-hexadiene exhibit an essentially syndiotactic structure (again the syndiotactic degree depending on the type of catalyst, specifically increasing with increasing the steric hindrance of the phosphine ligand bonded to the cobalt atom). These results clearly indicate that the monomer structure may strongly influence the polymerization stereoselectivity.

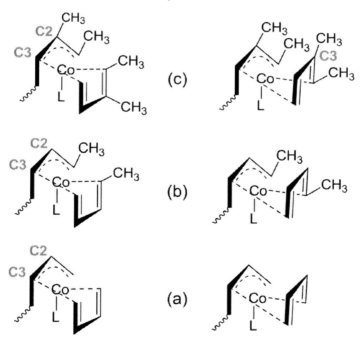

Figure 28. Possible orientations of incoming diene monomer and butadienyl group in the homopolymerization of *(a)* butadiene; *(b)* E-1,3-pentadiene; *(c)* 3-methyl-1,3-pentadiene with $CoCl_2(PRPh_2)_2$/MAO.

The formation of 1,2 syndiotactic polymers from butadiene, E-1,3 pentadiene and 1,3-hexadiene, and of isotactic polymers from 3-methyl-1,3-pentadiene, by using the same polymerization catalyst, can be explained, according to the diene polymerization mechanism [8,102-107], as follows: in case of butadiene (Figure 28a), E-1,3-pentadiene (Figure 28b), and 1,3-hexadiene (not shown) the favorite incoming monomer-butadienyl group orientation is the *exo-exo* one while, in the case of 3-methyl-1,3-pentadiene (Figure 28c), the preferred orientation is the *exo-endo* one.

By insertion of the incoming monomer at C3 of the butadienyl group, a 1,2 isotactic dyad is obtained in the case of the *exo-endo* orientation, while a 1,2 syndiotactic dyad is obtained in the case of the *exo-exo* orientation. Most probably in the polymerization of internal substituted dienes, such as 3-methyl-1,3-pentadiene, the presence of a methyl on the C2 carbon of the butadienyl group and on the C3 carbon of the incoming monomer, forces the two groups to assume an *exo-endo* orientation, even if this particular orientation is not the favourite one when a ligand (less or more hindered) is bonded to the metal. In other words, the incoming monomer prefers suffering the hindrance of the ligand rather than that originating from the butadienyl group.

4. POLYMERIZATION OF BORBORNENE

Norbornene (NB) can be polymerized by transition metal catalysts by two different catalytic routes (Figure 29): *a)* ring-opening metathesis polymerization (ROMP), which gives polymers containing double bonds in the main chain; *b)* vinyl addition polymerization, which gives completely saturated polymers [6,7]. Cationic and radical initiators are also active for NB polymerization, but give products of low molecular weight containing rearranged monomer units.

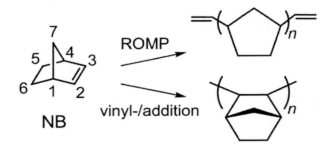

Figure 29. Transition metal catalytic routes for norbornene polymerization.

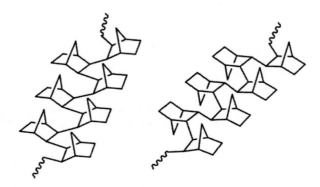

Figure 30. Schematic representation of disyndiotactic (left) and diisotactic (right) polynorbornene.

Vinyl-type polynorbornene (PNB) in particular exhibits properties that make it suitable for optical and electronic applications. Due to the industrial relevance of these polymers, several catalysts have been tested for its preparation, mainly based on Ni and on zirconocenes, but also on Ti, Cr, Co, and Pd [6,7]. A norbornene unit derived from 2,3 monomer insertion (numbering as in Figure 29) contains two asymmetric carbon atoms; which means that atactic, as well as stereoregular polymers (e.g., diisotactic and disyndiotactic, Figure 30) can be foreseen for PNB.

Crystalline, stereoregular vinyl-type poly(norbornene)s were obtained up to now only with the systems $CrCl_2(dppa)$/MAO, giving a diheterotactic poynorbornene [88,151], and $TiCl_4$/$AlEt_2Cl$, giving a disyndiotactc polynorbornene [152-154]; all the other systems used, including cobalt catalysts, gave essentially amorphous polymers.

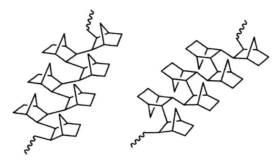

Figure 30. Schematic representation of disyndiotactic (left) and diisotactic (right) polynorbornene.

4.1. Polymerization of Norbornene with Cobalt Catalysts

Several cobalt(II) compounds (e.g., $CoCl_2$, Co(II) stearate, substituted bis(1,3-diketo) cobalt(II)), in combination with MAO, were used to polymerize norbornene [155-157]. These systems were found to be extremely active when used in chlorobenzene as solvent, and, as told above, they gave amorphous polymers, soluble in organic solvents in spite of the high molecular weight exhibited ($>1\times10^6$ g·mol^{-1}). More recently, cobalt complexes with phosphorus ligands (e.g., diphenylalkylphosphines, trialkylphosphines) were also used as catalysts precursors, in combination with MAO; high molecular weight, amorphous vinyl-type polymers were also obtained in this case [158]. The results obtained in the polymerization of norbornene with cobalt phosphine complexes are reported in Table 16; the ^{1}H and ^{13}C NMR spectra of the polynorbornene obtained with $CoCl_2(PR_3)_2$-MAO are shown in Figure 31.

4.2. Polymerization of Norbornene with Chromium Catalysts

As concern the copolymerization of norbornene with chromium catalysts, only a few papers were reported in the literature. The papers by Heitz [159,160] regard the norbornene polymerization with $[CpCrMeCl]_2$-MAO (Cp = C_5H_5, C_5Me_5, C_9H_7, $C_{13}H_9$) systems leading to partially crystalline materials, while Bochmann [161] reported on the polymerization of norbornene with catalysts based on chromium (II) allyl ($Cr[1,3-C_3H_5(SiMe_3)_2]_2$) and chromium (IV) alkyl ($Cr(CH_2SiMe_3)_4$) giving, respectively, insoluble vinyl-type and very low molecular weight polynorbornenes. Nothing was said, however, about the structure of the above polymers.

Very recently a crystalline vinyl-type polynorbornene (Figure 32) was obtained with the Cr(II) bidentate phosphine complexes based catalysts (Table 17) described above for the polymerization of 1,3-dienes.

Table 16. Polymerization of norbornene with cobalt phosphine based catalysts [a]

Solvent (type)	Co-complex	Time (min)	conv (%)	M_n [c] ($g \times mol^{-1}$)	M_w/M_n [c]
toluene	$CoCl_2(P^tBu_2H)_2$	1440	47	ns [d]	
o-DCB		1	36	45800	5.5
toluene	$CoCl_2(P^tBu_2Me)_2$	1440	100	846000	1.7
o-DCB		1	87	121800	3.4
toluene	$CoCl_2(PCyp_3)_2$	1440	100	ns [d]	
o-DCB		1	62	110000	2.1
toluene	$CoCl_2(PCyPh_2)_2$	1440	19	402300	2.9
o-DCB		1	100	89000	5.2

[a] Polymerization conditions: total volume, 18 mL; NB, 2 g; Co, 1×10^{-5} mol; Al/Co molar ratio = 1000; temperature, 20°C. [b] Given in kg of PNB mol Co^{-1} h^{-1}. [c] Determined by SEC in o-DCB by using standard polystyrene calibration. [d] Insoluble.

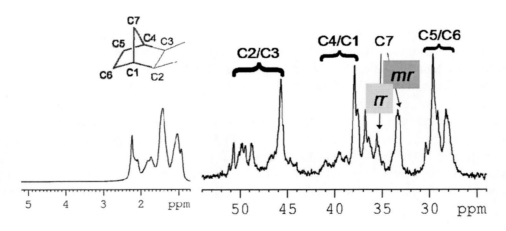

Figure 31. ^1H NMR (on the left) and ^{13}C NMR (on the right) spectra of vinyl-type polynorbornene ($C_2D_2Cl_4$ as solvent, HMDS as internal standard, 103°C) obtained with $CoCl_2(P^iPrPh_2)_2$–MAO.

The polynorbornenes obtained exhibited, after fractionation, a significant crystallinity. Using a combination of NMR (Figure 33), X-ray diffraction and molecular modelling, it was possible to establish the polynorbornene structure which resulted to be diheterotactic [151], a quite unusual structure in the field of polyolefins by means of stereospecific polymerization.

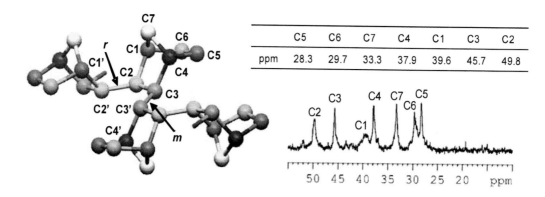

	C5	C6	C7	C4	C1	C3	C2
ppm	28.3	29.7	33.3	37.9	39.6	45.7	49.8

Figure 33. ^{13}C NMR spectrum (C$_2$D$_2$Cl$_4$, HMDS as internal standard, 103°C) of the heptane insoluble fraction of the polynorbornene obtained with CrCl$_2$(dppa)-MAO at -30°C. The structure and numbering scheme of 2,3-*exo*-diheterotactic polynorbornene are also shown: magnetically equivalent carbons have the same colour. Main-chain bonds across *r* and *m* dyads are indicated while hydrogens are omitted.

Table 17. Polymerization of norbornene with chromium(II) catalysts

Run	Cr-compound	Polymerization[a]		Polymer	
		time (min)	yield (%)	M_w[b] (g/mol)	T_g[c] (°C)
1	CrCl$_2$(dmpm)$_2$	13	44.9	1270	126
2	CrCl$_2$(dmpe)$_2$	60	25.3	1380	104
3	CrCl$_2$(depe)$_2$	60	18.4	1155	102
4	CrCl$_2$(dppm)	5	66.1	1490	140
5	CrCl$_2$(dppe)	55	34.5	1425	99
6	CrCl$_2$(dppa)	15	50.7	1305	88
7	CrCl$_2$(dppa)	1320	54.8	2760	135

a) Polymerization conditions: norbornene, 2.45 g; toluene, total volume 16 mL; MAO, Al/Cr = 1000; Cr, 5×10-6 mol (1×10-5 in run 7); polymerization temperature, +20°C (-30°C in run 7).
b) Molecular weight, determined by GPC analysis.
c) Glass transition temperature, determined by DSC analysis.

CONCLUSION

Since the beginning in the early 1950s, much work has been done in the field of homo- and copolymerization of vinyl monomers; various catalysts based on different transition metal compounds and aluminum-alkyls have been discovered and developed, and several polymers with different structure have been obtained from various types of olefins, cycloolefins and diolefins.

The progress in phosphorus based catalyst architecture indicates the importance of phosphorus ligands in polymerization catalysis. In contrast to most of the known catalyst systems, for which the structural variations are restricted, the catalysts with phosphorus ligands possess a high potential of structural change. In fact the great variety of synthetic methods applicable to the phosphorus chemistry leads to new type of vinyl monomers polymerization catalysts that can bring to the development of important fields of interest: *i)* microstructural control *via* improved catalyst architecture; *ii)* increase of polymerization activity; *iii)* identification of polymerization active species; *iv)* new polymer materials.

Catalysts based on transition metal phosphine derivatives were first used for the C2/CO copolymerization. In particular, Pd(II) phosphine complexes based catalysts permitted to obtain for the first time perfectly alternating C2/CO copolymers, opening a new chapter in the history of polymers. These perfectly alternating co- or terpolymers were easily accessible by phosphorus based palladium catalyzed polymerization of readily available, cheap feedstocks like CO and α-olefins. Catalyst activity, selectivity and polymer molecular weight were found to be strongly dependent on the phosphine ligand nature (*i.e.*, their steric and electronic properties, strongly depending on the type of substituents on the phosphorus atoms).

Palladium catalysts based on phosphine complexes were successively discontinued, due to the C2/CO copolymers commercial failure, probably related to their imperfect stability, especially when exposed to high temperature for long periods or when subjected to repeat cycles of melting and solidification.

A renewed interest for catalysts based on phosphine complexes arose from the discovery by Soga showing that triphenylphosphine was able to affect the catalyst stereospecificity in the polymerization of butadiene with cobalt derivatives. This fact prompted the researchers to systematically explore the polymerization of butadiene with catalysts based on transition metal complexes with different phosphine ligands, obtaining the following quite interesting results:

(i)   catalysts based on cobalt phosphine complexes allowed to manage polybutadiene microstructure, in a similar manner to the polymerization of α-olefins catalyzed by titanium or zirconium metallocenes [162,163]. Polybutadienes with controlled microstructure (*cis*-1,4; 1,2; mixed structure *cis*-1,4/1,2 with variable 1,2 content) were obtained, simply varying the type of ligand on the cobalt atom. Moreover, the same catalysts permitted to polymerize various types of conjugated diolefins, obtaining stereoregular polymers (*e.g.*, 1,2 syndiotactic and isotactic polymers from terminally substituted butadienes; *cis*-1,4/3,4 perfectly alternating polyisoprenes), which had not been possible to prepare with previous catalysts, giving useful information for a better comprehension of the diene polymerization mechanism;

(ii) catalysts based on bidentate phosphine chromium complexes allowed to obtain isotactic or syndiotactic 1,2 polybutadienes by varying the type of phosphine ligand, exhibiting a catalyst activity and stereospecificity much higher with respect to those of the known chromium systems. It is worthwhile to note that 1,2 syndiotactic polybutadiene is a polymer of industrial interest, mainly used for shoes soles manufacturing;

(iii) finally, chromium phosphine complexes based catalysts permitted to obtain for the first time a crystalline polymer from norbornene. This novel polymer exhibited a 2,3-*exo*-diheterotactic structure, a rather unusual structure in the field of vinyl polymers.

On the basis of the above results, it appears of scientific relevance and industrial potential interest to examine the behavior of other transition metal (early and late) phosphine complexes in the homo- and copolymerization not only of olefins and diolefins, but also in case of vinyl polar monomers.

REFERENCES

[1]   Kissin, Y. V. in *"Isospecific polymerization of olefins"* Springer-Verlag, USA, 1985.
[2]   Matsugi, T.; Fujita, T. *Chem. Soc. Rev.*, 2008, 37, 1264.
[3]   Camacho, D. H; Guan, Z. *Chem. Commun.*, 2010, 46, 7879.
[4]   Takeuchi, D. *Dalton Trans.*, 2010, 39, 311.
[5]   Nishiura, M.; Hou, Z. *Nature Chemistry*, 2010, 2, 257.
[6]   Janiak, C.; Lassahn, P.G. *J. Mol. Catal. A: Chem.*, 2001, 166, 193.
[7]   Blank, F.; Janiak, C. *Coord. Chem. Rev.*, 2009, 253, 827.
[8]   Porri, L.; Giarrusso, A. *"Conjugated Diene Polymerization"* in *Comprehensive Polymer Science,* Eastmond, G.; Edwith, A.; Russo, S.; Sigwalt, P.; Eds.; Pergamon Press Ltd., Oxford, 1989, vol. 4, pp 53-108.
[9]   Thiele, S. K. H.; Wilson, D. R. *J. Macromol. Sci. Part C: Polymer Reviews*, 2003, C43, 581.
[10]   Osakada, K; Takeuchi, D. *Adv. Polym. Sci.*, 2004, 171, 137.
[11]   Friebe, L.; Oskar Nuyken, O.; Obrecht, W. *Adv. Polym. Sci.* 2006, 204, 1.
[12]   Ricci, G.; Masi, F.; Boglia, A.; Sommazzi, A.; Ricci, M. in *"Advances in Organometallic Chemistry Research"*, K. Yamamoto Ed., Nova Science Publisher, Inc., USA 2007, pp. 1-36.
[13]   Ricci, G.; Sommazzi, A.; Masi, F.; Ricci, M.; Boglia, A.; Leone, G. *Coord. Chem. Rev.*, 2010, 254, 661.
[14]   Kaminsky, W. in *Synthesis of Polyolefins with Homogeneous Ziegler-Natta Catalysts of High Activity,* Seymour & Cheng, 1986, 257.
[15]   Brintzinger, H. H.; Fischer, D; Mülhaupt, R; Rieger, B; Waymouth, R.M. *Angew. Chem. Int. Ed*, 1995, 34, 1143.
[16]   Ittel, S. D.; Johnson, K.; Brookhart, M. *Chem. Rev.* 2000, 100, 1169.
[17]   Gibson, V.C.; Spitzmesser, S.K. *Chem. Rev.* 2003, 103, 283.
[18]   Bianchini, C.; Giambastiani, G.; Guerrero Rios, I.; Mantovani, G.; Meli, A.; Segarra, A. M. *Coord. Chem. Rev.* 2006, 250, 1391.
[19]   Ballauf, F.; Bayer, O.; Leichmann, L. G. *Patent* 863,711, 1941.
[20]   Reppe, W.; Mangini, A. *US Patent* 2,577,208, 1951.
[21]   Shryne, T. M.; Holler, H. V. *US Patent* 3,984,398 1976.
[22]   Shryne, T. M. *US Patent* 3,984,388 1976.
[23]   Klabunde, U.; Ittel, I. *J. Mol. Catal.* 1987, 41, 123.
[24]   Iwashita, Y.; Sakurabata, M. *Tetrahedron Lett.* 1971, 2409.
[25]   Sen, A.; Brumbaugh, J. S. *J. Organomet. Chem.* 1985, 279 C5.
[26]   Gouch, A. *British Patent* 1,081,304 1961
[27]   Zhao, A. X.; Chien, J. C. W. *J. Polym. Sci. Polym. Chem.* 1992, 30, 2735.
[28]   Fenton, D. M. *US Patent* 3,530,109, 1970.
[29]   Nozaki, K. *US Patent.* 3,689,460, 1972.
[30]   Nozaki, K. *US Patent* 3,694,412, 1972.

[31]   Nozaki, K. *US Patent* 3,85,123, 1974.

[32]   Fenton, D. M. *US Patent* 4,076,911, 1978.

[33]   Hudgin, D. E. *US Patent.* 3,948,873, 1976.

[34]   Sen, A.; Lai, T. W. *J. Am. Chem. Soc.* 1982, 104, 3520.

[35]   Lai, T. W.; Sen, A. *Organometallics* 1984, 3, 866.

[36]   Drent, E. *Eur. Patent* 121965, 1984.

[37]   Sommazzi, A.; Garbassi, F.; Mestroni, G.; Milani, B. *US Patent 5310871,* 1994.

[38]   Sen, A. *Chemtech* 1986, 48.

[39]   Drent, E. *Eur. Patent* 229408, 1986.

[40]   Drent, E. *US Patent* 4,778,279, 1988.

[41]   Drent, E.; van Broekhoven, J. A. M.; Doyle, M. *J. Organomet. Chem.* 1991, 417, 235.

[42]   Drent, E.; Budzelaar, P. H. M. *Chem. Rev.* 1996, 96, 663.

[43]   van Broekhoven, J. A. M.; Drent, E.; Klei, E. *Eur. Patent* 213671, 1987.

[44]   Sommazzi, A.; Garbassi, F.; Milani, B. *8th Int. Symp. Homogeneous Catalysis*, Amsterdam, 1992.

[45]   Dierkes, P.; van Leeuwen, P. W. N. M. *J. Chem. Soc. Dalton Trans.* 1999, 1519.

[46]   van Broekhoven, J. A. M.; Wife, R. L. *Eur. Patent* 257663, 1987.

[47]   Van Doorn, J. A.; Meijboom, N.; Wife, R. L. *Eur. Patent* 288196, 1988.

[48]   Van Doorn, J. A.; Meijboom, N. *Eur. Patent* 290075, 1988.

[49]   Van Doorn, J. A.; Meijboom, N.; Wife, R. L. *Eur. Patent*, 294000, 1988.

[50]   Wong, P. K.; Keijsper, J. J.; Van der Made, A. W. *Eur. Patent* 408155, 1991.

[51]   Dossett, S. J.; Gillon, A.; Guy Orpen, A.; Fleming, J. S.; Pringle, P. G.; Wass, D. F.; Jones, M. D. *Chem. Commun.* 2001, 699.

[52]   Bianchini, C.; Man Lee, H.; Meli; A.; Oberhauser, W.; Peruzzini, M.; Vizza, F. *Organometallics* 2002, 21, 16.

[53]   Bianchini, C.; Man Lee, H.; Meli, A.; Moneti, S.; Vizza, F.; Fontani, M.; Zanello, P. *Macromolecules* 1999, 32, 4183.

[54]   Milani, B.; Vincentini, L.; Sommazzi, A.; Garbassi, F.; Chiarparin, E.; Zangrando, E.; Mestroni, G. *J. Chem. Soc. Dalton Trans.* 1996, 16, 3139.

[55]   Drent, E.; van Dijk, R.; van Ginkel, R.; van Oort, B.; Pugh, R. I. *Chem. Commun.* 2002, 964.

[56]   Jiang, Z.; Sen, A. *Macromolecules* 1994, 27, 7215.

[57]   Verspui, G.; Papadogianakis, G.; Sheldon, R. A. *Chem. Commun.* 1998, 401.

[58]   Bianchini, C.; Man Lee, H.; Meli, A.; Moneti, S.; Patinec, V.; Petrucci, G.; Vizza, F. *Macromolecules* 1999, 32, 3859.

[59]   Lindner, E.; Schmid, M.; Wegner, J.; Nachtigal, C. *J. Organomet. Chem.* 2000, 602, 173.

[60]   Horne, S. E. Jr.; Kichi, J. P.; Shipman, J. J.; Folt, V. L.; Gibbs, C. T. *Ind. Eng. Chem.* 1956, 48, 784.

[61]   Natta, G.; Porri, L.; Mazzanti, G. (Montecatini SpA), *Ital. Pat. 536631* (1955) (*Chem. Abstr.* 1959, 53, 3756).

[62]   Sinn, H.; Bliemeister, J.; Clausnitzer, D.; Winter, L.; Zarncke, O. in "*Transition Metals and Organometallics as Catalysts for Olefin Polymerization*" W. Kaminsky, H. Sinn Eds., Springer-Verlag, Berlin Heidelberg New York, 1988, pp. 257-268.

[63] Bliemeister, J.; Hagendorf, W.; Harder, A.; Heitmann, B.; Schimmel, I.; Schmedt, E.; Schnuchel, W.; Sinn, H.; Tikwe, L.; von Thiene, N.; Urlass, K.; Winter, H.; Zarncke, O. in *"Ziegler Catalysts"* G. Fink, R. Mülhaupt, H.H. Brintzinger Eds., Springer-Verlag, Berlin Heidelberg New York, 1995, pp. 57-82.

[64] Ricci, G.; Italia, S.; Comitani, C.; Porri, L. *Polymer Commun.,* 1991, 32, 514.

[65] Ricci, G.; Italia, S.; Porri, L. *Macromol. Chem. Phys.,* 1994, 195, 1389.

[66] Ricci, G.; Porri, L. *Polymer,* 1997, 38, 4499.

[67] Ricci, G.; Zetta, L.; Alberti, E.; Motta, T.; Canetti, M.; Bertini, F. *J. Polym. Sci Part A: Polym. Chem.,* 2007, 45, 4635.

[68] Zambelli, A.; Ammendola, P.; Proto, A. *Macromolecules,* 1989, 22, 2126.

[69] Oliva, L.; Longo, P.; Grassi, A.; Ammendola, P.; Pellecchia, C. *Die Makromol. Chem., Rapid Commun.,* 1990, 11, 519.

[70] Venditto, V.; De Rosa, C.; Guerra, G.; Napolitano, R. *Polymer,* 1992, 33, 3547.

[71] Ricci, G.; Italia, S.; Giarrusso, A.; Porri, L. *J. Organomet. Chem.,* 1993, 451, 67.

[72] Ricci, G.; Panagia, A.; Porri, L. *Polymer* 1996, 37, 363.

[73] Ricci, G.; Bosisio, C.; Porri, L. *Macromol. Chem., Rapid Commun.,* 1996, 17, 781.

[74] Porri, L.; Ricci, G.; Giarrusso, A. in *"Metalorganic Catalysts for Synthesis and Polymerization"* Walter Kaminsky Ed., Springer-Verlag Berlin Heidelberg, 1999, pp. 519-530.

[75] Porri, L.; Giarrusso, A.; Ricci, G. in *"Metallocene-Based Polyolefins"* J. Scheirs and W. Kaminsky Eds., John Wiley & Sons Ltd., 2000, pp. 115-141.

[76] Longo, P.; Oliva, P.; Proto, A.; Zambelli, A. *Gazz. Chim. It.* 1996, 126, 377.

[77] Ricci, G.; Italia, S.; Porri, L. *Macromolecules,* 1994, 27, 868.

[78] Ricci, G.; Alberti, E.; Zetta, L.; Motta, T.; Bertini, F.; Mendichi, R.; Arosio, P.; Famulari, A.; Meille, S. V. *Macromolecules,* 2005, 38, 8353.

[79] Longo, P.; Guerra, G.; Grisi, F.; Pizzuti, S.; Zambelli, A. *Macromol. Chem. Phys.,* 1998, 199, 149.

[80] Ricci, G.; Porri, L. *Macromol. Chem. Phys.,* 1997, 198, 3647.

[81] Ricci, G.; Battistella, M.; Porri, L. *Macromolecules,* 2001, 34, 5766.

[82] Ricci, G.; Battistella, M.; Bertini, F.; Porri, L. *Polymer Bulletin,* 2002, 48, 25.

[83] Ricci, G.; Forni, A.; Boglia, A.; Sonzogni, M. *Organometallics,* 2004, 23, 3727.

[84] Ricci, G.; Forni, A.; Boglia, A.; Motta, T. *J. Mol. Catal. A: Chem.,* 2005, 226, 235.

[85] Ricci, G.; Forni, A.; Boglia, A.; Motta, T.; Zannoni, G.; Canetti, M.; Bertini, F. *Macromolecules,* 2005, 38, 1064.

[86] Ricci, G.; Forni, A.; Boglia, A.; Sommazzi, A.; Masi, F. *J. Organomet. Chem.,* 2005, 690, 1845.

[87] Ricci, G.; Boglia, A.; Motta, T. *J. Mol. Catal. A: Chem.,* 2007, 267, 102.

[88] Ricci, G.; Boglia, A.; Boccia, A. C.; Zetta, L. *Macromol. Symp.,* 2007, 260, 172.

[89] Ricci, G.; Leone, G.; Boglia, A.; Masi, F.; Sommazzi, A. in *"Cobalt: Characteristics, Compounds, and Applications"*, Lucas J. Vidmar Ed., Nova Science Publisher, Inc., USA 2011, pp. 39-81.

[90] Ricci, G.; Leone, G.; Masi, F.; Sommazzi, A. in *"Chromium: Environmental, Medical and Material Studies"*, Margaret P. Salden Ed., Nova Science Publishers, Inc., USA 2011, pp. 121-140.

[91] Ricci, G.; Motta, T.; Boglia, A.; Alberti, E.; Zetta, L.; Bertini, F.; Arosio, P.; Famulari, A.; Meille, S. V. *Macromolecules,* 2005, 38, 8345.

[92] Ricci, G.; Boglia, A.; Motta, T.; Bertini, F.; Boccia, A. C.; Zetta, L.; Alberti, E.; Famulari, A.; Arosio, P.; Meille, S. V. *J. Polym. Sci. Part A: Polym. Chem.*, 2007, 45, 5339.

[93] Ricci, G.; Bertini, F.; Boccia, A. C.; Zetta, L.; Alberti, E.; Pirozzi, B.; Giarrusso, A.; Porri, L. *Macromolecules*, 2007, 40, 7238.

[94] Pirozzi, B.; Napolitano, R.; Giusto, G.; Esposito, S.; Ricci, G. *Macromolecules*, 2007, 40, 8962.

[95] Ricci, G.; Leone, G.; Boglia, A.; Bertini, F.; Boccia, A. C.; Zetta, L. *Macromolecules*, 2009, 48, 3048.

[96] Ricci, G.; Leone, G.; Boglia, A.; Bertini, F.; Boccia, A. C.; Zetta, L. *Macromolecules*, 2009, 42, 3048.

[97] Ricci, G.; Leone, G.; Boglia, A.; Boccia, A.C.; Zetta, L. *Macromolecules*, 2009, 42, 9263.

[98] Porri, L. in *"Structural Order in Polymers"* F. Ciardelli, P. Giusti Eds., Pergamon Press Ltd. Oxford, 1981, 51.

[99] Destri, S.; Gallazzi, M. C.; Giarrusso, A.; Porri, L. *Makromol. Chem., Rapid Commun.*, 1980, 1, 293.

[100] Destri, S.; Gatti, G.; Porri, L. *Makromol. Chem., Rapid Commun.*, 1981, 2, 605.

[101] Bolognesi, A.; Destri, S.; Porri, L.; Wang, F. *Makromol. Chem., Rapid Commun.*, 1982, 3, 187.

[102] Porri, L.; Giarrusso, A.; Ricci, G. *Prog. Polym. Sci.*, 1991, 16, 405.

[103] Porri, L.; Giarrusso, A.; Ricci, G. *Makromol. Chem., Macromol. Symp.*, 1991, 48/49, 239.

[104] Porri, L.; Giarrusso, A.; Ricci, G. *Makromol. Chem., Macromol. Symp.*, 1993, 66, 231.

[105] Porri, L.; Giarrusso, A.; Ricci, G. *Polymer Science, Ser. A*, 1994, 36, 1421.

[106] Porri, L.; Giarrusso, A.; Ricci, G. *Macromol. Symp.*, 1995, 89, 383.

[107] Porri, L.; Giarrusso, A.; Ricci, G. *Macromol. Symp.*, 2002, 178, 55.

[108] Cugini, C.; Rombolà, O. A.; Giarrusso, A.; Porri, L.; Ricci, G. *Macromol. Chem. Phys.*, 2005, 206, 1684.

[109] Taube, R.; Schmidt, U.; Gehrke, J.-P.; Böme, P.; Langlotz, J.; Wache, S. *Makromol. Chem., Rapid Commun.*, 1993, 66, 245.

[110] Taube, R.; Windisch, H.; Maiwald, S. *Macromol. Symp.*, 1995, 89, 393.

[111] Tobisch, S.; Bögel, H.; Taube, R. *Organometallics*, 1996, 15, 3563.

[112] Peluso, A.; Improta, R.; Zambelli, A. *Macromolecules*, 1997, 30, 2219.

[113] Guerra, G.; Cavallo, L.; Corradini, P.; Fusco, R. *Macromolecules*, 1997, 30, 677.

[114] Tobisch, S.; Bögel, H.; Taube, R.; *Organometallics*, 1998, 17, 1177.

[115] Tobisch, S.; Taube, R. *Organometallics*, 1999, 18, 3045.

[116] Tobisch, S.; Taube, R. *Organometallics*, 1999, 18, 5204.

[117] Improta, R.; Peluso, A. *Macromolecules*, 1999, 32, 6852.

[118] Peluso, A.; Improta, R.; Zambelli, A. *Organometallics*, 2000, 19, 411.

[119] Costabile, C.; Milano, G.; Cavallo, L.; Guerra, G. *Macromolecules*, 2001, 354, 7952.

[120] Tobisch, S. *Organometallics*, 2003, 22, 2729.

[121] Costabile, C.; Guerra, G.; Longo, P.; Pragliola, S. *Macromolecules*, 2004, 37, 2016.

[122] Costabile, C.; Milano, G.; Cavallo, L.; Longo, P.; Guerra, G.; Zambelli, A. *Polymer*, 2004, 45, 467.

[123] Racanelli, P.; Porri, L. *Eur. Polym. J.*, 1970, 6, 751.

[124] Ricci, G.; Italia, S.; Comitani, C.; Porri, L. *Polymer Commun.*, 1991, 32, 514.

[125] Furukawa, J.; Haga, K.; Kobayashi, E.; Iseda, Y.; Yoshimoto T.; Sakamoto, K. *Polym. J.*, 1971, 2, 371.

[126] Ashitaka, H.; Isikawa, H.; Veno, H. *J. Polym. Sci. Pol. Chem. Ed.*, 1983, 21, 1853.

[127] Ashitaka, H.; Jinda, K.; Veno, H. *J. Polym. Sci. Pol. Chem. Ed.*, 1983, 21, 1951.

[128] Ashitaka, H.; Inaishi, K.; Veno, H. *J. Polym. Sci. Pol. Chem. Ed.*, 1983, 21, 1973.

[129] Ashitaka, H.; Jinda, K.; Veno, H. *J. Polym. Sci. Pol. Chem. Ed.*, 1983, 21, 1989.

[130] Ricci, G., Italia, S.; Porri, L. *Polym. Commun.*, 1988, 29, 305.

[131] Cooper, W.; Eaves, D. E.; Vaughan, G. *Adv. Chem. Ser.*, 1966, 52, 46.

[132] Takeuchi, M.; Shiono, T.;Soga, K. *Polym. Int.*, 1992, 29, 209.

[133] Takeuchi, M.; Shiono, T.; Soga, K. *Polym. Int.*, 1995, 36, 41.

[134] Takeuchi, M.; Shiono, T.; Soga, K. *Macromol. Chem. Phys.*, 1996, 197, 729.

[135] Ricci, G.; Boglia, A.; Santi, R.; Sommazzi, A.; Masi, F. *Italian Patent* MI03A 001807 (2003) to Polimeri Europa.

[136] Ricci, G.; Boglia, A.; Forni, A.; Santi, R.; Sommazzi, A.; Masi, F. *Italian Patent* MI03A 001808 (2003) to Polimeri Europa.

[137] Ricci, G.; Boglia, A.; Santi, R.; Sommazzi, A.; Masi, F. *Italian Patent* MI03A 001809 (2003) to Polimeri Europa.

[138] van Leeuwen, P.W.N.M.; Kamer, P.C.J.; Reek, J.N.H.; Dierkes, P. *Chem. Rev.*, 2000, 100, 2741.

[139] Freixa, Z.; van Leeuwen, P. W. N. M. *Dalton Trans.*, 2003, 1890.

[140] Tolman, C. *Chemical Reviews.*, 1977, 77, 313.

[141] Natta, G; Porri, L; Zanini, G; Palvarini, A. *Chim. Ind. (Milan)*, 1959, 41, 1163.

[142] Halasa, F; Massiein, J. M. in *Kirk-Othmer Encyclopedia of Chemical Technology*, 4th ed., J.I. Kroschwitz ed., John Wiley and Sons, New York, 1989, vol. 8.

[143] Tate, D. P; Bethea, T. W. in *Encyclopedia of Polymer Science and Engineering*, 2nd ed., H. F. Mark Ed., John Wiley and Sons, New York, 1989, vol. 2.

[144] Kerns, M; Henning, S; Rachita, M. "*Butadiene Polymers*" in *Encyclopedia of Polymer Science and Technology*, H. F. Mark ed., Wiley, 2003, Vol. 5, p. 317.

[145] Betz, P; Jolly, P. W.; Kruger, C; Zakrewski, U. *Organometallics*, 1991, 10, 3520.

[146] Girolami, G. S.; Wilkinson, G; Galas, A. M. R; Thornton-Pett, M; Hursthouse, M. .B. *J. Chem. Soc. Dalton Trans.*, 1985, 1339.

[147] Hermes, A.R; Girolami, G. S. *Inorg. Chem.*, 1988, 27, 1775.

[148] Ricci, G; Morganti, D; Sommazzi, A; Santi, R; Masi, F. *J. Mol. Cat A: Chemicals*, 2003, 204/205, 287.

[149] Ricci, G.; Italia, S.; Giarrusso A.; Porri, L. *J. Organomet. Chem.*, 1993, 451, 67.

[150] Ricci, G.; Bosisio, C.; Porri, L. *Macromol. Rapid Commun.*, 1996, 17, 781.

[151] Ricci, G.; Boglia, A.; Boccia, A.C.; Zetta, L.; Famulari, A.; Meille, S.V. *Macromolecules*, 2008, 41, 3109.

[152] Porri, L.; Meille, S.V.; Famulari, A.; Buono, A.; Ricci, G. *WO Patent* 2010/05224.

[153] Buono, A.; Famulari, A.; Meille, S. V.; Ricci, G.; Porri, L. *Macromolecules*, 2011, 44, 3681.

[154] Ricci, G.; Leone, G.; Rapallo, A.; Biagini, A.; Guglielmetti, G.; Porri, L. *Polymer*, 2011, 52, 5708.

[155] Alt, F. P.; Heitz, W. *Macromol. Chem. Phys.*, 1998, 199, 1951.

[156] Sacchi, M. C.; Sonzogni, M.; Losio, S.; Forlini, F.; Locatelli, P.; Tritto, I.; Licchelli, M. *Macromol. Chem. Phys.*, 2001, 202, 2052.

[157] Pelascini, F.; Peruch, F.; Lutz, P. J.; Wesolek, M.; Kress, J., *Macromol. Rapid Commun.* 2003, 24, 768.

[158] Leone, G. Boglia, A.; Boccia, A. C.; Taglialatela Scafati, S.; Bertini, F.; Ricci, G. *Macromolecules*, 2009, 42, 9231.

[159] Haselwander, T. F. A; Heitz, W; Maskos, M. *Macromol. Rapid Commun.*, 1997, 18, 689.

[160] Peucker, U; Heitz, W. *Macromol. Rapid Commun.*, 1998, 19, 159.

[161] Woodman, T. J; Sarazin, Y; Garrat, S; Fink, G; Bochmann, M. *J. Mol. Catal. A: Chem.*, 2005, 235, 88.

[162] Soga, K.; Shiono, T. *Prog. Polym. Sci.,* 1997, 22, 1503.

[163] Resconi, L.; Cavallo, L.; Fait, A.; Piemontesi, F. *Chem. Rev.*, 2000, 100, 1253.

In: Phosphorus: Properties, Health Effects and the Environment   ISBN: 978-1-62081-399-7
Editors: Ming Yue Chen and Da-Xia Yang   © 2012 Nova Science Publishers, Inc.

Chapter 3

EFFECTS OF PHOSPHORUS DOPING ON THE ELECTRICAL PROPERTIES OF DIAMOND AND CARBON NANOTUBES

Qingyi Shao[*], Aqing Chen, Guangwen Wang and Juan Zhang

Laboratory of Quantum Information Technology, School of Physics and
Telecommunication Engineering, South China Normal University, China

ABSTRACT

Phosphorus as the n-type dopant, is widely used in the semiconductor industry. As a potential dopant, it is also possible for application in the nanoelectronics industry in the future. However, phosphorus is highly toxic, can cause harm to human health, and brings the corresponding environmental pollution. A brief review is given on the theoretical and experimental works devoted to the phosphorus doping of diamond and carbon nanotubes (CNTs). The doping usually has an important effect on the chemical and physical properties of diamond and CNTs. In order to better understand the bonding mechanisms of the phosphorus-doped diamond films, and the influences of the phosphorus-doped concentration on the diamond lattice integrity and conductivity, we calculate the electronic structures of the phosphorus-doped diamond with different phosphorus concentration and the density of states in the phosphorus-doped diamond films with a vacant lattice site by the first principle method. The calculation results show the phosphorus atom only affects the bonds of a few atoms in its vicinity, and the conductivity increases as the doped concentration increases. Also in the diamond lattice with a total number of 64 atoms and introducing a vacancy into the non-nearest neighbor lattice site of a phosphorus atom, we have found that both the injuries of the phosphorus-doped diamond films and the n-type electron conductivity of diamond films could be improved. The characteristics of phosphorus-doped and boron /phosphorus co-doped single wall carbon nanotubes (B-PSWNTs) are also studied by using the First-Principle method based on density function theory (DFT). The formation energy of the P-doped single carbon nanotube increases with its diameter. The total energy of the P-doped single

---

[*] E-mail address: qyshao@163.com.

carbon nanotube in the same diameter decreases with the increasing doping rate. The position of impurity level may depend on the C-P-C bond angle. It is feasible to substitute a phosphorus atom for a carbon atom in SWCNT. P-doped carbon nanotubes are n type semiconductors. Mayer bond order, band structure, electron density and density of states are calculated in B-PSWNTs. It concludes that the B-PSWNTs have special band structure which is quite different from B-N co-doped carbon nanotubes, and that metallic SWNTs will be converted to semiconductor due to B/P co-doping which breaks the symmetrical structure. There are more sp3 hybridizations in B/P doped SWNT than those in intrinsic SWNT. The band structure of B-PSWNTs is special owing to the special band structure of P doped SWNTs. Besides, Mulliken charge population and the quantum conductance are also calculated to study the quantum transport characteristics of B-PSWNT hetero-junction. It is found that the position of p-n junction in this hetero-junction will be changed as the applied electric field by the Mulliken charge population analysis, and it performs the characteristics of diode.

INTRODUCTION

Diamond, an allotrope of carbon, has many excellent characteristics, such as extremely high degree of hardness and wear-resisting performance, high breakdown voltage and electron-hole mobility, excellently thermal conductivity and biological compatibility, low dielectric coefficient and good chemical inertness. Diamond semiconductor devices can be used in the adverse circumstances of high temperature, high pressure and strong radiation and other harsh environments. Diamond has an extremely attractive prospect in the semiconductor industries and microelectronic fields. Because the PN junction is the basic structure of the semiconductor electronic devices, it needs to be prepared with the P-type diamond and the N-type diamond.

The present technology of the P-doped diamond thin films (mainly boron-doped films) has become quite mature and is fully used in the treatment of the environment [1–4], medicine [5,6] and industries [7–9]. However the preparations of the N-doped diamond thin films are quite difficult, the impurity levels of the N-diamond films are relatively deep, and the electrical resistivity is very high [10,11]. The N-doped diamond thin films can't meet the technical requirements of the semiconductor electronic devices. Thus these difficulties limit the application of the N-doped diamond thin films in the electronics fields. The impure atoms of the N-type diamond mainly contain lithium, sodium, nitrogen, phosphorus, oxygen, and sulfur. Seeking appropriate donors and improving the experimental technique is a long term goal for material scientists.

In order to get the appropriate donors, some people tried with these atoms such as aluminum, phosphorus and sulfur. Among those donor atoms, the phosphorus atoms and sulfur atoms were studied most besides the nitrogen atoms. In 1990, Koblar Jackson and his teammates theoretically studied the donor level and the crystal lattice relaxation of the phosphorus-doped diamond. And they concluded that the crystal lattice relaxation had a great impact on the stability of the phosphorus atoms in the diamond crystal lattice [12].

In 1991, experiments succeeded on the conductivity of the phosphorus-doped diamond thin films including PN junction devices [13]. In 1997, the N-type conductance of phosphorus-doped homogeneous extension diamond thin films were prepared successfully by the microwave plasma chemistry gas phase deposition method [14]. But the impurity levels (hot activation energy) which formed in phosphorus-doped diamond were generally 0.6 eV [15,16]. And the electronic mobility was too low to be satisfactory. Moreover, there were different measurement results about the activation energy of the phosphorus-doped diamond thin films, such as 0.43 eV [14], and 0.54±0.02 eV [17].

It was possible to manufacture good N-type diamond devices with the phosphorus atoms as the dopant. But the reports of physical properties of the phosphorus-doped diamonds, which contained the formation mechanism of the impurity levels, the activation energy, and electron mobility, were very few. In recent years, despite many improvements and enhancements in the phosphorus-doped diamond experiments, there was not enough theoretical research. We calculated the energy band structures and the density of states of the different concentrations' phosphorus-doped diamond unit cells with the first principle of the density functional theory (DFT), and analyzed their electronic structures. These methods enable us to understand the bond properties between the impurity atoms and the carbon atoms, the situations of the electric charge distributions, and the influences after introducing the phosphorus impurity atoms. We also studied the influences of the vacancy in the phosphorus-doped diamond thin films, and found improvement on their conductivity.

On the other hand, since the carbon nanotubes were discovered [18], they have attracted the attention of numerous research groups because of their outstanding mechanical and electronic properties. A single-wall carbon nanotube (SWNT) can be described as a graphite sheet rolled into a cylindrical shape so that the structure is of one dimension [19] with a diameter of about 0.7-10.0 nm. Carbon nanotubes are regarded as the ultimate fiber with regard to its strength in the direction of the nanotubes axis [20], and its electronic structure can be either metallic or semiconducting depending on its diameter and chirality [21].

At low temperature, a SWNT is a quantum wire in which the electrons flow in the wire without being scattered by scattering centers [22]. Based on those outstanding characteristics, carbon nano-tubes have been studied in a wide range of areas, including field emitter for flat panel displays [23, 24], carbon nanotubes field-effect transistors [25] micro-electronics devices, chemic sensors [26], press sensors [27], etc. What's more, chemical doping [28] is expected to substantially increase the density of free charge carriers and thereby to enhance the electrical and thermal conductivity.

There are many theoretical and experimental studies on doped carbon nanotubes such as boron- and N-doped carbon nano-tubes [29~33]. Boron or nitrogen-doped carbon nanotubes were synthesized by chemical vapor deposition (CVD) [34, 35], phosphorus-doped carbon nanontubes also was synthesized [36]. It is easier to inject B impurities into the carbon nanotubes with a small diameter than ones with a big diameter. The ionization potential (IP) of B-doped zigzag (10, 0) carbon nanotubes is about 0.2 eV.

The work function of N-doped carbon nanotubes is lower than that of pristine carbon nanotubes. Otherwise, work function and ionization potential of N-doped carbon nanotubes vary with the position of N impurities in carbon nanotubes. Both the IP and the work function decrease with energy gap of semiconducting carbon nanotubes and increase with the local density of states on Fermi energy level owing to the presence of impurities. Yong-Ju Kang's calculations [37] show that defects such as vacancies severely modify the electronic structure of carbon nanotubes, resulting in a metal-to-semiconductor transition. Chemical doping also can convert the metallic SWTN to semiconductor, which has been discussed by Xu et al [38]. whose study showed that those boron/nitrogen co-doping metallic SWNTs will be converted to semiconductors. The constituting B, C and N elements are homogenously distributed within the SWNTs tube shells with no appreciable phase-separated B, N and C domains. This kind of SWNTs have been synthesized by using the Bias-Assisted Hot filament CVD [39]. The doped carbon nanotubes will be P type or N type semiconductor, just as diamond film which is doped with phosphorus is N type semiconductor which has been synthesized with microwave inductive plasma chemic vapor deposition by Chen et al. [40]. Cruz-Silva et al. [41] used a solution of ferrocene, triphenylphosphine, and benzylamine in conjunction with spray pyrolysis to synthesize phosphorus-nitrogen doped multiwall carbon nanotubes forming hetero-doped carbon nanotubes. SWNTs are often synthesized with the mixture of metallic and semiconducting SWNTs. It is always difficult to separate the semiconductor SWNTs from metallic ones, which holds back the development of application of SWNTs. Carbon nanotubes behave as a metal or as a semiconductor depending on the chirality and diameter that it is hard to attain homogeneous semiconducting carbon nanotubes in experiment.

With the purpose of exploring the properties of P-doped CNTs and solving the problem of separating the semiconducting carbon nanotubes from the metallic ones to get the homogeneous semiconducting carbon nanotubes in experiment in nano-electronic field, in this chapter we gave the electronic structure of P doped SWNTs further, such as how both the concentration of P impurity and the position of P atom in SWNT affect the electronic structure, which has been discussed in detail by the first principle calculation based density of function theory to explore the basic electronic structure characteristic of P-doped SWNT by attaining the change of the formation energy of SWNT after P presence and analyzing the effects of the position of P in SWNT. Substitutional P dopants within the nanotube C lattices is sp^3 coordinated rather than sp^2 coordinated in B doped CNTs [42]. Besides, we calculated boron-/phosphorus-doped carbon nanotubes to explore the reasons for such a characteristics of metal-to-semiconductor transition deeply and concluded that broken symmetric structure and sp^3 hybridization are responsible for metal-to-semiconductor transition. Another important characteristic of the B-P co-doped SWNT you will found in this chapter is that both B impurity level and one of P impurity levels are located between the Fermi energy level and the conduction band but another P impurity level is located between the Fermi energy level and the valence band, which is quite different from the band structure of B-N tubes. Besides, Mulliken charge population and quantum conductance are calculated to characterize quantum transport.

It is found that this heterojunction displays the structure of n-p-n junction if extra electrical field is not applied. However, it turns to diode gradually as the electric field increasing. Besides, the position of p-n junction shifts to the two layers which are between the two layers of P and B atoms when the electric field is applied along the tube axis and increases gradually.

1. THE MODEL AND METHOD OF CACULATION

We did the calculation for the phosphorus-doped diamond with American Accelrys Corporation Materials Studio 4.4 CASTEP (Cambridge serial total energy package) [43]. The valence electrons are described by Local atomic basis set and Numerical periodic boundary conditions in this software package. The interactions between electrons and ions are generally described by the norm-conserving pseudopotential and the ultrasoft pseudopotential [44]. We use the ultrasoft pseudopotential to describe the interactions between the valence electrons and the ions. The exchange-correlation energy functions are expressed by the PBE parametric form of the generalized gradient approximation (GGA) [45]. In all the geometry optimization computation, the computational precision of the total energy is 1.0×10^{-5} eV atom^{-1}, and the cut-off energy value is 280.0 eV. All the super cells are permitted to relax. The stress of each atom in the diamond crystal lattice is smaller than 0.3 eV atom^{-1}, and the stress of each structural unit is smaller than 0.05 GPa, and the atomic displacement from two successive structural parameters changing is less than 1.0×10^{-4} nm, so that they maintain the real structures under the geometry optimization. The K value of the undoped diamond crystal cell is $12 \times 12 \times 12$, and the K values of doped diamond super cells, in which the atomic ratios are 1:15, 1:23, 1:31, 1:47, 1:63, 1:71, 1:95, are separately $4 \times 7 \times 7$, $2 \times 7 \times 7$, $4 \times 4 \times 7$, $2 \times 4 \times 7$, $4 \times 4 \times 4$, $2 \times 2 \times 7$, $2 \times 4 \times 4$.

First-principles quantum mechanics used to explore the properties of crystals and surfaces in materials such as semiconductors, ceramics, metals, minerals, and zeolites, are employed to calculate the properties of P doped and B-P codoped SWNTs. The First-principles based on DFT is the precise calculation method to explore the electronic structure currently [46]. Many calculations in published papers [47, 48] have been completed by it. In this chapter, we focus on zigzag tubes and armchair tube including (5,0), (6,0), (7,0), (8,0), (9,0) and (10,0) type tube, in whose cell there are 20, 24, 28, 32, 36, and 40 atoms, respectively. The calculations are completed by Castep package [49] and DMOL3 code [50, 51] for P doped SWNTs and B-PSWNTs, respectively.

For the case of P doped SWNTs, We substitute a C atom in carbon framework with a P atom in different position. In order to study the effects of the P impurity concentration upon SWNT, the PC_{39}, P_2C_{38}, and P_3C_{37} tubes are constructed. The general-gradient potential approximation (GGA) [52] of PBE for exchange and correlation functional was used. The calculations were expended using plane waves basis with a cutoff energy of 470 eV. We used Normal-conserving pseudopotential [53, 54] to perform the interaction between ions and electrons. Geometry optimization was performed with convergence toleration of 2×10^{-5} eV/atom. The pressure on every atom is less than 0.05 eV/Å and stress is less than 0.1 GPa.

For the case of B-PSWNTs, a (9, 0) and a (6, 6) type single carbon nanotubes with 72 and 96 atoms, respectively, are to study the characteristic of metallic SWNTs with different chirality. We substitute four C atoms in carbon framework with two B atoms two P atoms for (9, 0) type SWNTs, and substitute two C atoms with a B atom and a P atom for (6, 6) type, respectively, just as Figure 5 shows. The chosen tubes are the periodic supercell, whose band structure is independent of the length of SWNTs representing the common band structure of doped SWNTs which can be obtained from the Maciel's results [36]. In order to make the results of calculation reliable and make the characteristics of such heterojunction correct, two exchange–correlation function, namely, the generalized gradient approximation (GGA) for (9, 0) type and LDA for (6, 6) type, are employed to optimize geometrical structures and calculate the properties of B-PSWNT with the Perdew-Burke-Ernzerh [52] and PWC [55] of correlation gradient correction, respectively, which accompanies the convergence tolerance of energy of 1.0×10^{-5} Ha (1 Ha = 27.2114 eV), the maximum force of 0.002 Ha/Å, and the maximum displacement of 0.005 Å. The electronic wave functions are expanded in double-numeric polarized basis set with an orbital cutoff of 5.0 Å.

The type of treatments of core electrons is All Electron forms owing to no heavy atoms in the whole system. The k-points are set $1 \times 1 \times 6$ in the first Brillouin zone for all structures.

2. RESULTS

2.1. The Analysis of the Total Energies and the Electronic Structures of P-Doped Diamond

In order to study the different concentrations' phosphorus-doped diamond crystal lattices, we separately calculated the diamond unit cell and several phosphorus-doped diamond super cells, in which the atomic ratios between phosphorus atoms and carbon atoms are 1:15, 1:23, 1:31, 1:47, 1:63, 1:71, 1:95. Because a phosphorus atomic radius is bigger than a carbon's, a phosphorus atom can substitute for a carbon atom when it is introduced into the diamond crystal lattice. The phosphorus atomic radius is 110 pm, and the carbon atomic radius is 77 pm. When the phosphorus atoms are introduced into the diamond crystal cells to substitute for carbon atoms, they will cause the inflations of the diamond super cells and distort the diamond crystal lattices. Then they will have a great impact on the diamond structures, the bond types and the electric charge spatial distribution [56]. As the doped concentrations are reduced, the bond angles which come from the combination of a phosphorus atom and four nearest neighbor carbon atoms are also reduced, but they change only a little. The impurity phosphorus atoms have a great impact on the bond angles of the nearest neighbor carbon atoms, but have little influence on the bond angles of the farther carbon atoms. What's more, there is nearly no influence on the bond angles out of several atomic radius distance. In order to further understand the influences of the phosphorus atoms on the diamond crystal lattices, we analyzed the relations between the bond lengths and the phosphorus atomic concentrations. The results are showed in Table 1.Table 1 describes the bond lengths and the electric charge distributions between the phosphorus atoms and the nearest carbon atoms. By the data of the table, we find that the electric charge distributions of the carbon bonds of the undoped diamond are as many as five or six times of the doped diamonds', and the bond lengths have increased by 0.1588–0.17332 Å (10.25%~11.19%). These were the same as the document [12]. Lombardi and his teammates also obtained the similar results by theoretically calculating the interactions between the hydrogen atoms and the impurity atoms in the diamond crystals. They found that the phosphorus atoms had the smallest energy in the T_d symmetrical position, all the nearest neighbor atoms of the phosphorus atoms relaxed outward and the phosphorus ions and the neutral phosphorus atoms had the same geometry structures in the T_d symmetrical position [57].

Table 1. The electric charge distributions of the phosphorus nearest neighbor atoms

P/C	Bond	Population	Length (Å)
1:15	C 003–P 001	0.55	1.72203
1:23	C 009–P 001	0.55	1.71803
1:31	C 002–P 001	0.60	1.71607
1:47	C 036–P 001	0.59	1.71369
1:63	C 061–P 001	0.68	1.70791
1:71	C 040–P 001	0.56	1.71134
1:95	C 010–P 001	0.69	1.70751
0:8	C 001–C 002	2.99	1.54871

As the doping concentrations were reduced, the electric charge distributions of the bonds increased gradually, but the bond lengths were reduced gradually. These showed that the combinations of the C-P bonds would be improved as the concentration of the phosphorus atoms was reduced. Thus, when the bond lengths shortened, the integrities of the diamond crystal lattices could be improved. In the experiment of the preparations of the P-doped diamond thin films by the microwave enhancement plasma chemistry gas phase deposition, Koizumi found that the homogeneity extension diamond thin films got worse with the P/C ratios increased [14]. Therefore, it also demonstrated the accuracy of our computational results in the experiment. When the diamond thin films were doped in low concentrations, the carrier concentrations were very low. According to the formula of the semiconductor's conductivity $\sigma = ne\mu$ (n is current carrier density), their electric conductivities were too low to meet the actual requirements.

The changes of the total energy after a phosphorus atom substituting for a carbon atom were shown in Table 2. The energy variations ($\Delta E = E_2 - E_1$) after a phosphorus atom substituting for a carbon atom would be reduced as the phosphorus atom concentrations increased possibly due to the aggravation of the P-doped diamond crystal lattices' inflation and the decrease of interactions between parts of the electrons and the nucleuses. It demonstrated that when the concentration of the phosphorus atoms in the diamond crystals was higher and the inflations of the diamond crystal lattices were more serious, the SP^3 carbon bonds would be more unstable and they would be converted to the SP^2 more easily. When the diamonds have been doped high, we may obtain the appropriate electronic conductivity, but the diamond crystal lattices will be damaged seriously. Therefore, if we want to obtain the ideal diamond thin films, we must make sure that the impurity atoms do not damage the diamond structures when they are introduced into the diamond crystal lattices by efficient experimental methods.

The valence electronic structure of a phosphorus atom is $3S^2 3P^3$, while the valence electronic structure of a carbon atom is $2S^2 2P^2$. By the limitation of the periodic arrangements of crystal lattices, the electronic orbits of the phosphorus atoms are compelled to hybridize in the SP^3. But the residual electrons always go into the orbits of the anti-bonds of the higher energy, and form the impurity levels near the bottom of the conduction bands. Because of the covalent bonds between the phosphorus atoms and the four nearest neighbor carbon atoms, the residual valence electrons of the phosphorus atoms can become the mutual local charges of the four nearest carbon atoms.

Table 2. The changes of the P-doped diamond crystal lattice energy

Numbers of total atoms	Total energy before doping (E_1 (keV))	Total energy after doping (E_2 (keV))	Changes of energy (ΔE(keV))
16	-2.47830196	-2.49776669	-0.01946473
24	-3.71745398	-3.73680229	-0.01934831
32	-4.95661760	-4.97574041	-0.01912281
48	-7.43492948	-7.45393921	-0.01900973
64	-9.91321221	-9.93204790	-0.01883569
72	-11.1523980	-11.1713091	-0.0189111
96	-14.8698961	-14.8886010	-0.0187049

Thus, these make the C-P bonds have a small amount of ionic characteristics. Then the conductivity of the semiconductors can be improved. According to the Mulliken Population analysis of the phosphorus-doped diamonds, we find that besides a delocalized electron, small parts of the phosphorus ion charges are uniformly close to the four nearest neighbor carbon atoms probably because the phosphorus ionic radius is bigger than the carbon ionic radius. For maintaining the stable structures, the carbon ions adsorb small parts of the phosphorus ionic charges, and develop covalent bonds of the stronger ionic characteristics. Therefore, the electrons of the phosphorus-doped diamond thin films in the impurity levels are provided by the p-orbits electrons of the phosphorus atoms. But these electrons have some ionizing energy, and are generally limited to a very small region. They can not move freely in the diamond crystal lattices. So reducing the ionizing energy of the most outer shell electrons of the impurity atoms or their barrier heights can effectively improve the current carrier concentrations.

2.2. The Influences of Vacancies on the P-Doped Diamond Thin Films

The above analysis showed obviously that although the high concentration doping in the phosphorus-doped diamonds could enhance the conductivity of the thin films, it also damaged the integrities of the diamond thin films. Therefore, we thought that introducing some vacancies into the appropriate positions could enhance the impurity concentrations of the phosphorus atoms, then improve the conductivity of the thin films, and also effectively reduce the damages of the phosphorus-doped diamond thin films. We researched the 64 atom super cells of the phosphorus-doped diamond crystal lattices, and considered two different circumstances as follows: the first one is introducing a vacancy into the position of the nearest neighbor of a phosphorus atom, and the other one is introducing a vacancy into the position of several atomic distances from a phosphorus atom. Their PDOS are showed [56]. We found that the low energy levels (approximately lower than -13 eV) were mainly occupied by the s electrons, and the high energy levels (bigger than -13 eV) were mainly occupied by the p electrons. The situations are very similar to those of the diamond. The results of the Mulliken Population analysis and the optimized structures gave rise to our findings. On the one hand, there were more phosphorus atomic orbits occupied by the electrons after introducing a vacancy into the phosphorus-doped diamond crystal lattice. And before introducing the vacancy, the p orbits were occupied by 2.45 electrons. Then after introducing the vacancy, the p orbits were occupied by 2.66 electrons. On the other hand, before introducing a vacancy into the phosphorus-doped diamond, the bond lengths between the phosphorus atom and the nearest neighbor carbon atoms were 1.70791 Å, the bond angles between the phosphorus atom and the nearest neighbor carbon atoms were 109.471°, and the bond angles of the nearest neighbor carbon atom were approximately 113.238°. After introducing a vacancy into the phosphorus-doped diamond, the bond lengths between the phosphorus atom and the nearest neighbor carbon atoms were 1.95552 Å, the bond angles between the phosphorus atom and the nearest neighbor carbon atoms were 86.605°, and the bond angles of the nearest neighbor carbon atoms were approximately 108.064°. So the bond lengths were increased by 0.24761 Å, and the bond angles were reduced by more than 10°. It was possible that after introducing a vacancy into the phosphorus-doped diamond, the phosphorus atom would move close to the vacancy. Then it would cause the bond lengths to increase and the bond angles to reduce. And it would limit the inflation of the phosphorus-doped diamond crystal lattices. This method could solve the question of the inflation of the phosphorus-doped diamond crystal lattices to a certain extent. The Fermi energy level moved toward the valence band and even entered it, so the N-type semiconductor became the P-type semiconductor, which did not meet our expectancies.

By the other method when introducing a vacancy into the position of the several atomic distances from a phosphorus atom, we obtained a better result [56]. The energy levels less than 15 eV were occupied by the s electrons while the energy levels higher than 15 eV were occupied by the p electrons. The numbers of the energy levels which were occupied by the p electrons with this method were less than with the fist method, and more than with the no vacancy method. In the computation result, the bond lengths between the phosphorus atom and the nearest neighbor carbon atoms were 1.71430 Å, the bond angles between the phosphorus atom and the nearest neighbor carbon atoms were 108.894°, and the bond angles of the nearest neighbor carbon atoms were approximately 111.218°. Compared with the phosphorus-doped diamonds without a vacancy, the integrities of the crystal lattices were greatly improved, and the energy band gap became smaller due to the impurity levels near the Fermi energy level. Therefore, this method could effectively improve the electron conductivity. In order to further study the influences of the vacancies on the electron conductivity by this method, we calculated the Plane-wave Density of States (PDOS) of the phosphorus-doped diamonds in which the concentration of the phosphorus atoms had been enhanced [56]. When the concentration of the phosphorus doping atoms was enhanced, the width of the forbidden band obviously became smaller, and the Fermi energy level moved closer to the conduction band. It indicated that the electron ionizing energy or the potential barrier of the impurity level across the conduction band was reduced. And it was possible that there were more free electrons entering the conduction band. Thus the concentration of the free current carriers could be enhanced, and the electron conductivity of the N-type diamond thin films could be improved effectively.

2.3. The Optimized Geometry Structure and Total Energy of P Doped SWNTs

The geometry structure of P-doped SWNTs with different diameters has been optimized [58]. We can see that a C atom in hexagon of a carbon nanotube frame is substituted with a P atom. Because the P atom radius is bigger than C atom radius, the regular hexagon frame is distorted. The length of C-P bond is 1.79 Å.

The angles of C-P-C is varied from 94.042°-100.348°, which agrees with the results reported by Cruz-Silva [41]. The P atom has been pushed out from the graphene layer in order to form a stable framework.

The formation energy [29] of the substitutional P impurity by comparing the total energy to that of a pristine SWNT has been calculated to discuss the stability of a P-doped SWNT. The formation energy can be defined by the following formula:

$$\Delta E = E\left(PC_{n-1}\right) - \frac{n-1}{n}E\left(C_{n-1}\right) - E(P) \tag{1}$$

Here, $E(PC_{n-1})$ and $E(C_n)$ represent the total energies of a P-doped and pristine SWNT, respectively, and $E(P)$ represents the energy per atom in phosphorus. Because $E(P)$ is constant, the above formula can be rewritten as

$$\delta = \Delta E + E(P) = E(PC_{n-1}) - \frac{n-1}{n}E(C) \tag{2}$$

Table 3 indicates the relationship between the diameter of P-doped SWNT and δ [58]. It is noteworthy that δ increases with diameter in both zigzag and armchair tubes indicating that narrower tubes are more favorable for phosphorus doping, which is similar to the results of B-doped SWNT reported by Koretsune et al [29].

According to their theory, we think that in order to stretch the P-C bonds, the carbon atoms should be pushed or the P atom should be moved higher beyond the graphite layer accompanied by symmetry breaking, when graphite layer is doped substitutionally with P atom. For the tubes with big curvature, P atom can be injected when the tubes are distorted slightly. However, for the tubes with small curvature they need to be distorted intensely. But another important reason we think is the form of C-P bond. When graphite layer is doped with P atoms, P atoms interact with the nearby C atoms exhibiting sp^2 and sp^3 hybridization.

But there is more sp^3 hybridization in tubes with narrower diameter accompanied by lower energy. So, the P-doped SWNT with narrow diameters is easily synthesized.

We have calculated the total energy to discuss the stability of P-doped SWNT with different impurity concentrations. The total energy of doped SWNT decreases as the increase of impurity concentration, which indicates that it is easier to synthesize doped carbon nanotubes when the impurity concentration becomes higher. The total energy of P-doped SWNT is lower than that of pristine SWNT leading to the fact that P-doped SWNT is more stable than pristine SWNT. So it is likely possible to synthesize P-doped SWNT with substitutional doping in experiment.

Table 3. δ for different diameters

Diameter(nm)	δ (eV)
0.391(5,0)	-179.7941
0.470(6,0)	-179.6111
0.548(7,0)	-179.0883
0.662(8,0)	-178.9906
0.705(9,0)	-178.6971
0.783(10,0)	-178.4553

2.4. The band Structure and Density of State of P Doped SWNTs

In order to study electrical characteristics of P-doped carbon nanotubes well, both band structure and density of states of (5, 0), (7, 0), (8, 0) and (10, 0) tubes, respectively, are calculated. Figure 1 shows the band structure of (5, 0), (7, 0), (8, 0) and (10, 0) P-doped SWNT.

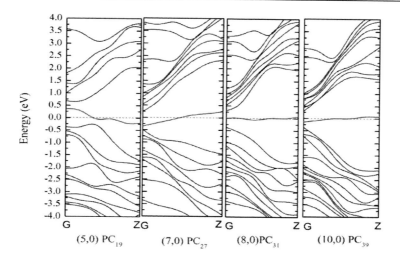

Figure 1. Band structures of (5,0) PC$_{19}$, (7,0) PC$_{27}$, (8,0) PC$_{31}$, and (10,0) PC$_{39}$ type P-doped SWNTs respectively.

According to Figure 1, the presence of P introduces an impurity energy level near the Fermi energy level, while impurity energy levels of (7,0) PC$_{27}$, and (10,0) PC$_{39}$ are close to valence band top across the Fermi energy level and the impurity energy levels of (5, 0) PC$_{19}$ are close to conduction band bottom across the Fermi level. But the impurity level of (8, 0) PC$_{31}$ crosses the Fermi energy in the middle of the gap between valence band top and conduction band bottom. Just as described in Figure 2 (c) and 3(d), the electrons from p orbit belong to P atom without becoming bond. So they mainly contribute to the DOS near Fermi energy level. Each carbon atom has six electrons which occupy $1s^2$, $2s^2$ and $2p^2$ atomic orbitals. The $2s$ orbital and two $2p$ orbitals are hybridized forming three sp^2 hybridized orbitals. These hybrid orbitals form σ bonds. Each carbon atom has an excess electron which has been hybridized but forms a π orbital perpendicular to the graphite sheet plane.

According to Figure 2 (d), although there are numerous electrons from p orbital to contribute to valence band and conduction band, there are also a few electrons from s orbital to contribute to valence band and conduction band. Besides, there are few electrons from s orbital near Fermi energy level contributing to valence band and conduction band [see Figure 2 (b)]. According to the PDOS of P-doped SWNT, however, just as described in Figure 2 (d), there are a few electrons from s orbital near Fermi energy level. Therefore the electrons from s orbital are mainly from P atom. By comparing Figure 2 (a) with (b), it is obvious that the peak in Fermi energy level mainly results from the impurity levels of P atoms. Figure 2 (c) reveals that some peaks locating between -4 and -1 eV are mainly due to electrons from p orbitals of P impurities. But there are also a few electrons from s orbitals for those peaks. There is a mixing of p and s atomic orbitals at the same level, which leads to that p orbital and s orbital are hybridized. The peak above Fermi energy level also mainly arises from the result of hybridization of p and s orbital.

The band structure of pristine (10, 0) SWNT and P-doped SWNT is shown in Figure 3 (a)-(d). Pristine zigzag (10,0) carbon nanotubes have the D$_{10h}$ symmetry [30, 59, 60]. Figure 3 (a) shows the band structure of pristine (10, 0) carbon nanotubes, from which we can see that zigzag (10, 0) carbon nanotube is direct gap semiconductor and that the energy bands show a large doubly degeneracy at the zone boundary.

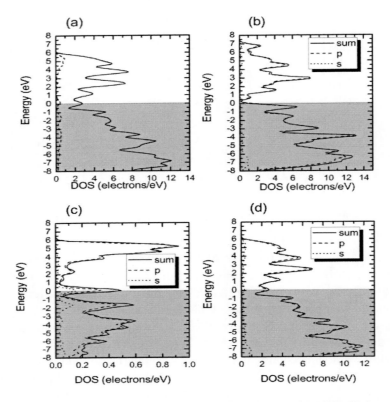

Figure 2. Total density of states (TDOS) of (a) P-doped (7,0) SWNT and TDOS of P impurities described by the dash line. Partial density of states (PDOS) of (b) pristine (7,0) SWNT, (c) P impurities and (d) P-doped (7,0) SWNT. The Fermi level is at 0 eV.

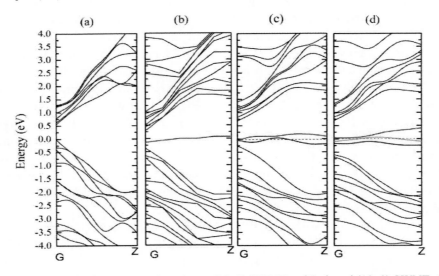

Figure 3. energy band structures of pristine zigzag (10, 0) SWNT and P-doped (10, 0) SWNT: (a) C_{40}, (b) PC_{39}, (c) P_2C_{38}, and (d) P_3C_{37}.

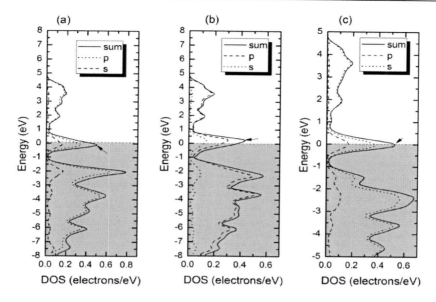

Figure 4. PDOS of (a) No 1 P, (b) No 2 P and (c) No 3 P atoms respectively.

The band gap is 0.57 eV approximately, which is similar to that reported in some paper [46]. Valence band top and conduction band bottom correspond to π-energy bonding band and π^{*}-energy anti-bonding band respectively. Figures 3(b) - (d) are the energy band structures of PC_{39}, P_2C_{38} and P_3C_{37}, respectively and there are impurity energy levels near Fermi energy level. Figure 3 (b) shows clearly that impurity energy levels cross the Fermi energy level and the impurity energy level is closer to valence band top than to conduction band bottom. Figure 3 (c) shows the two impurity energy levels. One of them crosses Fermi energy but the other is under Fermi energy level. There are three impurity energy levels shown in Figure 3(d). One is between Fermi energy level and conduction band bottom, the other is across Fermi energy and the last one is between Fermi level and valence band top. We mark the different positions of P atom with No. 1, No. 2 and No. 3 in the structure of P_3C_{37} SWNT [58]. The DOS of No. 1, No. 2 and No. 3 atoms are shown in Figures 4 (a) - (c), respectively.

The peak located below the Fermi energy level is an impurity peak just as Figure 4 (a) shows. It illustrates that there is an impurity energy level under the Fermi energy level. The reason for that is the C-P-C bond angle with 95.686° which is close to the typical angle of sp^3 hybridization. It suggests that there may be sp^3 hybridization between C atoms and P atoms to lead to σ bond. So an impurity energy level is introduced between Fermi energy level and valence band top. There is a sharp peak up the Fermi energy level shown in Figure 4 (b) which corresponds to the DOS of No. 2 P atom. The C-P-C angle composed with No. 2 P atom and C atoms is 99.1°, so there may be no sp^3 hybridization between No. 2 P atom and nearby C atoms. The P atom has one valence electron more than C atom. Therefore an impurity energy level is generated between Fermi energy and conduction band bottom. The C-P-C angle composed with No. 3 P atom and C atoms is among the angle composed with No. 1 P atom and C atoms and the angle composed with No. 2 P atom and C atoms. Therefore, the No. 3 P impurity energy level is located between No. 1 P and No. 2 P impurity energy level, which is described well in Figure 3 (d). Other P doped SWNTs have the same characteristics as (10, 0) P doped SWNT. According to Figure 4, it is noticeable that the peaks of P impurity near Fermi energy mainly result from that the s and p atomic orbitals of P atom are hybridized.

2.5. Optimized Geometry Structure and Total Energy of B-P Co-Doped SWNTs

Figure 5 shows the geometry structure of B/P-doped SWNTs. It can be seen that the structure of (6, 6) type is similar to one of (9, 0) type. For the geometry structure of (9, 0), two B atoms and two P atoms substitute for four C atoms located at the corner of hexagon, respectively.

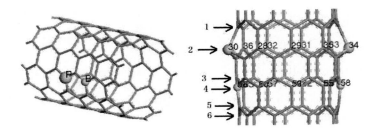

Figure 5. Structure of B–P doped SWNT. (a), (b) are the structures of (6, 6) and (9, 0) type, respectively.

The B atoms are faced to the P atoms directly with the distance of 2.767 Å. P atoms are pulled out of the graphite sheet. Two reasons can account for that formed structure. One reason is that the radius of P atom is larger than that of C atom and another one is that there is more sp^3 hybridization in C-P chemical bonding, just discussed in section 2.1. The bond angles of C-P-C are in the range of 99-103° and bond lengths are in the range of 1.705-1.798 Å. The ΔE can be used to illustrate the stability of B-PSWNTs under electric field, which is defined as follows:

$$\Delta E = E^{'} - E \qquad (3)$$

where and are the total energy of B-PSWNT under the different electric field and without field, respectively. The difference of total energies becomes bigger as the electric field increase. These results suggest that that B-PSWNT may get more stable under an extra electric field.

The band structures of intrinsic SWNTs and B-PSWNTs are calculated, respectively [61]. A gap of about 0.4626 eV appears in band structure of the doped (9, 0) type SWNTs. However, there is no energy gap in intrinsic (9, 0) type SWNT but an energy level crosses the Fermi energy level. The band structure of another metallic (6, 6) type SWNTs is also calculated in order to illustrate the common phenomenon that the metallic SWNTs will be converted to semiconductor resulted from the presence of B and P atoms. There is also a band gap of about 0.6 eV in the band structure of (6, 6) type B-PSWNTs. Therefore, it is concluded that the metallic SWNT is converted to semiconductor after B/P co-doping, which agrees well with the results of Xu et al. [38]. As far as we know, there is no exact theory to account for such a characteristic. However, we think the main reasons are that the presence of impurities destroys the symmetry of geometry structure, which is viewed as Jahn-Teller effects [62~ 66] and that the chemical bonding becomes stronger because of sp^3 hybridization.

According to some theories [60, 67], the (9, 0) type SWNT has D_{9d} symmetry, which causes a degeneracy of the energy bands at the boundary of the Brillouin zone. The energy levels of SWNTs are symmetrically disposed about E = 0 which locate at the six corners of the Brillouin zone. That is to say that Fermi energy is located at E = 0. The requirement of periodic boundary conditions for SWNTs is expressed as follows:

$$\vec{k} - \vec{c} = 2\pi v \tag{4}$$

where $\vec{c}$ is the circumferential vector, which defines a series of parallel lines, each corresponding to a different integer value line, giving rise to a set of dispersion relations $E_v(k)$, one for each subband v. The existence of gap depends on whether there exist subbands passing though the corners of the Brillouin zone or not. There exist such subbands for metallic SWNTs, but no such subbands for semiconductors. When B atoms and P atoms are injected into the structure of (9, 0) type SWNT, the symmetry of SWNT is broken leading to a broken symmetry of Brillouin zone. Therefore, there is no subbands passing through the corners of the Brillouin zone and a gap arises. There is always an energy gap at the Fermi energy level in one dimension case whenever the symmetry is broken according to the Jahn-Teller effects. In order to understand the complex electronic structure of B-PSWNTs, the PDOS of (9, 0) B-PSWNT are calculated just as shown in Figure 6. There are two impurity levels due to the presence of P atoms at ~ 0.4 and ~ -0.75 eV and another impurity level due to the presence of B atoms at ~ 0.7 eV, respectively, by comparing the PDOS of P and B atoms with the energy band structure in Figure 6.

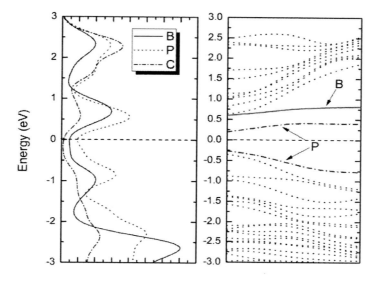

Figure 6. Energy band structure of B-PSWNTs and LDOS of B, P and C atom, respectively. The Fermi energy is defined at zero.

That is quite different from the B/N-doped SWNTs. The reason for P impurity level dispersion was explained [58]. Figure 6 also shows that the values of DOS of C atoms are zero near Fermi energy level from the LDOS of C atoms. It suggests that there are no energy levels of C atoms near the Fermi energy level but energy gap comes out. Another reason considered is that the B/P-doped SWNT form a heterojunction because of electrons diffusion owing to the difference from electrons concentrations, which leads to depletion region. It makes the energy gap get wider. Mulliken population and Mayer bond order [68, 69] were calculated to understand the bonding form [61]. Both the valences of P_{30} and of P_{34} are 3.2, while the valence of B_{56} is 3.1 as the same as that of B_{58}. The total valence indicates how many single bonds are associated with the atom [69].

Therefore, both P atom and B atom form about three bonds. The values of bond orders of P atoms forming bonding with three C atoms are 0.99, 0.99 and 0.90, while those of B atoms forming bonding with three C atoms are 1.03, 1.04 and 0.94. Being different with above cases, those of C atoms forming bonding each other are in the range of 1.11-1.35. The sp^3 hybridization mainly forms a single bond.

Therefore, there is more sp^3 hybridization in P atom than that in B atoms as well as that in C atoms. Therefore, it can be concluded that there is more sp^3 hybridization in B/P-doped SWNT than that in intrinsic SWNT, which can be another important reason of presence of an energy gap. The Mayer total valence of each C atom in the second, third, fourth and fifth layer is closed to four indicating each C atom with four bonds.

The deformation densities are calculated to analyze the bonding forms further. The deformation densities of intrinsic (9, 0) type SWNT and B/P-doped SWNT are plotted [61]. The deformation density of the layer which C atoms locate at in intrinsic SWNT, is homogeneous. However, the deformation density is homogeneous inside of annulus but not well-proportioned outside for B-PSWNTs.

There are fewer electrons in the red area called bonding area, which gets wider after boron and phosphorous are injected. It indicates that there is more sp^3 hybridization in that area. It also can be seen that the deformation density is not homogeneous inside and outside of the annulus, which suggests that there is more sp^3 hybridization in the bonding formed by P atoms and C atoms than that formed by B atom and C atom. The bonds of B-PSWNT become stronger in comparison to the similar bonds of intrinsic SWNT.

According to the distribution of deformation density of the layers B and P atoms locate at, there are lots of delocalized orbitals. Therefore, the electron transfer will happen in B/Pdoped SWNT. The space charge region is produced when the electron transfer happens.

2.6. Quantum Conductance of B-P SWNTs

Quantum conductance is calculated to study the quantum transport of this hetero-junction. Carbon nanotubes are the quasi one dimensional nano-wire. The electrons are transported in the form of ballistic transports when the length of nano-wire is shorter than the mean free path of an electron under the low temperature. Ballistic transport consists of single electron conduction with no phase and momentum relaxation. When chemical dopants are introduced into the C lattice, the impurity-induced backscattering becomes severely strong [70], yielding a very small mean free path so that electrons are strongly backscattered on the impurity level. However, quasiballistic behavior is restored under the proper condition according to Avriller's work [71] which mainly studied the effect of tube length and the magnetic field on the quantum conductance of CNTs. Doping by physisorption or chemical substitutions made great impact on the quantum transport of CNTs. Adessi's study [72] which demonstrated that doping by physisorption will decrease charge-carrier mobilities much less than chemical substitution introducing strong backscattering at the resonance energies of the "quasi bound" states associated with the defect potential well. Three type transport regimes including quasi-ballistic, intermediate and localized regime have been studied by Avriller et al. [73]. The case of (9, 0) considered in this chapter is quite different from the case Avriller group studied. Comparing Avriller's work in which characteristic transport length scales like the elastic mean free path and the localization length were studied, the length of this tube is about 0.7032 nm which is great shorter than the mean free path or the elastic mean free path (about 17.8 nm in this case). Therefore, our study focuses on the ballistic transport of B-P-doped SWNTs. The feature of quantum transport of the p-n junction region is the main study in this section. The quantum conductance G can be attained by Landauer formula [67, 74] which demonstrates that quantum conductance G is determined by the number of the energy level across the Fermi energy level. The Landauer formula is written as:

$$G = G_0 M$$

(5)

$$G_0 = q^2/h = 38.7 \, \mu s$$

(6)

where M is the number of energy level across the Fermi energy level. Since the number of sub-energy band equal to the integral value of the density of states, the distribution of G under various electric fields as a function of energy range can be described. A uniform extra electric field is applied along the direction of the tubes to calculate the characteristic of electron transport. The range of electric field strength varies from -1.0 to 1.0 V/Å. The quantum conductance is shown [61]. We define that the electric field is positive along the Z direction. The quantum conductance of intrinsic (9, 0) type SWNT is 2 G_0 and that of B/P-doped SWNT is about 1.3 G_0 when electric field strength is 0 V/ Å. Substitutional doping in CNTs will induce backscattering efficiency which reduced charge mobility and will strongly impact on the on-current capability of CNTs [72]. But the main reason for the decrease of the conductance is effects of the build-in field formed by B/P co-doping. The blow phenomenon can well interpret such result. When the electric field strength increases up to 0.5 V/ Å, there are few changes of G. As electric field increases to 1 V/ Å, the quantum conductance G is up to 2 G_0. Therefore, the heterojunction of B/P SWNTs may be broken down under the electric field with 1 V/ Å according to varied value of quantum conductance as a function of electrical field. This can be explained by the Tunneling Effect because the junction described in the next paragraph becomes narrow under the electric field with 1 V/Å. When the electric field strength is -0.5 V/Å, the quantum conductance G is closed to 3 G_0. What's more, the quantum conductance G will increase to 5 G_0 under the electric field with -1 V/Å. The potential barrier weakens as the positive increase of the electrical field resulting in the increase of the quantum conductance. While the electrical field becomes negative, the carries can be transported under the electrical field. It is, hence, concluded that the B/P-doped SWNT behaves as p-n junction.

The electronic distribution in the B-PSWNTs is determined by Mulliken charge population [61]. The electronegative of C atom is larger than that of B atom resulting in the fact that the fifth layer B atoms locate in are positive and that the nearest neighbor layers are in reverse. However, the second layer P atoms locate in is positive because P atoms give electronics to the C atoms to take part in sp3 hybridization, which is quite different from the fifth layer. It can be seen that the p-n junction main locates between the second and the third layer without applying of the extra electric field while the position of p–n junction shift to the interface between the third and the fourth layer gradually as electric field increase. Therefore, the p-n junction has the tendency to be formed between the layers in which P and B atoms locate. It is important to note that the length of p-n junction get longer when the electric field is 0.25 V/ Å. Since the charge of the second layer is nearly zero, which can leads to decrease of the conduction. But the length will become shorter as the electric field increase, resulting in the increase of conduction. The above results agree well with what the previous paragraph demonstrates.

CONCLUSION

With the first principle computation, we have researched the lattice expansion phenomenon of the phosphorus-doped diamond unit cells with different concentrations, the bond nature and charge distributions of the phosphorus atoms in the crystal lattices, and the influences of the vacancies on the physical properties of phosphorus-doped diamond thin films. First, the phosphorus atom affects only the bond nature obviously in its vicinity of a few atoms, and the closer the atoms, the greater the impacts. The smaller the concentrations of the phosphorus atoms, the stronger the C-P bonds and the more stable the structure. Second, introducing some vacancies into the right positions of the phosphorus-doped diamond thin films not only reduce the damages of the diamond thin films, but also effectively improve the electrical conductivity of the N-type diamond thin films.

We also have studied the basic electronic structure of P-doped SWNT by the First Principle Theory based DFT. The formation energy of P-doped SWNT is related to the diameters. The narrower diameters are, the lower formation energy is. Therefore, the system gets more stable. It can be concluded that the total energy of P-doped SWNT is lower than that of pristine SWNT, and the total energy will get lower with the impurity concentration increase by analyzing the total energy of P-doped carbon nanotubes. It is feasible to substitute a carbon atom with a phosphorus atom in SWNT in theory. By analyzing of DOS and PDOS, we can see that the DOS near Fermi energy level attribute to the electronics from the *p* orbital and the impurity energy level may be affected by the C-P-C angle and the *sp* hybridization leads to the impurity peak, so the presence of P atom affects the physical property of SWNT in a certain sense.

On the other hand, by calculating the characteristics of B-P doped (9, 0) and (6, 6) type SWNT using the first principle based on DFT, it concludes that the metallic SWNT can be convert to semiconductor by the B/P co-doping. The main reasons are that the symmetry is broken and that there are more sp3 hybridizations in B/P-doped SWNT than those in intrinsic SWNT. It is also obtained that the band structure of B-PSWNTs is special owing to the special band structure of P-doped SWNTs. Lastly, Mulliken charge population and the quantum conductance of that heterojunction are calculated to study the electrons transport. The study of quantum conductance suggests that this heterojunction has the characteristics of p–n junction. Finally, it is found that the position of p-n junction of B-PSWNTs will be changed under the electric field by the analysis of the Mulliken charge population.

Doping is important for chemical and physical performance of SWNT as the promising nano-material in the future. The P-doped carbon nano-tubes enrich the material for fabricating nano-device. The other significance of above results is that it may provide some theory for studying the device applied to nano-integrated circuits in the future. For the phosphorus-doped diamond, this study shows the influences of the phosphorus-doping concentrations on the electrical conductivity and the integrity of the diamond crystal lattice. Increasing the amount of vacancies in the non-nearest neighbor positions of phosphorus atoms could prepare the appropriate N-type diamond thin films in accordance with requirements of the conductivity.

REFERENCES

[1] P-A. Michaud, M. Panizza, L. Ouattara, T. Diaco, G. Foti, and Ch. Comninellis *J Appli Electrochem*, 33, 151(2003).

[2] M. F. Wu, G. H. Zhao, M. F. Li, L. Liu, and D.M. Li, *J Hazardous Mater* 163, 26(2009).

[3] X. P. Zhu, J. R. Ni, and L. Peng, *Water Res.*, 43, 4347(2009).

[4] E. Chatzisymeon, N. P. Xekoukoulotakis, E. Diamadopoulos, A. Katsaounis, and D, Mantzavinos, *Water Res.*, 43, 3999(2009).

[5] Y. Altun, B. Dogan-Topal, B. Uslu, and S. A. Ozkan, *Electrochim. Acta.*, 54, 1893(2009).

[6] E. Nicolau, I. Gonzalez, M. Flynn, K. Griebenow, and C. R. Cabrera, *Adv. Space Res.*, 44, 965(2009).

[7] J. Z. Zhu, D. R. Lu, and G. X. Zhang. *J. Shanghai. Univ.*, 2, 311(1998)

[8] C. Provent, W. Haenni, E. Santoli, and P. Rychen, *Electrochim. Acta.*, 49, 3737(2004).

[9] R. Torz-Piotrowska, A. Wrzyszczynski, K. Paprocki, and E. Staryga, *Opt. Mater.*, 31, 1870(2009).

[10] S. A. Kajihara, A. Antonelli, J. Bernholc, and R. Car, *Phys. Rev. Lett.*, 66, 2010(1991).

[11] J. Birrell, J. E. Gerbi, O. Auciello, J. M. Gibson, D. M. Gruen, and J. A. Carlisle, *J. Appl. Phys.*, 93, 5606(2003).

[12] K. Jackson, M. R. Pederson, and J. G. Harrison, *Phys. Rev.*, B 41, 12641(1990).

[13] K. Okano, H. Kiyota, T. Iwasaki, T. Kurosu, M. Iida, and T. Nakamura, *Appl. Phys. Lett.*, 58, 840(1990).

[14] S. Koizumi, M. Kamo, Y. Sato, H. Ozaki, and T. Inuzuka, *Appl. Phys. Lett.*, 71, 1065(1997).

[15] M. Suzuki, H. Yoshida, N. Sakuma, T. Ono, T. Sakai, and S. Koizumi, *Appl. Phys. Lett.*, 84, 2349(2004).

[16] S. Koizumi, T. Teraji, and H. Kanda, *Diamond Relat. Mater.*, 9, 935(2000).

[17] Y. Koide, S. Koizumi, H. Kanda, M. Suzuki, H. Yoshida, N. Sakuma, T. Ono, and T. Sakai, *Appl. Phys. Lett.*, 86, 232105(2005).

[18] S. Iijima, *Nature,* 354, 56 (1991).

[19] M. José-Yacamán, M. Miki-Yoshida, L. Rendón, and J. G. Santiesteban, *Applied physics. Letters,* 62, 202 (1993).

[20] G. Overney, W. Zhong, and D. Tomanek, *Zeitschrift für Physik D Atoms, Molecules and Clusters,* 27, 93 (1993).

[21] M. S Dresselhaus, G. Dresselhaus, and R. Saito, *Carbon,* 33, 883 (1995).

[22] J. C Charlier, X. Blase, and S. Roche, *Reviews of modern physics,* 79, 677 (2007).

[23] S. M. Hou, Z. X. Zhang, W. M. Liu, J. Luo, G. M Zhang, Z. N. Gu, X. Y. Zhao, L. M. Peng, J. L. Wu, and Z. Y. Xue, *Science in China Series G: Physics Mechanics and Astronomy,* 46, 33 (2003).

[24] Q. K. Wang, C. C. Zhu, C. H. Tian, and Y. S. Shi, *Chin. J. Electron. Devices,* 27, 543 (2004).

[25] S. J Tans, A. R. M Verschueren, and C. Dekker, *Nature,* 393, 49 (1998).

[26] J. and Cao, Q. Wang, and H. Dai, *Phys. Rev. Lett.,* 90, 157601 (2003).

[27] R. J Grow, Q. Wang, J. Cao, D. Wang, and H. Dai, *Applied Physics Letters,* 86, 093104 (2005).

[28] R. S Lee, H. J Kim, J. E Fischer, A. Thess, and R. E Smalley, *Nature,* 388, 255 (1997).

[29] T. Koretsune and S. Saito, *Phys. Rev.,* B 77, 165417 (2008).

[30] S. H. Lim, R. Li, W. Ji, and J. Lin, *Phys. Rev.,* B 76, 195406 (2007).

[31] S. Ishii, T. Watanabe, S. Ueda, S. Tsuda, T. Yamaguchi, and Y. Takano, *Applied Physics Letters,* 92, 202116 (2008).

[32] Y. S Min, E. J Bae, U. J Kim, E. H Lee, N. Park, C. S Hwang, and W. Park, *Applied Physics Letters,* 93, 043113 (2008).

[33] Q. L Williams, X. Liu, W. Walters Jr, J. G Zhou, T. Y Edwards, F. L Smith, G. E Williams, and B. L Mosley, *Applied Physics Letters,* 91, 143116 (2007).

[34] P. Ayala, M. H. Rümmeli, T. Gemming, E. Kauppinen, H. Kuzmany, and T. Pichler, *physica status solidi., (b)* 245, 1935 (2008).

[35] A. Caillard, C. Charles, R. W Boswell, and P. Brault, *Plasma Science, IEEE Transactions on* 36, 882 (2008).

[36] I. O. Maciel, J. Campos-Delgado, E. Cruz-Silva, M. A. Pimenta, B. G. Sumpter, V. Meunier, F. Lopez-Urias, E. Munoz-Sandoval, H. Terrones, M. Terrones, and A. Jorio, *Nano. Lett.,* 9, 2267 (2009).

[37] Y. J Kang, Y. H Kim, and K. J Chang, *Curr Appl Phys* 9, S7 (2009).

[38] Z. Xu, W. Lu, W. Wang, C. Gu, K. Liu, X. Bai, E. Wang, and H. Dai, *Advanced Materials,* 20, 3615 (2008).

[39] W. L Wang, X. D Bai, K. H Liu, Z. Xu, D. Golberg, Y. Bando, and E. G Wang, *J. Am. Chem. Soc.,* 128, 6530 (2006).

[40] C. F Chen, C. L Tsai, and C. L Lin, *Materials chemistry and physics,* 72, 210 (2001).

[41] E. Cruz-Silva, D. A Cullen, L. Gu, and J. M. Romo-Herrera, *ACS nano.,* 2, 441 (2008).

[42] W. L. Wang, X. D. Bai, and E. G. Wang, *International Journal of Nanoscience,* 6, 431 (2007).

[43] M. D. Segall, P. J. D. Lindan, and M. J. J. Probert, *J. Phys.-Condens Matter,* 14, 2717(2002).

[44] D. Vanderbilt, *Phys. Rev.,* B 41, 7892(1990).

[45] J. P. Perdew, K. Burke, and M. Ernzerhof, *Phys. Rev. Lett.,* 77, 3865(1996).

[46] K. Watanabe, M. Sakairi, H. Takahashi, K. Takahiro, S. Nagata, and S. Hirai, *ELECTROCHEMISTRY-TOKYO,- 69, 407 (2001).*

[47] X. H. Yan, Y. Xiao, J. W. Ding, Z. H. Guo, Y. R. Yang, and D. L. Wang, *Phys. Rev., B* 75, 195442 (2007).

[48] J. Zhao, H. Park, J. Han, and J. P Lu, *The Journal of Physical Chemistry, B* 108, 4227 (2004).

[49] M. D. Segall, P. J. Lindan, M. J. Probert, C. J. Pickard, P. J. Hasnip, S. J. Clark, and M. C. Payne, *Journal of Physics: Condensed Matter,* 14, 2717 (2002).

[50] B. Delley, *The Journal of chemical physics,* 92, 508 (1990).

[51] B. Delley, *The Journal of Chemical Physics,* 113, 7756 (2000).

[52] J. P Perdew, K. Burke, and M. Ernzerhof, *Phys. Rev. Lett.,* 77, 3865 (1996).

[53] N. Troullier and J. L Martins, *Phys. Rev., B* 43, 1993 (1991).

[54] L. Kleinman and D. M. Bylander, *Phys. Rev. Lett.,* 48, 1425 (1982).

[55] J. P Perdew and Y. Wang, *Phys. Rev., B* 45, 13244 (1992).

[56] G. W. Wang, and Q. Y. Shao, *Science in China, Series G: Physics, Mechanics, Astronomy,* 53, 1248(2010).

[57] E. B. Lombardi, A. Mainwood, and K. Osuch, *Phys. Rev., B* 70, 205201(2004).

[58] A. Q. Chen, Q. Y. Shao, and Z. C. Lin, *Sci. China Ser. G-Phys. Mech. Astron.,* 52, 1139(2009).

[59] H. Pan, Y. P. Feng, and J. Y. Lin, *Phys. Rev., B* 70, 245425 (2004).

[60] R. Saito, G. Dresselhaus, M. S Dresselhaus, and others, Physical properties of carbon nanotubes, Imperial College Press, London (2003).

[61] A. Q. Chen, Q. Y. Shao, and Z. Li, *J. Nanopart. Res.,* 13, 2275(2011).

[62] H. A Jahn and E. Teller, *Proceedings of the Royal Society of London. Series A, Mathematical and Physical Sciences,* 161, 220 (1937).

[63] R. Janes and E. A Moore, Metal-ligand bonding, Open University Press, Cambridge CB4 0WF (2004).

[64] F. G. Klärner, *Angewandte Chemie International Edition,* 40, 3977 (2001).

[65] M. J Bearpark, L. Blancafort, and M. A Robb, *Molecular Physics,* 100, 1735 (2002).

[66] Cheryl D. Stevenson and Yong Seol Kim, *J. Am. Chem. Soc.,* 122 (13), 3211 (2000).

[67] S. Datta, Quantum transport: atom to transistor, Cambridge Univ Press, New York (2005)

[68] R. S Mulliken, *The Journal of Chemical Physics,* 23, 1841 (1955).

[69] I. Mayer, *International Journal of Quantum Chemistry,* 29, 477 (1986).

[70] B. Biel, X. Blase, F. Triozon, and S. Roche, *Phys. Rev. Lett.,* 102, 96803 (2009).

[71] R. Avriller, S. Latil, F. Triozon, X. Blase, and S. Roche, *Phys. Rev., B* 74, 121406 (2006).

[72] C. Adessi, S. Roche, and X. Blase, *Phys. Rev., B* 73, 125414 (2006).

[73] R. Avriller, S. Roche, F. Triozon, X. Blase, and S. Latil, *Modern Physics Letters, B* 21, 1955 (2007).

[74] B. J Van Wees, H. Van Houten, C. W. J Beenakker, J. G Williamson, L. P Kouwenhoven, D. Van der Marel, and C. T Foxon, *Phys. Rev. Lett.,*60, 848 (1988).

In: Phosphorus: Properties, Health Effects and the Environment   ISBN: 978-1-62081-399-7
Editors: Ming Yue Chen and Da-Xia Yang   © 2012 Nova Science Publishers, Inc.

Chapter 4

LIMITING NUTRIENT AND EUTROPHICATION IN AQUATIC SYSTEMS - THE NITROGEN/PHOSPHORUS DILEMMA

Lars Håkanson

Department of Aquatic Sciences and Assessmentm SLU,
UPPSALA, Sweden

ABSTRACT

Remedial methods to lower eutrophication should not focus on nitrogen, but on phosphorus, because there are many major uncertainties related to (a) the quantification of atmospheric N_2-fixation by cyanobacteria, (b) wet and dry deposition of nitrogen, (c) the algorithm regulating the particulate fraction for nitrogen and hence also (d) sedimentation of particulate nitrogen and (e) denitrification. Occasional very high concentrations of cyanobacteria may may be quantitatively explained by high total phosphorus (TP) concentrations, high temperatures (higher than 15 °C) and/or low TN:TP ratios (lower than 15 by weight). So, there are no general validated mass-balance models for nitrogen which have been tested for independent coastal systems and been demonstrated to yield good predictive power for N only for P. Any N-model can be tuned, using different calibration constant sets for different systems, to give perfect descriptive power, but such tuning may obscure the true aspects of how natural systems work, just like a deodorant covers a bad smell. Because plankton cells include both nitrogen and phosphorus (given by the standard composition $C_{106}N_{16}P$), because both nutrients are transported to water systems by the same rivers, and because there is in many systems a potential for phosphorus-driven atmospheric N_2 fixation by cyanobacteria, one generally finds a marked co-variation between P- and N-concentrations in aquatic systems. Primary production (e.g., in g C per m^3 per day) cannot be predicted from concentrations (e.g., in mg per m^3) of dissolved nutrients, such as DIN (dissolved inorganic nitrogen), DIP, phosphate, nitrate or ammonia which are frequently below detection and have very high coefficients of variation (CV), but can only be predicted well from total concentrations of nutrients (TN or TP), i.e., from the total pools of the nutrients in the system.

BACKGROUND

The question about "limiting" nutrient is certainly central in aquatic ecology and has been treated in numerous papers and textbooks (e.g., Dillon and Rigler, 1974; Smith, 1979; Riley and Prepas, 1985; Howarth, 1988; Hecky and Kilham, 1988; Evans et al., 1996; Wetzel, 2001; Håkanson and Bryhn, 2008a). Fig. 1 illustrates key questions related to the concept of "limiting" nutrient and the nitrogen/phosphorus dilemma. It shows the main processes regulating fluxes of nutrients (nitrogen and phosphorus) to a given aquatic system (atmospheric input, river inflow), internal fluxes (biouptake, sedimentation, resuspension, diffusion, denitrification and burial) including the very important relationship between the amount of the nutrient in dissolved (bioavailable) form and the amount in particulate form (the only part that can settle out due to gravity). The average composition of algae ($C_{106}N_{16}P$) is reflected in the Redfield ratio (N/P = 7.2 by mass). So, by definition, algae need both nitrogen and phosphorus and one focus of eutrophication studies concerns the factors limiting the phytoplankton biomass, often expressed by chlorophyll-a concentrations in the water. Note that the actual phytoplankton biomass at any given moment in a system is a function of the initial phytoplankton production minus predation on phytoplankton by herbivorous zooplankton minus the death of phytoplankton regulated by the turnover time of the phytoplankton (see Håkanson and Boulion, 2002).

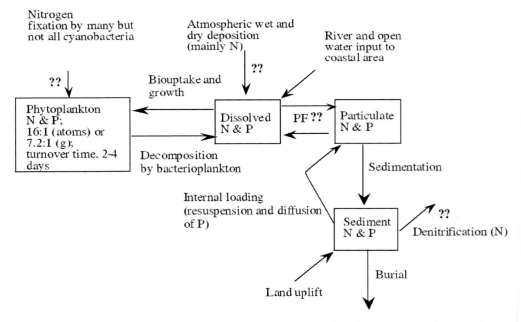

Figure 1. Overview of important transport processes and mechanisms related to the concept of "limiting" nutrient.

An important point in fig. 1 concerns the equilibrium between nutrients in dissolved and particulate phases, the timescales of these interactions and what is actually meant by "limiting" nutrient. At short timescales (seconds to days), it is evident that the causal agent regulating/limiting primary production is the concentration of the nutrient in bioavailable forms, such as DIN (dissolved inorganic nitrogen) and DIP, nitrate, phosphate and ammonia.

Short-term nutrient limitation is often determined by measuring DIN and DIP-concentrations, or by adding DIN and/or DIP to water samples in bioassays. However, information on DIN and DIP from real aquatic systems often provide poor guidance in management decisions because:

- DIN and DIP are quickly regenerated (Dodds, 2003). For example, zooplankton may excrete enough DIN to cover for more than 100% of what is consumed by phytoplankton (Mann, 1982). In highly productive systems, there may even be difficulties to actually measure nutrients in dissolved forms since these forms are picked up so rapidly by the algae. Dodds (2003) suggested that only when the levels of DIN are much higher than the levels of DIP (e.g., 100:1), it is unlikely that DIN is limiting and only if DIN/DIP < 1, it is unlikely that P is the limiting nutrient. He also concluded that DIN and DIP are poor predictors of nutrient status in aquatic systems compared to TN and TP.

- Phytoplankton and other primary producers also take up dissolved organic N and P (Huang and Hong, 1999; Seitzinger and Sanders, 1999; Vidal et al., 1999).

- DIN and DIP are highly variable (see table 1) and are, hence, very poor predictors of phytoplankton biomass and primary production (as measured by chlorophyll concentrations; see fig. 2).

- Primary production in natural waters may be limited by different nutrients in the long run compared to shorter time perspectives, see Redfield (1958). Based on differences in nutrient ratios between phytoplankton and seawater, Redfield (1958) hypothesized that P was the long-term regulating nutrient, while N deficits were eventually counteracted by nitrogen fixation. Schindler (1977, 1978) tested this hypothesis in several whole-lake experiments and found that primary production was governed by P inputs and unaffected by N inputs, and that results from bioassays were therefore irrelevant for management purposes. Redfield's hypothesis has also been successfully tested in modeling work for the global ocean (Tyrrell, 1999) and the Baltic Proper (Savchuk and Wulff, 1999). However, Vahtera et al. (2007) have used a "vicious circle" theory to suggest that both nutrients should be abated to the Baltic Sea since they may have different long-term importance at different times of the year.

- Fig. 3 gives another angle to the problem of using the TN/TP or the DIN/DIP-ratios in contexts related to "limiting" nutrient and if remedial actions should focus on nitrogen or phosphorus (the management dilemma). The data in fig. 3 emanate from the Himmerfjärden Bay on the Swedish east coast in the Baltic Proper. From the TN/TP data, one may be tempted to conclude that nutrient reductions should focus on phosphorus because the TN/TP-ratio is higher than the Redfield ratio of 7.2; using the DIN/DIP-ratio, the argument could be that nutrient reductions should focus on nitrogen because the DIN/DIP-ratio is often lower than 7.2. Our point is that neither of these arguments are valid because the primary production (biomass per time unit) is not regulated by concentrations or ratios based on concentrations but by the availability (emissions plus regeneration) of bioavailable forms, such as DIN and DIP.

- Fig. 4 illustrates another problem related to the concept of "limiting" nutrient. Using data from the Baltic Sea, this figure gives a situation where the chlorophyll-a concentrations show a typical seasonal "twin peak" pattern with a pronounced peak in April. The higher the primary production, the more bioavailable nitrogen (nitrate, ammonium, etc.) and phosphorus (phosphate) are being used by the algae (the spring bloom is mainly diatoms) and eventually the nitrate concentration drops to almost zero and the primary production decreases - but the important point is that the primary production, the phytoplankton biomass and hence also the concentration of chlorophyll-a remain high during the entire growing season!

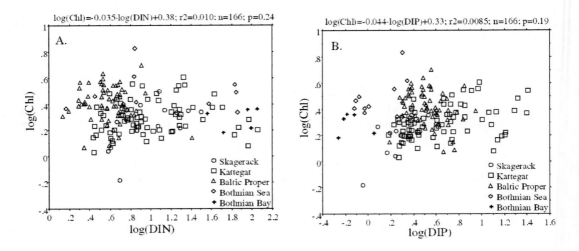

Figure 2. Empirical data from the Baltic Sea, Kattegat and Skagerack on mean monthly chlorophyll-a concentrations (logarithmic data) versus empirical data (log) on DIN and DIP, respectively. The figure also gives the equations for the regressions and the corresponding r^2-values (from Håkanson and Bryhn, 2008a).

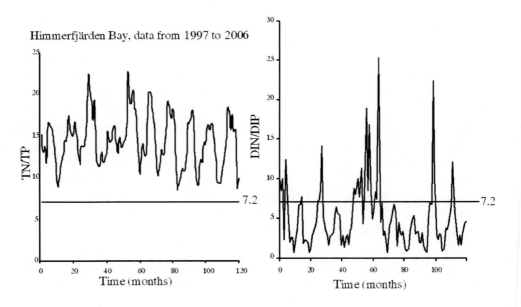

Figure 3. Monthly mean values on the TN/TP-ratio and the DIN/DIP-ratio (by weight) from the surface-water layer in the Himmerfjärden Bay (Swedish coast, Baltic Proper) using data from 1997 to 2006 (from Håkanson and Bryhn, 2008a).

So, the concentrations of the bioavailable fractions, such as DIN and DIP in µg/l or other *concentration* units, cannot as such regulate primary phytoplankton *production* in µg/l·day (or other units), since primary production is a flux including a time dimension and the nutrient concentration is a concentration without any time dimension. The central aspect has to do with the flux of DIN and DIP to any given system and the regeneration of new DIN and DIP related to bacterial degradation of organic matter containing N and P. The concentration of DIN and DIP may be very low and the primary phytoplankton production and biomass can be high as in fig. 4 because the regeneration and/or inflow of DIN and DIP are high. The regeneration of DIN and DIP concerns the amount of TN and TP available in the water mass, i.e., TN and TP represent the pool of the nutrients in the water, which can contribute with new DIN and DIP. It should be stressed that phytoplankton has a typical turnover time of about 3 days and bacterioplankton has a typical turnover time of slightly less than 3 days (see Håkanson and Boulion, 2002). This means that within a month there can be 10 generations of phytoplankton which would need both DIN and DIP and in the proportions given by the Redfield ratio (7.2 in grams).

There are four highlighted spots with question marks in fig. 1 indicating that it is very difficult to quantify these processes in a general manner. Three of them are denitrification, atmospheric wet and dry deposition and nitrogen fixation, e.g., by certain forms of cyanobacteria. Fig. 1 also highlights another major uncertainty related to the understanding of nitrogen fluxes in water systems, the particulate fraction, which is necessary for quantifying sedimentation. Atmospheric nitrogen fixation is often very important in contexts of mass-balance calculations for nitrogen (see Rahm et al., 2000). Without empirically well-tested algorithms to quantify nitrogen fixation, crucial questions related to the effectiveness of the remedial measures to reduce nutrient discharges to aquatic systems cannot be properly evaluated, since costly nitrogen reductions may be compensated for by nitrogen fixation by cyanobacteria. It also means that it is generally very difficult to understand, model and predict changes in measured TN-concentrations in the water phase, since such changes in concentrations are always mechanistically governed by mass-balances, i.e., the quantification of the most important transport processes regulating the given concentrations.

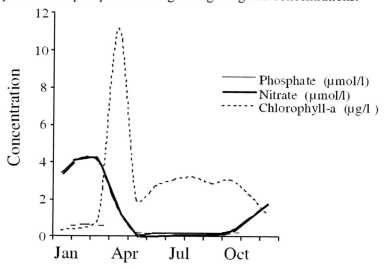

Figure 4. Variations in chlorophyll-a concentrations, phosphate and nitrate in the Baltic Sea (using data from the Gotland deep between 1993 to 2003; data from SMHI, Sweden).

Håkanson et al. (2007c) have presented a model for total cyanobacteria in marine systems based on TP, TN, salinity and water temperature, which gave an r^2 of 0.78 when tested against empirical data. This model will be used in this work and it is explained in a coming section. It should be stressed that the nitrogen fixation rates in, e.g., the Baltic Sea have been substantially revised upwards during the last decade due to better measurement techniques and better understanding of the process (Capone, 2001; Wasmund et al., 2005). This explains the wide uncertainty interval for nitrogen fixation given in table 2.

Table 1A. Monthly CV-values (coefficients of variation) for TN, DIN, TP, DIP, DIN/DIP and TN/TP in the Himmerfjärden Bay (in the Baltic Proper). (from Håkanson and Bryhn, 2008a). B. Coefficients of variation (CV) for twelve water variables based on data from 58 Swedish lakes (from Håkanson et al., 2007c). The values describe conditions during the growing season and are typically based on 66 measurements in each lake and in no case less than 6

A. Month	TN	DIN	TP	DIP	DIN/DIP	TN/TP
Jan	0.13	0.30	0.10	0.10	0.57	0.12
Feb	0.11	0.26	0.09	0.12	0.54	0.13
Mar	0.14	0.47	0.15	0.47	1.05	0.16
Apr	0.16	1.49	0.24	0.92	2.01	0.27
May	0.15	1.20	0.23	0.58	1.38	0.19
Jun	0.12	1.52	0.18	0.51	1.62	0.17
Jul	0.10	1.27	0.16	0.68	1.53	0.11
Aug	0.09	1.50	0.13	0.61	1.58	0.12
Sep	0.10	1.39	0.21	0.90	1.52	0.16
Oct	0.11	0.99	0.28	0.63	1.90	0.24
Nov	0.14	0.59	0.24	0.30	0.77	0.17
Dec	0.24	0.42	0.19	0.20	0.62	0.20

B. Variables	Median	Min	Max
Cyanobacteria	1.76	0.64	3.91
Ammonium	0.74	0.42	3.91
Nitrate + nitrite	0.73	0.09	2.78
Total algal biomass	0.68	0.34	1.83
Phosphate	0.58	0.24	1.14
Chlorophyll	0.43	0.25	1.29
Total-P	0.37	0.23	0.78
Total-N	0.24	0.04	0.72
Secchi depth	0.21	0.11	0.51
Temperature	0.14	0.10	0.37
Calcium	0.11	0.03	0.83
pH	0.04	0.01	0.09

Table 2. Uncertainties in key nutrient fluxes to the Baltic Proper (modified from Håkanson and Bryhn, 2008a)

A. Nitrogen	
In to Baltic Proper	1000·tons TN/yr
From land uplift	400-600
From rivers	300-600
From the Bothnian Sea	300-400
From Kattegat	100-150
From wet and dry deposition on the water surface	200-300
From nitrogen fixation by cyanobacteria	100-900
Sum annual input of TN	1400-2950
Total from Sweden	40-50
Realistic Swedish reductions	about 5
B. Phosphorus	
In to Baltic Proper	1000·tons TP/yr
From land uplift	110-140
From rivers	30-40
From the Bothnian Sea	10-15
From Kattegat	10-15
From wet and dry deposition on the water surface	about 1
Sum annual input of TN	160-210
Total from Sweden	1.5-2
Realistic Swedish reductions	about 0.75

From this, one can conclude that nutrient reductions for coastal areas should generally focus on phosphorus rather than on nitrogen. The main reasons for not combating eutrophication with nitrogen abatement are:

- Due to the generally large uncertainties related to the quantification of nitrogen fixation, wet and dry deposition, sedimentation and denitrification, it is difficult or impossible to predict the outcome, and cost-effectiveness, of nitrogen reductions. This should be valid for many aquatic systems.
- Lower TN-concentrations may increase the risk of cyanobacterial blooms.
- Arguments for nitrogen abatement are often backed by laboratory experiments with DIN and DIP – and such results often provide very scant information for management decisions for real aquatic systems.
- Primary production in the coastal zone generally seems to be limited by phosphorus in the long-term (monthly, annual and multi-annual) time perspective.

EMPIRICALLY-BASED MODELS FOR OPERATIONAL BIOINDICATORS

Predicting Secchi Depth

To most people, clear waters with large Secchi depths are more attractive than turbid waters. Many factors are known to influence the Secchi depth (the "sight" depth where a white and black disc lowered through the water is lost from eye sight; Secchi, 1866; Vollenweider, 1958, 1960; Carlson, 1977, 1980; Højerslev, 1978; Preisendorfer, 1986). The Secchi depth is a direct reflection of the amount of suspended particulate matter (SPM) scattering light in the water and it is also used as a key component in an algorithm expressing a water quality index for coastal waters (see Vollenweider et al., 1998). SPM and Secchi depth depend on, (1) autochthonous production (the amount of plankton, detritus, etc. produced in the system; more plankton, etc. mean a lower Secchi depth); (2) allochthonous materials (such as humic and minerogenic substances supplied to the coastal area from outside sources, such as tributaries); (3) the amount of resuspended material (materials resuspended from the sediment bed via wind/wave activity, slope processes, etc.) and in the Baltic Sea material supplied to the system from land uplift (including, e.g., nutrients, iron and clay particles). A high sedimentation leads to high amounts of resuspendable materials; high resuspension leads to high internal loading of nutrients and increased production; a high amount of colored substances in estuaries means a smaller photic zone and a lower production; a high input of allochthonous substances and a high production would mean a high sedimentation, etc. Wallin et al. (1992) showed that the Secchi depth should be much greater than that observed if only plankton cells were responsible for the light extinction. This observation means that particles other than plankton cells may be the most important factors for determining the Secchi depth in many coastal areas. It was also concluded that the empirical relationship between Secchi depth and chlorophyll-a largely depends on the chlorophyll-a concentration co-varying with the total amount of suspended particles. This correlation has also been discussed in other studies (Kiefer and Austin, 1974; Tilzer, 1988). The maximum depth of the photic zone is generally set to about two times the Secchi depth, and the effective (or mean) depth of the photic zone, a key regulator of macrophyte expansion, is often set equal to the Secchi depth (see Håkanson, 2006).

Several studies have quantified and ranked variables of significance to predict how Secchi depths vary among water systems (see Wallin et al., 1992; Nürnberg and Shaw, 1998).

1. Dynamically modeled TP-concentrations may first be transformed into SPM-concentrations (which scatter light and regulate Secchi depth) by means of a regression shown in fig. 5. However, SPM-concentrations do not change as quickly as the phosphorus concentrations for several reasons (e.g., that dissolved phosphorus is being picked up so rapidly by phytoplankton and because TP-concentrations can vary and increase very much in connection with the water turnover in the fall when SPM-concentrations do not change as much). So, a smoothing function has been used for the regression (Håkanson and Peters, 1995 describe the smoothing function). It gives an exponential smoothing similar to a running mean value and these calculations have used an averaging time of 3 months. A smoothing function is written as SMTH(Input, Averaging time, Initial value). This means that the SPM-concentration is given by:

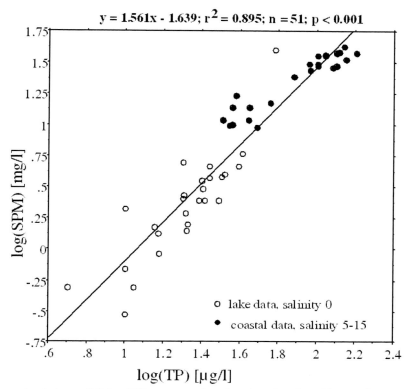

Figure 5. A regression between SPM and TP-concentrations based on data from 51 coastal areas and lakes (from Håkanson and Bryhn, 2008a).

$$SPM = SMTH(10^{\wedge}(1.56 \cdot \log(TP) - 1.64), 3, 1) \tag{1}$$

Where the SPM-value from the regression is the initial value, the averaging time is set to 3 months, and the initial value is set to 1 mg/l (but this only affects the SPM-values for the first few months in a simulation).

2. Fig. 6 gives a nomogram illustrating the relationship between Secchi depth, SPM and salinity (from Håkanson, 2006). This nomogram has been constructed using eq. 2.

$$SPM_{SW} = 10^{\wedge}(-0.3 - 2 \cdot (\log(Sec) - (10^{\wedge}(0.15 \cdot \log(1 + Sal_{SW}) + 0.3) - 1)) / ((10^{\wedge}(0.15 \cdot \log(1 + Sal_{SW}) + 0.3) - 1) + 0.5)) \tag{2}$$

3. In areas with a relatively high input of freshwater and colored humic substances, one should also expect that the Secchi depth would be somewhat reduced, as compared to the values predicted using eq. 2 (see Håkanson, 2006).

So, eq. 1 will translate dynamically modeled TP-concentration into SPM-values and together with modeled data on salinity and water fluxes, the Secchi depths will be predicted using fig. 6.

SPM is directly related to many variables of general use in water management as indicators of water clarity, e.g., the depth of the photic zone (see Jørgensen and Johnsen, 1989; Wetzel, 2001; Kalff, 2002; Panagiotopoulos and Sempere, 2005). Suspended particles will settle out on the bottom and the organic fraction will be subject to bacterial decomposition (= mineralization). This will influence the oxygen concentration in the sediments and hence also the survival of zoobenthos, an important food for fish. SPM influences primary production of phytoplankton, benthic algae, macro algae and macrophytes, the production and biomass of bacterioplankton, and hence also the secondary production, e.g., of zooplankton, zoobenthos and fish. The effects of SPM on recycling processes of organic matter, major nutrients and pollutants determine the ecological significance of SPM in any given aquatic environment. Understanding the mechanisms that control the distribution of SPM in aquatic systems is an issue of both theoretical and applied concern, as physical, chemical and biological processes ultimately shape aquatic ecosystems (Håkanson, 2006).

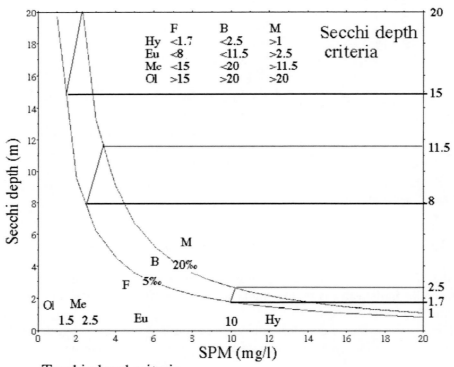

Figure 6. Illustration of the relationship between Secchi depth, SPM in surface water and salinity in surface water and trophic categories for fresh water systems (salinity < 5 psu), brackish systems (salinity 5-20 psu) and marine coastal systems (salinity > 20 psu). From Håkanson and Bryhn, (2008a).

Table 3. Characteristic features in (A) freshwater-dominated systems, (B) brackish systems and (C) marine coastal systems of different trophic levels (see also OECD, 1982; Håkanson and Jansson, 1983; Wallin et al., 1992; Håkanson and Boulion, 2002; Håkanson et al., 2007a). All data represent characteristic (median) values for the growing season for the surface-water layer

A. Freshwater-dominated systems, salinity < 5 psu					
Trophic level	Secchi* (m)	Chl-a (µg/l)	Total-N (µg/l)	Total-P (µg/l)	Cyanobacteria** (µg ww/l)
Oligotrophic	>5	<2	<60	<8	<2.2
Mesotrophic	3-5	2-6	60-180	8-25	2.2-250
Eutrophic	1-3	6-20	180-430	25-60	250-1400
Hypertrophic	<1	>20	>430	>60	>1400
B. Brackish systems, salinity 5-20 psu					
Oligotrophic	>8	<2	<70	<10	<9.5
Mesotrophic	4.5-8	2-6	70-220	10-30	9.5-380
Eutrophic	1.5-4.5	6-20	220-650	30-90	380-2500
Hypertrophic	<1.5	>20	>650	>90	>2500
C. Marine systems, salinity >20 psu					
Oligotrophic	>11	<2	<110	<15	<55
Mesotrophic	6-11	2-6	110-290	15-40	55-680
Eutrophic	2-6	6-20	290-940	40-130	680-4040
Hypertrophic	<2	>20	>940	>130	>4040

Relationships between chlorophyll, TP, TN and salinity calculated from Håkanson (2006).

* Secchi depth calculated from Håkanson (2006).

** Concentration of cyanobacteria (CB) calculated using the model from Håkanson et al., 2007c when TN/TP is set to 15 (weight ratio), surface water temperature to 17.5 °C and the salinity to 2.5, 12.5 and 36, respectively for fresh water, brackish and marine systems.

The curves for the salinities 0, 5 and 20 psu are shown in fig. 6 and the corresponding Secchi depths at the limits for the different trophic categories (oligotrophy, mesotrophy, eutrophy and hypertrophy) given in table 3. Shallow and wind/wave exposed sites/areas are generally dominated by processes of fine particles erosion and transport. The relationships between winds, waves and SPM-concentrations have been investigated in several studies (see Hellström, 1991; Kristensen et al., 1992). A high wind speed might increase SPM and decrease the Secchi depth. However, not only the prevailing wind situation is of importance, but also the frequency of resuspensions (Floderus and Håkanson, 1989). If there are many resuspensions per month, it is likely that there is less material on the bottom to be resuspended. The wind direction is also of interest. If the fetch is large, the wave base (i.e., the water depth down to which the wave orbitals can resuspend fine particles) can be deep. Studies by Andersson (2000) demonstrate that resuspension correlates with winds higher than 7 m/s in four different archipelago areas in the Baltic Proper, whereas studies by Eckhéll et al. (2000) indicate that wind speeds higher than 14 m/s correlate best with resuspension. Burban et al. (1989, 1990) have demonstrated that changes in water turbulence, SPM and salinity are also key regulatory factors for the aggregation and flocculation of suspended particles and hence also for the fall velocity. In the summer, when the water temperature is high, the biological production is also high and this affects SPM and the Secchi depth.

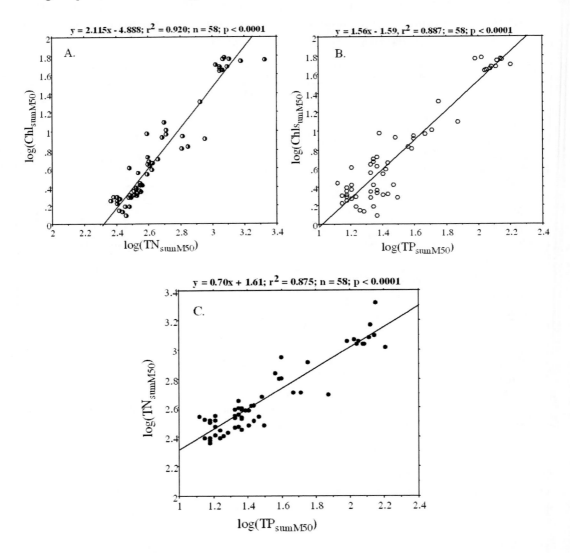

Figure 7. The relationship between chlorophyll-a concentrations, total nitrogen (TN) and total phosphorus (TP) concentrations in brackish coastal areas based on logarithmic data and median values (M50) for the growing season. The figure also gives the regression lines and basic statistics (r^2-value = the coefficient of determination, r = the correlation coefficient, n = number of data in the regression and p = the statistical uncertainty level). Data from Wallin et al. (1992), Meeuwig et al. (2000), Nordvarg (2001) and Bryhn et al. (2007).

PREDICTING CHLOROPHYLL – A CONCENTRATIONS

Typical chlorophyll-a concentrations for the Baltic Sea and parts of the North Sea are generally lower than 2 μg/l (oligotrophic conditions) and are found in the northern parts of the

Bothnian Bay and the outer parts of the North Sea, while values higher than 20 µg/l (hypertrophic conditions) are often found in, e.g., the Vistula and Oder lagoons. Typical chlorophyll data in the Baltic Proper at different depth intervals show that the highest values, as expected, are to be found in the upper layer and that the mean chlorophyll-value of about 2 µg/l in the surface-water layer (down to the theoretical wave base at 44 m in the Baltic Proper) is close to the boundary between oligotrophy and mesotrophy.

Generally, chlorophyll-a concentrations are predicted from light conditions (or water temperature) and nutrient concentrations (e.g., Dillon and Rigler, 1974; Smith, 1979; Riley and Prepas, 1985; Evans et al., 1996; Håkanson and Bryhn, 2008a). In the following, chlorophyll-a concentrations will be predicted in two different ways. These approaches use the basic regressions shown in fig. 7.

Chlorophyll from TN

One model is based on empirical median TN-concentrations from the summer period (see fig. 7A; $r^2 = 0.92$), the other on empirical median TP-concentrations (see fig. 7B; $r^2 = 0.89$). From fig. 7C, one can also note that over a wide range (these data emanate from Baltic Sea coastal areas and from the Ringkobing Fjord, Denmark; see Håkanson et al., 2007), there is a strong correlation between TP and TN-concentrations ($r^2 = 0.88$), which is also used in the following to predict TN from dynamically modeled TP-concentrations.

To obtain a better causal link between empirical TN-concentrations and chlorophyll, the regressions shown in fig. 7 have been multiplied with a simple dimensional moderator (Y_{DayL}) based on the number of hours with daylight each month (HDL, see table 4), e.g., for the Bothnian Bay (BB), we have $Y_{DayLBB} = HDL_{BB}/12$, where 12 is the average number of hours with daylight per month.

This means that Chl-values in the Bothnian Bay (BB; the same approach is used for all systems) are calculated from:

$$Chl_{TNBB} = Y_{DayLBB} \cdot 10^{\wedge}(2.115 \cdot \log(TN_{BB}) - 4.888) \tag{4}$$

Chlorophyll from TP

The second empirical approach to predict chlorophyll-a concentrations (Chl in µg/l) is shown in fig. 8 (this approach is also described by Håkanson and Bryhn, 2008a). From comprehensive empirical data covering very wide domains in trophic level and salinity for the growing season, it has been demonstrated (see Håkanson et al., 2007a) that the salinity influences the Chl/TP-ratio. Fig. 8A gives the model (using "if-than-else" statements and a technique with dimensionless moderators). The correspondence between modeled and empirical data for the Chl/TP-ratio for the growing season is shown in fig. 8B. The model is simple to use. It predicts chlorophyll from TP and salinity as $Chl = Y_{sal} \cdot TP$, where Y_{sal} is the dimensionless moderator quantifying how variations in salinity would generally influence variations in chlorophyll.

Table 4. Daylight table giving average number of hours with daylight different months at different latitudes on the northern hemisphere

Month	Equator	10°	20°	30°	40°	50°	60°	70°	80°	Pole
January	12:07	11:35	11:02	10:24	9:37	8:30	6:38	0:00	0:00	0:00
February	12:07	11:49	11:21	11:10	10:42	10:07	9:11	7:20	0:00	0:00
March	12:07	12:04	12:00	11:57	11:53	11:48	11:41	11:28	10:52	0:00
April	12:07	12:21	12:36	12:53	13:14	13:44	14:31	16:06	24:00	24:00
May	12:07	12:34	13:04	14:22	15:22	17:04	22:13	24:00	24:00	24:00
June	12:07	12:42	13:20	14:04	15:00	16:21	18:49	24:00	24:00	24:00
July	12:07	12:40	13:16	13:56	14:49	15:38	17:31	24:00	24:00	24:00
August	12:07	12:28	12:50	13:16	13:48	14:33	15:46	18:26	24:00	24:00
September	12:07	12:12	12:17	12:23	12:31	12:42	13:00	13:34	15:16	24:00
October	12:07	11:55	11:42	11:28	11:10	10:47	10:11	9:03	5:10	0:00
November	12:07	11:40	11:12	10:40	10:01	9:06	7:37	3:06	0:00	0:00
December	12:07	11:32	10:56	10:14	9:20	8:05	5:54	0:00	0:00	0:00

From: http://encarta.msn.com/media_701500905/Hours_of_Daylight_by_Latitude.html.

To obtain seasonal/monthly variations, the following predictions will (1) also apply the same dimensional moderator (Y_{DayL}) based on the number of hours with daylight each month as used in eq. 4, (2) use modeled values of the dissolved fraction of phosphorus, since this is the only fraction that can be taken up by phytoplankton and since values of the dissolved fraction of phosphorus (DF), and (3) use a boundary condition related to low water temperatures given by (example for the Bothnian Bay):

If $SWT_{BB} > 4$ °C then $Y_{SWTBB} = 1$ else $Y_{SWTBB} = (SWT_{BB}+0.1)/4$ (5)

This water temperature moderator will not influence modeled chlorophyll values when the surface-water temperature is higher than 4 °C, but it will lower predicted chlorophyll values during the winter time, and since there is also primary production under ice, the constant 0.1 is added. This moderator has been used and motivated before (see Håkanson and Eklund, 2007), and it will not influence modeled chlorophyll values very much, but it will prove better predictions of chlorophyll in the wintertime.

This means that using this approach Chl is predicted from:

$Chl_{emodBB} = Y_{DayL} \cdot DF_{SWBB} \cdot Y_{sal} \cdot Y_{SWT} \cdot TP$ (6)

So, by accounting for variations in salinity among coastal areas, one can increase the predictive power and applicability range of regression models between chlorophyll and nutrients.

Chlorophyll from Phytoplankton Production

The third approach is to predict chlorophyll-a concentrations from primary phytoplankton production (PrimP; using an approach given by Håkanson and Boulion, 2002). With this method, Chl-values are first calculated from modeled primary phytoplankton production (PrimP):

A.

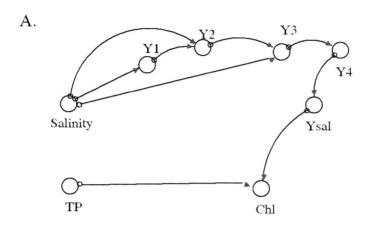

Chl = Ysal·TP[chlorophyll-a concentration in µg/l]
TP   = [TP-concentration in water in µg/l]
Ysal = Y4 [dimensionless moderator for the influence of salinity on chlorophyll]
Y1   = if Salinity < 2.5 psu then (0.20-0.1·(Salinity/2.5-1)) else (0.20+0.02·(Salinity/2.5-1))
Y2   = if Salinity < 12.5 then Y1 else (0.28-0.1·(Salinity/12.5-1))
Y3   = if Salinity > 40 then (0.06-0.1·(Salinity/40-1)) else Y2
Y4   = if Y3 < 0.012 then 0.012 elseY3

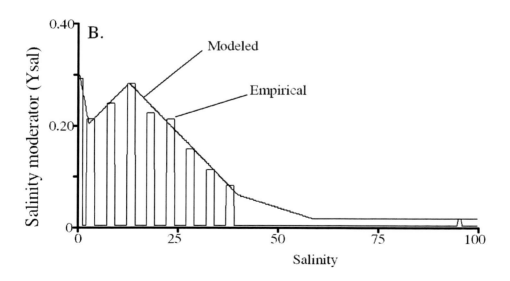

Figure 8. A. Illustration of the model for how salinity influences the Chl/TP-ratio (the Y_{sal}-moderator) and the equations. B. Illustration of how the model describes the empirical median values for the salinity moderator (from Håkanson and Bryhn, 2008a).

PrimP = 30.6·Chl$^{0.927}$ (7)
(r^2 = 0.88; n = 102)

In eq. 7, PrimP is calculated as μg C/l·day and chlorophyll-a concentrations in μg/l. PrimP is calculated from phosphorus uptake from water (in dissolved form) by phytoplankton. Using the standard chemical composition of phytoplankton related to the Redfield ratio ($C_{106}N_{16}P$; the carbon content is a factor of 41.1 higher than the phosphorus content) and by applying dimensional adjustments (from day to month), one can calculate chlorophyll values from:

Chl$_{modBB}$ = (F$_{TPbioupBB}$/(V$_{SWBB}$)·10^3·(12/365)·
(41.1/30.6))$^{(1/0.927)}$ (8)

Predicting Concentrations of Cyanobacteria

Photolithoautotrophic bacteria (sometimes called bluegreen algae; here referred to as cyanobacteria), play two key roles in eutrophication contexts: they can form extensive nuisance blooms that may be toxic (Smith, 2003), and many (but not all) cyanobacterial species can fix large amounts of dissolved gaseous nitrogen of atmospheric origin (Rahm et al., 2000; Tõnno, 2004). In the Baltic Sea, they constitute the dominating form of harmful algal blooms, although other harmful algae may be more important in other brackish and marine areas.

Quantifying nitrogen fixation is often essential for estimating the nitrogen balance in marine waters and understanding the causes of marine eutrophication. Since nitrogen fixation is triggered by high temperatures, low non-gaseous nitrogen concentrations and high phosphorus concentrations in the water, this process may determine which nutrient regulates primary production in the long run, and thus which nutrient should be abated in order to remediate marine eutrophication (Savchuk and Wulff, 1999; Tyrrell, 1999).

Fig. 1 gives the main processes regulating external fluxes (atmospheric input and river inflow) of nutrients (nitrogen and phosphorus) to a given aquatic system, internal fluxes (sedimentation, resuspension, diffusion, denitrification and burial) including the very important relationship between the amount of the nutrient in dissolved and particulate forms. The focus of this section concerns nitrogen fixation by cyanobacteria.

Many papers discuss nitrogen fixation in the Baltic Sea (see Wasmund, 1997; Rahm et al., 2000; Larsson et al., 2001; Wasmund et al., 2005). The aim of this section is to use an empirically-based model from Håkanson et al. (2007c) to predict cyanobacteria and nitrogen fixation in the Baltic Proper. This model will be outlined in the next section.

Table 2 also provides background for this section. It summarizes transport processes to, within and from the Baltic Proper. The value given here for the nitrogen fixation is 130,000 tons per year. This value indicates an order-of-magnitude figure for the nitrogen fixation in the Baltic Proper. The value is, however, very uncertain. For example, Melvasalo et al. (1983) and Leppänen et al. (1988) have given values of 100,000 t/yr, Rönner (1985) stated 130,000 for the Baltic Proper and the Gulf of Finland, and Rahm et al. (2000) gave an interval of 30,000 to 260,000 t/yr for the period 1992 to 1997. Yearly estimations on nitrogen fixation from the Baltic Proper according to Larsson et al. (2001) are found in table 5. The summer increase in TN strongly coincided with the blooms of N-fixating cyanobacteria in 1997 and

1998 and these values are about 60% of those calculated by Wasmund et al. (2001). Wasmund et al. (2005) estimated the N-fixation rate in the Baltic Proper to about a factor of 2 higher than the values in table 5 (434,000 – 792,000 t/yr), while earlier estimates have generally been much lower and have not included night measurements, the complete growing season, or the important contribution from phytoplankton smaller than 10 µm.

Table 5. Yearly N-fixation in tons per year in the Baltic
Proper based on data from Larsson et al. (2001)

Year	Minimum	Maximum
1994	290,000	350,000
1995	360,000	420,000
1996	180,000	250,000
1997	340,000	430,000
1998	180,000	330,000

To quantify nitrogen fixation should be one of the most difficult and uncertain of all N-fluxes because the concentration of cyanobacteria show such very high coefficients of variation. This will be discussed in a following section.

It is important to identify all major sources of nutrient emissions not just to the Baltic Proper but to all polluted water systems and to quantify all major fluxes because this will determine the expectation one would have on different, often costly, measures to reduce nutrient emissions and improve the ecosystem conditions. If the total inflow of nitrogen to the Baltic Proper from countries and processes is 1,465,000 t/yr (table 2), and if Swedish anthropogenic emissions are just 8% (117,800/1,465,000) of all the nitrogen transport to the Baltic Proper, this will determine the expectations that one would have on Swedish nitrogen reductions, and also provide a possibility to compare the cost-effectiveness of different alternative approaches to reduce the nitrogen fluxes to the system.

The problem to understand and predict TN-concentrations in marine systems is, as stressed, accentuated by the fact that there are no (to the best of my knowledge) practically useful validated models to quantify the particulate fraction for nitrogen in saltwater systems. In mass-balance modeling, it is imperative to have a reliable algorithm for the particulate fraction, since the particulate fraction (PF) is the only fraction that by definition can settle out due to gravity.

From previous modeling work (see, e.g., Floderus, 1989), one can conclude that it is also very difficult to quantify denitrification (another question mark in fig. 1). Denitrification depends on sediment redox conditions, i.e., on sedimentation of degradable organic matter and the oxygen concentration in the deep-water layer, but also on the frequency of resuspension events, on the presence of mucus-binding bacteria, on the conditions for zoobenthos and bioturbation. Given this complexity, it is easy to understand why empirically well-tested algorithms to quantify denitrification on a monthly basis do not exist to the best of our knowledge. The atmospheric wet and dry deposition of nitrogen may (as indicated in fig. 1) be very large (in the same order as the tributary inflow) and patchy (Wulff et al., 2001), which means that for large coastal areas and smaller systems far away from measurement stations, the uncertainty in the value for the atmospheric wet and dry deposition of N is also generally very large.

The abundance of cyanobacteria is also related to the TN/TP-ratio. Cyanobacteria have been found to dominate lake primary production at TN/TP $\leq 29/1$ (by weight) and are much less abundant at higher ratios, while nitrogen-fixing cyanobacteria tend to dominate at TN/TP $\leq 22/1$ (Havens et al., 2003). Smith (1985) found TP to be a better predictor of the biomass of cyanobacteria (CB) than TN and TN/TP. The TN/TP-ratio is an important variable for the model used in this work. The DIP concentration is poorly correlated with cyanobacterial biomass in the Baltic Sea (Nausch et al., 2008).

The Model for Cyanobacteria

This approach concerns cyanobacteria in the water column but not in the benthic zone. In the derivation of the model, data from many databases were used (see Håkanson et al., 2007c) Fig. 9A gives the (log-log) regression between chlorophyll-a concentrations and total cyanobacteria (CB = median values for the growing season) using data for lakes. One can note a highly significant and mechanistically understandable strong positive co-variation between these two measures of primary production/biomass in water. Evidently, this relationship may look different had it been based on daily, weekly or monthly values and it is probable that this co-variation also exists for many marine systems. The following calculations first show maximum values for the nitrogen fixation. In a following section, we will also discuss the fraction of N-fixating species of the total biomass of cyanobacteria in the Baltic Proper.

The basic regression is given in fig. 9B. This regression includes data from more systems than the equation given by Smith (1985) and it also gives a higher r^2-value (0.76 as compared to 0.71).

$$CB^{0.25} = 5.85 \cdot \log(TP) - 4.01 \tag{10}$$
$$(r^2 = 0.76; n = 86)$$

In the literature, temperatures between 15 and 17 °C have been reported as the minimum for cyanobacteria blooms in freshwater systems and in the Baltic Sea (Reynolds and Walsby, 1975; Edler, 1979; Wasmund, 1997). It has also been shown that cyanobacteria require temperatures of about 20-21 °C to form blooms (Marumo and Asaoka, 1974; Lukatelich and McComb, 1986; McQueen and Lean, 1987). The optimal growth temperatures in laboratory experiments are usually around 25 °C for many species in temperate waters (Konopka and Brock, 1978; Robarts and Zohardy, 1987; Lehtimäki et al., 1997). With higher temperatures, the growth rate usually starts to decrease. In field data from the Baltic Sea (Wasmund, 1997), this decrease in growth rate is not shown because there are few occasions with temperatures higher than 20 °C.

Fig. 9C gives data on the relationship between CB (log(1+CB)) and SW-temperatures (SWT in °C) from 74 systems. One can note that all systems with higher CB-values than 100 µg/l (median values for the growing season) have temperatures higher than 15 °C. The temperature influences on CB are quantified in fig. 10, which gives a compilation of the model. This mean that the dimensionless moderator for temperature influences on CB (Y_{SWT}) is given by:

If SWT ≥ 15 °C, then

$Y_{SWTCB} = (15/17.5)·(1+0.63·((SWT/15)^{1.5}-1))$ else
$Y_{SWTCB} = (1+1·((SWT/15)^3-1))$ (11)

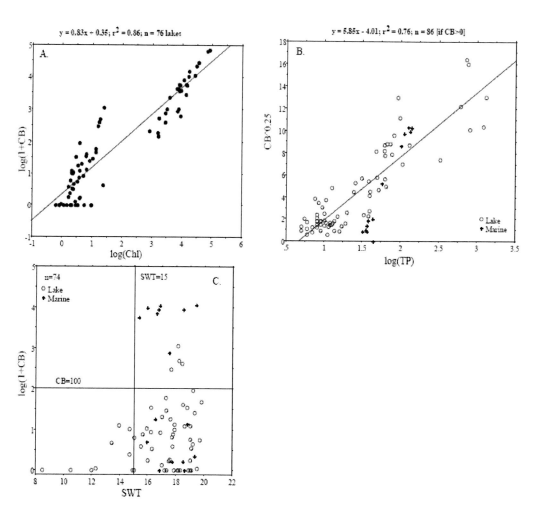

Figure 9. A. Regression between log(1+CB) and log(Chl) based on data from 76 lakes. B. Regression between CB (transformed to $CB^{0.25}$) and log(TP) (TP in μg/l) using median values for the growing season from 86 systems with CB-values higher than zero. C. Scatter plot between cyanobacteria (transformed into log(1+CB)) versus surface water temperatures (SWT in °C) based on data from 74 systems. The figure also gives the coefficients of determination (r^2) and the regression lines. Cyanobacteria (CB) in μg ww/l, chlorophyll-a concentrations (Chl) in μg/l. From Håkanson et al. (2007c).

So, if SWT = 15 °C, Y_{SWTCB} = 0.86; if SWT = 5, Y_{SWTCB} = 0.037; if SWT = 17.5, Y_{SWTCB} = 1; if SWT = 25, Y_{SWTCB} = 1.48, etc. When the temperature is 25 °C, the risks of getting high concentrations of cyanobacteria is factor of 1.48 higher than at 17.5 °C, if all else is constant.

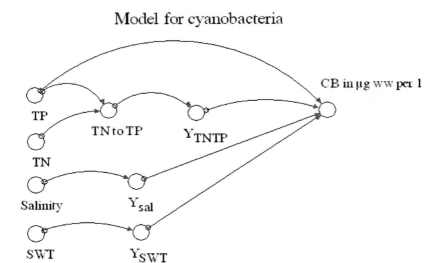

$$CB = ((5.85 \cdot \log(TP) - 4.01)^4) \cdot Y_{TNTP} \cdot Y_{SWT} \cdot Y_{sal}$$

CB in µg ww/l
Salinity in psu
SWT = Surface water temperature in °C
Total-N (TN) in µg/l
Total-P (TP) in µg/l

Y_{TNTP} = if TN/TP < 15 then (1-3·(TN/TP/15-1)) else 1
Y_{SWT} = if SWT □ 15 then (0.86+0.63·((SWT/15)^1.5-1)) else (1+1·((SWT/15)^3-1))
Y_{sal} = if salinity <10 then (2.1+1.1·((salinity/10)^2-1)) else (2.1-115·((salinity/10)^0.01-1))

Model domain: 4 < TP < 1300; 165 < TN < 6830; 0 < salinity < 40; 8 < SWT < 25

Figure 10. Outline of the model to predict median summer values of cyanobacteria in coastal areas. From Håkanson et al. (2007c).

In hypertrophic lakes, the biomass of cyanobacteria can be very high with concentrations of about 100 mg/l (Smith, 1985). Howarth et al. (1988a, b) found no data on N-fixing planktonic species in estuaries and coastal seas, except for the Baltic Sea and the Pell-Harvey estuary, Australia. Also results from Marino et al. (2006) support this general lack of N-fixing cyanobacteria in estuaries. There are more than 10 nitrogen fixating cyanobacteria species in the Baltic Proper (Wasmund et al., 2001). A field study in the Baltic Sea (Wasmund, 1997) indicated that in this brackish environment cyanobacteria have the highest biomass at 7 – 8 psu and that the blooms in Kattegat and Belt Sea are more frequent if the salinity is below 11.5 psu (see also Sellner, 1997). A laboratory experiment with cyanobacteria from the Baltic Sea supports the results that the highest growth rate was at salinities in the range between 5 and 10 psu (Lehtimäki et al., 1997).

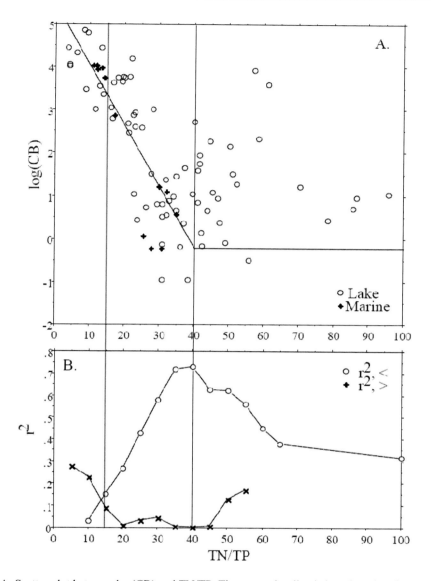

Figure 11. A. Scatter plot between log(CB) and TN/TP. The regression line is based on data from systems where TN/TP < 15. B. Compilation of r^2-values between log(CB) and TN/TP using data from systems when successively smaller (<) and higher (>) TN/TP-ratios have been omitted. The maximum r^2 is obtained for systems with smaller TN/TP than 40; very low r^2-values are obtained if the regressions are done for systems with TN/TP higher than 15. From Håkanson et al. (2007c).

In this model, the influences of the salinity (Sal) on cyanobacteria are motivated by empirical data from a large number of systems (see Håkanson et al., 2007c) and are expressed by eq. 12:

If the salinity < 10 psu, $Y_{sal} = (2.1 + 1.1 \cdot ((Sal/10)^2 - 1))$
else $Y_{sal} = (2.1 - 115 \cdot ((Sal/10)^{\wedge 0.01} - 1))$ (12)

This means that at a salinity of 10 psu, Y_{sal} is 2.1 and CB likely a factor of 2.1 higher than in freshwater systems; if the salinity is 5, Y_{sal} is 1.28; if the salinity is 20, Y_{sal} is 1.3; and if the salinity is 36, Y_{sal} is 0.62.

Fig. 11A shows a scatter plot between log(CB) and TN/TP. High CB-values only appear in systems with relatively low TN/TP. The regression between log(CB) and TN/TP attains a maximum value ($r^2 = 0.73$; log(CB)=0.142·TN/TP+5.47; n = 61) if only data from systems with TN/TP smaller than 40 are used. The upper curve (circles) in fig. 11B gives the r^2-values when only systems with TN/TP smaller than 10, 15, 20,….. 100 were used in the regressions. The lower curve in fig. 4.B gives similar results when only systems with higher TN/TP were used. Then, one can note that there is no statistically significant ($p < 0.01$) relationship between log(CB) and TN/TP if TN/TP is higher than 15.

This information is used in the model where the basic regression between CB and TP given by eq. 10 is complemented with a dimensionless moderator, Y_{TNTP} defined by:

If TN/TP < 15 then $Y_{TNTP} = (1-3 \cdot ((TN/TP)/15-1))$
else $Y_{TNTP} = 1$ $\hspace{4cm}$ (13)

This means that for systems with TN/TP (based on median or mean values for the growing season) higher than 15, one can use the basic regression without any correction for the TN/TP-ratio, but for systems with lower TN/TP, eq. 13 will provide a correction factor. If, e.g., TN/TP = 7.2, then $Y_{TNTP} = 2.56$, and the CB-value a factor of 2.56 higher than the value suggested by the basic regression.

The general model for cyanobacteria may give rather uncertain predictions for systems with high TN/TP and low temperatures. However, during such conditions, the N-fixation should be small. Predicting conditions with high CB is evidently most important. Due to the fact that all methods to estimate N-fixation in entire systems at longer time scales (such as month or years) are very uncertain, there is good reason to regard this approach as complementary – and not a competitor - to other approaches. Measured N-fixation tends to follow a similar pattern as the prevalence of cyanobacteria (Howarth et al., 1988a, b; Wasmund et al., 2001). Analyses using modern gene sequencing techniques have suggested that more organisms than we currently know may fix nitrogen in both lakes and marine systems (Zehr et al., 2003).

CONCLUSION

Savchuk et al. (2008) estimated pre-industrial nitrogen loadings and the same research group has presented the results behind the Baltic Sea Action Plan (BSAP, 2007), which requires massive reductions in N-input to the Baltic Sea. However, Håkanson and Bryhn (2008b) have, based on data from the Baltic Sea and many other coastal areas, demonstrated why remedial actions should not focus on nitrogen and they gave six main reasons:

1) It is not possible to predict how the Baltic Sea system – or most other aquatic systems - would respond to reductions in N-loading since there are many major uncertainties related to (a) the quantification of atmospheric N_2-fixation by

cyanobacteria, (b) wet and dry deposition of nitrogen, (c) the algorithm regulating the particulate fraction for nitrogen and hence also (d) sedimentation of particulate nitrogen and (e) denitrification.

2) Lowering the N-concentration the Baltic Sea with salinities from 3 to 17 psu is likely to favor the blooming of harmful cyanobacteria, and such events should be avoided. Occasional very high concentrations of cyanobacteria in the Baltic Sea - and elsewhere - may be quantitatively explained by high total phosphorus (TP) concentrations, high temperatures (higher than 15 °C) and/or low TN:TP ratios (lower than 15 by weight).

3) There are no general validated mass-balance models for nitrogen which have been tested for independent coastal systems and been demonstrated to yield good predictive power. Any N-model can be tuned, using different calibration constant sets for different systems, to give perfect descriptive power, but such tuning may obscure the true aspects of how natural systems work just like a deodorant covers a bad smell.

4) The general dynamic P-model, CoastMab, presented by Håkanson and Bryhn (2008b) gave good predictions ($r^2 = 0.98$ for modeled annual mean values regressed against empirical data) in a number of bassin basins, lakes and vertical layers without basin-specific tuning and without taking N-concentrations into account. These findings fundamentally contradict the popular "vicious circle theory" (Vahtera et al., 2007) which asserts that P-diffusion from deep sediments is driven by low oxygen concentrations created by sedimentation of N-limited diatoms. Instead, the P-cycle in the Baltic Sea appears to be largely or completely independent from N-inputs, similar to the case of Lake 227, most other lakes and the Stockholm Archipelago (Håkanson and Bryhn, 2008d; Schindler et al., 2008).

5) Because plankton cells include both nitrogen and phosphorus (given by the standard composition $C_{106}N_{16}P$), because both nutrients are transported to water systems by the same rivers, and because there is in many systems a potential for phosphorus-driven atmospheric N_2 fixation by cyanobacteria, one generally finds a marked co-variation between TP and TN-concentrations in aquatic systems, as shown using data from 495 systems covering very wide ranges in trophic status, size and form, latitudes and salinity (data sources and more details are given Håkanson et al., 2008a). It is interesting to note that only 9 of these 495 systems have TN/TP-ratios lower than the Redfield-ratio (based on weight) of 7.2 and that the coefficient of determination is about 0.6 for both the actual and the logarithmic data. When there is a major difference from the general relationship shown by the regression line in fig. 12, there should be specific causal reasons for this, if one first accounts for the scatter related to the inherent uncertainties in the data. So, phosphorus rather than nitrogen seems to limit the long-term (growing season period) primary production in the Baltic Sea and in most coastal areas of the world.

6) Primary production (e.g., in g C per m^3 per day) cannot be predicted from concentrations (e.g., in mg per m^3) of dissolved nutrients, such as DIN (dissolved inorganic nitrogen), DIP, phosphate, nitrate or ammonia which are frequently below detection and have very high coefficients of variation (CV), but can only be predicted well from total concentrations of nutrients (TN or TP), i.e., from the total pools of the nutrients in the system. The concentrations of dissolved nutrients can be low and

approach zero but the system can still maintain a high primary production because primary production is regulated by the regeneration and rapid recycling of dissolved nutrients (Håkanson and Bryhn, 2008b).

REFERENCES

Anderssson, M. H., Gullström, M., Asplund, M., and Öhman, M. C., 2007. Importance of using multiple sampling methodologies for estimating of fish community composition in offshore wind power construction areas of the Baltic Sea. *Ambio,* 36: 634-636.

BSAP. 2007, *HELCOM Baltic Sea Action Plan – HELCOM Ministerial Meeting,* Krakow, Poland, 15 November, 2007, 101 p. (see HELCOM website).

Burban, P.-Y., Lick, W. and Lick, J., 1989. The flocculation of fine-grained sediments in estuarine waters. *Journal of Geophysical Research,* 94: 8223-8330.

Burban, P.-Y., Xu, Y.-J., McNeiel, J. and Lick, W., 1990. Settling speeds of flocs in freash water and seawater. *Journal of Geophysical Research,* 95: 18213-18220.

Capone DG. Marine nitrogen fixation: what's the fuss? *Curr. Opin. Microbiol.* 2001; 4: 341-348.

Carlson, R.E. 1977. A trophic state index for lakes. *Limnology and Oceanography,* 22: 361-369.

Carlson, R.E., 1980. More complications in the chlorophyll - Secchi disk relationship. *Limnology and Oceanography,* 25: 379-382.

Højerslev, 1978; Preisendorfer, 1986).

Dillon, P.J. and Rigler, F.H., 1974. The phosphorus-chlorophyll relationship in lakes. *Limnol. Oceanogr.,* 19:767-773.

Dodds, W. K., 2003. Misuse of inorganic N and soluble reactive P concentrations to indicate nutrient status of surface waters. *Journal of the North American Benthological Society,* 22: 171–181.

Edler L. Phytoplankton succession in the Baltic Sea. *Acta Bot Fennica.* 1979; 110: 75-78.

Eckhéll, J., Jonsson, P., Meili, M and Carman, R., 2000. Storm influence on the accumulation and lamination of sediments in deep areas of the northwestern Baltic proper. *Ambio,* 29: 238-245.

Evans M.S., Arts M.T. and Robarts R.D., 1996. Algal productivity, algal biomass, and zooplankton biomass in a phosphorus-rich, saline lake: deviations from regression model predictions. *Can. J. Fish. Aquat. Sci.,* 53:1048-1060.

Floderus, S. and Håkanson, L. 1989. Resuspension, ephermal mud blankets and nitrogen cycling in Laholmsbukten, south east Kattegat. *Hydrobiologia,* 176/177: 61-75.

Floderus, S., Jähmlich S., Ekebom J. and Saarso, M., 1999. Particle flux and properties affecting the fate of bacterial productivity in the benthic boundary layer at a mud-bottom site in South-Central Gulf of Riga. *Journal of Marine Systems,* 23:233-250.

Håkanson, L., 2006. Suspended particulate matter in lakes, rivers and marine systems. *The Blackburn Press,* New Jersey, 331 p.

Håkanson, L. and Boulion, V., 2002. The Lake Foodweb - modelling predation and abiotic/biotic interactions. Backhuys Publishers, Leiden, 344 p.

Håkanson, L. and Peters, R.H., 1995. Predictive limnology. *Methods for predictive modelling.* SPB Academic Publishing, Amsterdam, 464 p.

Håkanson, L. and Bryhn, A.C., 2008a. Tools and criteria for sustainable coastal ecosystem management – with examples from the Baltic Sea and other aquatic systems. Springer Verlag, Berling, Heidelberg, 292 p.

Håkanson, L. and Bryhn, A.C., 2008b. Eutrophication in the Baltic Sea – present situation, nutrient transport processes, remedial strategies. Springer Verlag, Berlin, Heidelberg, 261 p.

Håkanson, L. and Bryhn, A.C., 2008c. A dynamic mass-balance model for phosphorus in lakes with a focus on criteria for applicability and boundary conditions. *Water, air and soil pollution,* 187: 119-147.

Håkanson, L., Bryhn, A. C., and Hytteborn, J. K., 2007. On the issue of limiting nutrient and predictions of cyanobacteria in aquatic systems. *Science of the Total Environment,* 379: 89-108.

Håkanson, L. and Boulion, V., 2002a. *The Lake Foodweb - modelling predation and abiotic/biotic interactions.* Backhuys Publishers, Leiden, 344 p.

Håkanson, L., Bryhn, A.C., and Eklund, J.M., 2007. Modelling phosphorus and suspended particulate matter in Ringkobing Fjord to understand regime shifts. *– J. Marine Systems,* 68: 65-90.

Håkanson, L. and Eklund, J.M., 2007. A dynamic mass-balance model for phosphorus fluxes and concentrations in coastal areas. *Ecol. Res.,* 22: 296-320.

Håkanson, L. and Peters, R.H., 1995. *Predictive limnology. Methods for predictive modelling.* SPB Academic Publishing, Amsterdam, 464 p.

Havens KE, James RT, East TL, Smith VH. N:P ratios, light limitation, and cyanobacterial dominance in a subtropical lake impacted by non-point source nutrient pollution. *Environ. Poll.* 2003; 122: 379-390.

Hecky, R.E. and Kilham, P., 1988. Nutrient limitation of phytoplancton in freshwater and marine environments: A rewiew of recent evidence on the effects of enrichment. *Limnol. Oceanogr.* 33, 796-822.

Hellström, T., 1991. The effect of resuspension on algal production in a shallow lake. *Hydrobiologia.* 213: 183-190.

Højerslev, N.K., 1978. Daylight measurements appropriate for photosynthetic studies in natural sea waters. *J. Cons. Int. Explor. Mer.,* 38: 131-146.

Howarth, R.W., 1988. Nutrient limitation of net primary production in marine ecosystems. *Ann. Rev. Ecol.,* 19, 89-110.

Howarth, R. W., Marino, R., Lane, J. and Cole, J.J., 1988a. Nitrogen fixation in freshwater, estuarine, and marine ecosystems. 1. Rates and importance. *Limnol. Oceanogr.,* 33: 669 – 687.

Howarth, R. W., Marino, R. and Cole, J. J., 1988b. Nitrogen fixation in freshwater, estuarine, and marine ecosystems: 2. Biogeochemical controls. *Limnol. Oceanogr.,* 33: 688-701.

Huang, B. and Hong, H., 1999. Alkaline phosphatase activity and utilization of dissolved organic phosphorus by algae in subtropical coastal waters. *Marine Pollution Bulletin,* 39: 205-211.

Jørgensen, S.E. and Johnsen, J., 1989. Principles of environmental science and technology (2nd edition). *Studies in environmental science,* 33. Elsevier, Amsterdam, 628 p.

Kalff J., 2002. *Limnology.* Prentice Hall, New Jersey, 592 p.

Kiefer, D.A. and Austin, R.W., 1974. The effect of varying phytoplankton concentration on submarine transmission in the Gulf of California. *Limnology and Oceanography,* 19: 55-64.

Konopka, A. and Brock, T. D., 1978. Effect of temperature on blue-green algae (Cyanobacteria) in Lake Mendota. *Applied and Environmental Microbiology,* 36: 572 – 576.

Kristensen, P., Søndergaard, M. and Jeppesen, E., 1992. Resuspension in a shallow eutrophic lake. *Hydrobiologia.* 228: 101-109.

Larsson, U., Hajdu, S., Walve, J., Elmgren, R., 2001. Baltic Sea nitrogen fixation estimated from the summer increase in upper mixed layer total nitrogen. *Limnology and Oceanography,* 46: 811-820.

Lehtimäki, J. Moisander, P. Sivonen, K. and Kononen, K., 1997. Growth, nitrogen Fixation, and Nodularin production by two Baltic Sea Cyanbacteria. *Applied and Environmental Microbiology,* 63: 1647 – 1656.

Leppänen, JM., Niemi, Å., and Rinne, I., 1988. *Nitrogen fixation of cyanobacteria (blue-green algae) and nitrogen cycle of the Baltic Sea, Symposis,* 6: 181-194.

Lukatelich, R. J. and McComb, A. J., 1986. Nutrient levels and the development of diatoms and blue-green algal blooms in a shallow Australian estuary. *Journal of Plankton Research,* 8: 597 – 618.

Mann, K.H., 1982. *Ecology of coastal waters. A systems approach.* Blackwell Scientific Publications, 322 p.

Marino, R., Chan, F., Howarth, R. W., Pace, M. L. and Likens, G. E., 2006. Ecological constraints on planktonic nitrogen fixation in saline estuaries. I. Nitrogen and trophical controls. *Marine Ecology Progress Series,* 309: 25 – 39.

Marumo, R. and Asaoka, O., 1974. Distribution of Pelagic Blue-green Algae in the Northen Pacific Ocean. *Journal of the Oceanographical Society of Japan,* 30: 77 – 85.

McQueen, D. J. and Lean, D. R. S., 1987. Influence of water temperature and nitrogen to phosphorus ratios on the dominance of blue-green algae in Lake St. George, Ontario. *Can. J. Fish. Aquat.,* 44: 598 – 604.

Melvasalo, T., Niemi, Å., Niemitö, L. and Rinne, I., 1983. On the importance of nitrogen fixation in the Baltic Sea ecosystem. Symposium on Ecological Investigations of the *Baltic Sea Environment,* Riga, 16-19 March 1983, pp.176 – 189.

Nausch, M., Nausch, G., Wasmund, N. and Nagel, K., 2008. Phosphorus pool variations and their relation to cyanobacteria development in the Baltic Sea: A three-year study. *Journal of Marine Systems,* 71: 99-111.

Nürnberg, G.K. and Shaw, M., 1998. Productivity of clear and humic lakes: nutrients, phytoplankton, bacteria. *Hydrobiologia,* 382: 97-112.

Odum, E., 1986. *Ecology.* Moscow (in Russian).

Panagiotopoulos, C. and R. Sempere, 2005. The molecular distribution of combined aldoses in sinking particles in various oceanic conditions. *Marine Chemistry,* 95: 31-49.

Preisendorfer, R.W., 1986. Secchi disk science: Visual optics of natural waters. *Limnolology and Oceanography,* 31: 909-926.

Rahm L, Jönsson A, Wulff F. Nitrogen fixation in the Baltic proper: an empirical study. *J. Mar. Sys.* 2000; 25: 239-248.

Redfield, A.C., 1958. The biological control of chemical factors in the environment. *Am. Sci.,* 46, 205-222.

Reynolds CS, Walsby AE. Water-blooms. *Biol. Rev.* 1975; 50: 437-481.

Riley E.T. and Prepas E.E., 1985. Comparison of the phosphorus-chlorophyll relationships in mixed and stratified lakes. *Can. J. Fish. Aquat. Sci.,* 42:831-835.

Robarts RD, Zohary T. Temperature effects on phytosynthetic capacity, respiration, and growth rates of bloom-forming cyanobacteria. *NZJ Mar. Freshw. Res.* 1987; 21: 391 – 399.

Rönner, U., 1985. Nitrogen transformations in the Baltic proper: denitrification counteracts eutrophication, *Ambio,* 14: 134-138.

Ryther, J.H. and Dunstan, W.M., 1971. Nitrogen, phosphorus, and eutrophication in the coastal marine environment. *Science,* 171, 1008-1013.

Savchuk, O.P. and Wulff, F., 1999. Modeling the Baltic Sea eutrophication in a decision support system. *Ambio,* 2-3: 141-148.

Savchuk, O. S., Wulff, F., Hille, S., Humborg, C. and Pollehne, F., 2008. The Baltic Sea a century ago - a reconstruction from model simulations, verified by observations. *Journal of Marine Systems,* 74:485-494.

Schindler, D.W., 1977. Evolution of phosphorus limitation in lakes. *Science,* 195, 260-262.

Schindler, D. W., Hecky, R. E., Findlay, D. L., Stainton, M. P., Parker, B. R., Patterson, M. J., Beaty, K. G., Lyng, M., and Kasian, S. E. M., 2008. Eutrophication of lakes cannot be controlled by reducing nitrogen input: results of a 37-year whole ecosystem experiment. *PNAS,* 105: 11254-11258.

Secchi, A., 1866. Relazione della esperienze fatta a bordo della pontificia pirocorvetta L'Immacolata Concezione per determinare la transparenza del mare. In: Cialdi, Cmdr.A., Sul moto ondoso del mare e su le corenti di esso specialment auquelle littorali, 2nd ed., p. 258-288. (Dep. of the navy. office of chief of naval operations. *ONI Transl.* A-655, Op-923 M4B).

Seitzinger, S. P. and Sanders, R. W., 1999. Atmospheric inputs of dissolved organic nitrogen stimulate estuarine bacteria and phytoplankton. *Limnology and Oceanography,* 44: 721-730.

Smith, V.H., 1979. Nutrient dependence of primary productivity in lakes. *Limnol. Oceanogr.,* 24:1051-1064.

Smith VH. Predictive models for the biomass of blue-green algae in lakes. *Wat. Resour. Bull.* 1985, 21: 433-439.

Smith VH. Eutrophication of Freshwater and Coastal Marine Ecosystems: A Global Problem. *Environ. Sci. Pollut. Res. Int.* 2003; 10: 126-139.

Tilzer, M.M., 1988. Secchi disk - chlorophyll relationships in a lake with highly variable phytoplankton biomass. *Hydrobiologia.* 162: 163-171.

Tõnno, I., 2004. *The impact of nitrogen and phosphorus concentration and N/P ratio on cyanobacterial dominance and N$_2$ fixation in some Estonian lakes.* Doctoral thesis, Tartu University Press, Tartu, 106 p.

Tyrrell, T., 1999. The relative influences of nitrogen and phosphorus on oceanic primary production. *Nature,* 688: 525-531.

Vahtera E., Conley, D. J., Gustafsson, B. G., Kuosa, H., Pitkänen, H., Savchuk, O. P., Tamminen, T., Viitasalo, M., Voss, M., Wasmund, N., and Wulff, F., 2007. *Internal Ecosystem Feedbacks Enhance Nitrogen-fixing Cyanobacteria Blooms and Complicate Management in the Baltic Sea. Ambio,* 36: 186-193.

Vollenweider, R.A. 1958. Sichttiefe und Production. *Verhandlungen der Internationalen Vereinigung der Limnologie,* 13: 142-143.

Vollenweider, R.A. 1960. Beitrage zür Kenntnis optischer Eigenschaften der Gewässer und Primärproduktion. *Mem. Ist. Ital. Idrobiol.,* 12: 201-244.

Vollenweider, R.A., 1968. The scientific basis of lake eutrophication, with particular reference to phosphorus and nitrogen as eutrophication factors. Tech. Rep. DAS/DSI/68.27, OECD, Paris, 159 p.

Vollenweider, R.A., Giovanardi, F., Montanari, G. and Rinaldi, A., 1998. Characterization of the trophic conditions of marine coastal waters with a special reference to the NW Adriatic Sea: Proposal for a trophic scale, turbidity and generalized water quality index. *Environmetrics,* 9: 329-357.

Wallin, M., Håkanson, L. and Persson, J. 1992. Load models for nutrients in coastal areas, especially from fish farms (in Swedish with English summary). *Nordiska ministerrådet,* 1992:502, Copenhagen, 207 p.

Wasmund, N., 1997. Occurrence of cyanobacterial blooms in the Baltic Sea in relation to environmental conditions. *Internationale Revue gesamten Hydrobiologie,* 82: 169-184.

Wasmund, N., Voss, M., and Lochte, K., 2001. Evidence of nitrogen fixation by non-heterocystous cyanobacteria in the Baltic Sea and re-calculation of a budget of nitrogen fixation. *Marine Ecology Progress Series,* 214: 1-14.

Wasmund, N., Nausch, G., Schneider, B., Nagel, K., Voss, M., 2005. Comparison of nitrogen fixation rates determined with different methods: a study in the Baltic Proper. *Mar. Ecol. Prog. Ser.,* 297: 23–31.

Wetzel R.G., 2001. Limnology. Academic Press, London, 1006 p.

Wulff, F., Rahm, L., Hallin, A. K., Sandberg, J., 2001. A nutrient budget model of the Baltic Sea. In: Wulff, F. et al., (Eds.), *A Systems Analysis of the Baltic Sea, Ecological Studies,* vol. 148. Springer, Berlin, pp. 353–372.

In: Phosphorus: Properties, Health Effects and the Environment   ISBN: 978-1-62081-399-7
Editors: Ming Yue Chen and Da-Xia Yang   © 2012 Nova Science Publishers, Inc.

Chapter 5

Study on the Environmental Response of Sedimentary Phosphorus of Shallow Lakes to Anthropogenic Impact in Lixia River Basin, China

Ying Zhang[1,2], Ling Liu[1], Chengpeng Lu[1,2] and Bao Qian[1]

[1]College of Hydrology and Water Resources, Hohai University, Nanjing, China
[2]School of Natural Resources, University of Nebraska-Lincoln, Lincoln, NE, US

Abstract

The Lixia River Basin in China has been seriously affected by long-term intensive industrial, urban and agricultural activities. The fractionation of phosphorus (P) in five lakes sediments from Lixia River Basin have been investigated by SMT methods for the first time in order to understand the environmental response mechanism of sedimentary P to anthropogenic impact and the eutrophication status of these lakes. The results showed that the non-apatite P (NAIP) and organic P (OP) were more sensitive to the anthropogenic impact than other fractions of P. Furthermore, NAIP had significant relationship with fishery pollution and OP had significant relationship with other polluted from basin inflow respectively. Considered the results of other biogeochemical elements (carbon and nitrogen), the viewpoint "Three Stages" of the lakes in Lixia River Basin sedimentary environment was proposed, which can define three periods, before 1970s, from 1970s to 1990s and after 1990s. The first period was considered as the background period of the lakes in study area. The second period was the time when industry and agricultural begin to develop, the surface area of lakes decreased significantly and pollute material flowed into lakes more and more. During the third period, the industrial, agricultural and fishery developed quickly, the lakes in Lixia River Basin had been subjected to various pollutant sources and led to the serious pollution and hyper-eutrophication.

1. INTRODUCTION

The eutrophication of lakes was induced by natural and anthropogenic impacts together. Cultural eutrophication has become a major environmental problem for freshwater lakes throughout the world [1, 2]. Therefore, the study on the evolution history of lake eutrophication is equal to the study on the interaction history of anthropogenic and nature. Recently, the impact of anthropogenic research have been developed in many fields and acted as one of the most important directions of global change. The study on the evolution history of lake ecosystem has been focused on the process of nature evolution firstly. However, it is transferred to focus on the process which combined with nature and cultural evolution together recently.

In historical times, the formation of lakes had been affected by many factors, such as global climate change, geological structure movement and sediment deposition. However, when the intensively of human activity has increased in recent 2000 years, The human activity had became the most important driving force of lake evolution, especially in the shallow lakes in the river-net plain area, where have the relatively high density of population. The sediment of lakes contains rich information of lake evolution process. The characteristic of sediments depends on the features of lakes or catchments. The composition of lake sediments generally reflects the environmental conditions in and around a water body that existed at the time of their accumulation [3].

The paleolimnological approach affords a long-term perspective on lake ecosystem changes that is not possible with short-term monitoring data [4]. Paleolimnological studies have employed sediment variables such as total organic carbon (TOC), total nitrogen (TN), C/N ratio, and phosphorus (P) fractions, to infer long-term changes in lake trophic status [3, 5, 6]. The concentration of P in sediment was arrived around 0.01 to 10 mg g^{-1}[7], which was much higher than the concentration of P in lake water column. The faint variation of environment was likely to induce the release of different fractions of sedimentary P into overlying water. As we known, the different fractions of P in sediment had different environmental chemical behavior and bioavailability [8]. Not all fractions of P could reflect the concentration of P in lake water column in the response depth of year [9]. Previous studies showed that the sedimentary P could represent the loss mass amount of P from the catchment [10] and the degree of soil erosion of lake catchment. Therefore, the study on the P fractions of sediment had significantly environment meaning. However, many studies were focused on the fractions of P distribution and the relationship with the concentration of P of overlying water. Little study was focused on the relationship between the P fractions to different human activities. The environmental response mechanisms of sedimentary of P to anthropogenic impact need further investigation.

Eutrophication had become a serious environmental problem in China and is regarded as a threat to water resources, human health, and social sustainable development [11]. The Huai River Basin is a unique region in China with high densities of both human population and water projects, and thus is experiencing a serious pollution problem [12]. The Lixia River Basin is the most important basin in the southeast lower reaches of the Huai River region that was thought to have undergone dramatic changes in lake area and tropic status [13]. The total area of lake surface had been decreased from 1113 km^2 in the 1950s` to 58.5 $km^2$ in the 1990s`, and it was keeping decreasing in present. Shallow lakes from the Lixia River basin in densely populated areas may receive high amounts of anthropogenic nutrients, and their relatively low volumes make them susceptible to reach high nutrient concentration and primary productivity [13, 14]. The sediment of most Lixia River Basin lakes had never been dredged and there was little study on the sedimentary environment of this area. The sediment could be preserved their original geochemical characteristics.

The objectives of this chapter were to: 1) observe the spatial and vertical variation of P fractions in sediment cores from Lixia River Basin; 2) explore the environmental response mechanism of sedimentary of P to anthropogenic impact and the eutrophication status of these lakes; 3) discuss the process of sedimentary environment of the lakes in Lixia River Basin combined with other biogeochemical elements (carbon and nitrogen).

2. Sampliing and Methods

2.1. Study Area

The samples were collected from Wujin (WJ) Lake, Jiulongkou (JLK) Lake, Dazong (DZ) Lake, Desheng (DS) Lake and Wugong (WG) Lake in the Lixia River basin (Figure 1). Some characteristics of these five lakes are presented in Table 1.

Table 1. Geographic and limnological features of the studied lakes

Lake	Position	Surface area (km^2)	Mean depth (m)	Trophic status	References
WJ Lake	32°57` N 119°50` E	5.1	2.0	hypereutrophication	[28]
JLK Lake	33°24` N 119°35` E	67	1.2	mesotrophication	[29]
DZ Lake	33°10` N 119°46` E	28	1.4	hypereutrophication	[30]
DS Lake	32°56` N 119°56` E	15	3.2	hypereutrophication	[25]
WG Lake	33°04` N 119°49` E	12.9	4.0	mesotrophication	[31]

2.2. Sediment Sampling and Analysis

Sediment cores and surface sediments were collected with a modified Kajak gravity corer in May 2009. The locations of sampling sites are shown in Figure 1. In Wujin Lake, Jiulongkou Lake and Dazong Lake, at each site, two sediment cores of 86 mm diameter and 20~30 cm long were collected. The two cores were located within 1 m proximity of one another. The cores were sliced into five subsamples of 1 cm thickness in the upper 5 cm and several subsamples of 2 cm thickness below the depth of 5 cm. The subsamples from the two cores were mixed from the same site and depth. In Wugong Lake and Desheng Lake, the upper 5cm surface sediments were collected simultaneously with a modified Kajak gravity corer. The samples were put into air-sealed plastic bags, kept cool (4 °C) on ice and protected from light in the field and during transport. After transportation (within 6 h) to the laboratory, the samples were sent to analysis immediately. Before the analysis, the subsamples were freeze-dried (CHRIST Inc., ALPHA 1-2) and homogenized. The rest of the samples were kept frozen.

Total nitrogen (TN %) was measured using the dichromate H_2SO_4 digestion method [15]. Total organic carbon (TOC %) was measured by an automatic TOC analyzer (Analytik Jena AG, Multi N/C2100). The sequential extraction procedure was based on a modified version of the Williams method (SMT), which has been proposed in the frame of the 'Standards, Measurements and Testing' program of the European Commission [16]. The SMT method is comprised of five steps [17]. Five fractions of P are determined, including total P (TP), non-apatite inorganic P (NAIP), apatite P (AP), inorganic P (IP), and organic P (OP). Tests for the determinations of the five forms of P were conducted onto the fraction of the sediment of the particle size less than 100 μm, which indicated that sieved sediment can be considered as the geochemically active fraction of sediments [18].

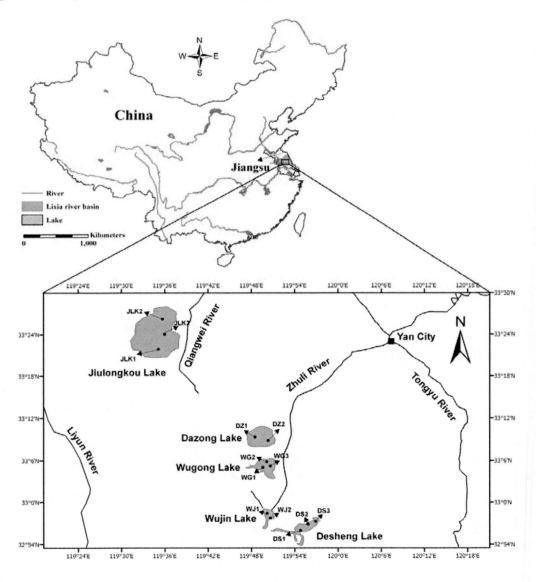

Figure 1. The map of sampling site.

3. RESULTS

3.1. The Vertical Distribution of Phosphorus Fractions

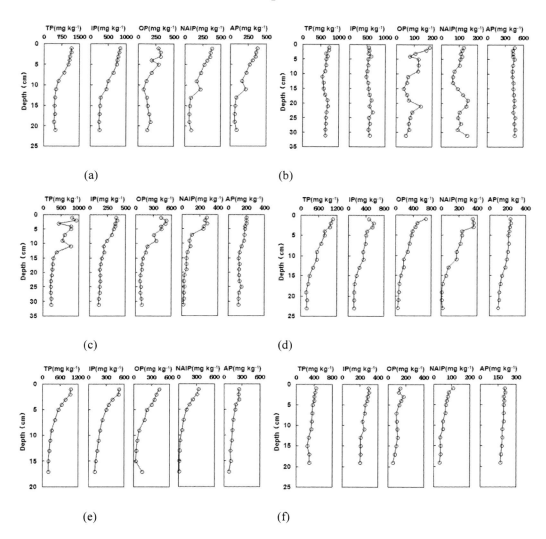

Figure 2. The vertical distribution of SMT-extracted P of sediment core (a.WJ1, b. WJ2, c. JLK1, d. JLK2, e. JLK3, f. DZ1).

Split cores revealed the heterogeneity of the sediment. The vertical distribution of TP varied markedly (Fig. 2). At WJ2 and DZ1 it was more or less homogeneous, while at other stations it decreased strongly above 15cm depth and kept relatively instant lower concentration below 15cm depth. The vertical distributions of IP were similar of TP in these sediment cores. Beside WJ2, the concentration of IP was decreased above 15~20cm depth and remained stable concentration below the deeper depth. However, the trend of decline in the upper layers of IP was less than the trend of TP. OP presented the fluctuated distribution in the upper 5cm depth and decreased with depth until the 15cm depth. NAIP and AP were the main components of IP. NAIP showed significantly decreased in the upper 15cm as OP (except WJ2). However, the vertical variation of AP was not obviously, in most of sampling sites (except WJ1) the AP maintained relatively constant concentration in the whole core.

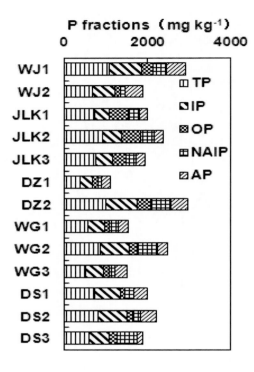

Figure 3. The distribution of P fractions of surface sediment in five lakes.

3.2. The Distribution of Surface Sediment

Fig. 3 showed that the P fractions of surface sediment in five lakes had their characteristics respectively. The average concentration of TP in five lakes was 748.73 ± 195.32 mg kg^{-1}. Among those lakes, the concentration of TP in the surface sediment of WJ1 and DS3 were higher than other sampling sites, the lowest value of TP was showed in DZ1. The average concentration of IP was 531.77 mg kg^{-1}, the lowest concentration of IP was presented in DZ1 (282.42 mg kg^{-1}) as TP, and the concentration of IP in WJ1 and DS3 were higher than other sites, the value was 775.60 mg kg^{-1} and 739.55 mg kg^{-1} respectively. The value of OP in five lakes was 230.59 ± 128.83 mg kg^{-1}, the concentration of OP in the JLK1 and JLK2 were significantly higher than other lakes, followed by JLK3 and DZ3. The concentration of OP in WJ2, Wugong Lake and Dazong Lake were relatively lower. The average concentration of NAIP of five lakes was 270.30 mg kg^{-1}. The value of NAIP in DZ3, WG2 and DS3 were approached 480 mg kg^{-1} and higher than other sampling sites. WJ2 and DZ1 had lower concentration of NAIP, which was around 100 mg kg^{-1}. The average concentration of AP in surface sediments was 285.74 mg kg^{-1}, the concentration of AP in surface sediment of Wujin Lake was higher than other lakes, and the value was 442.37 mg kg^{-1} and 431.57 mg kg^{-1}, respectively.

3.3. Total Nitrogen Distribution in Sediment Cores and Surface Sediments

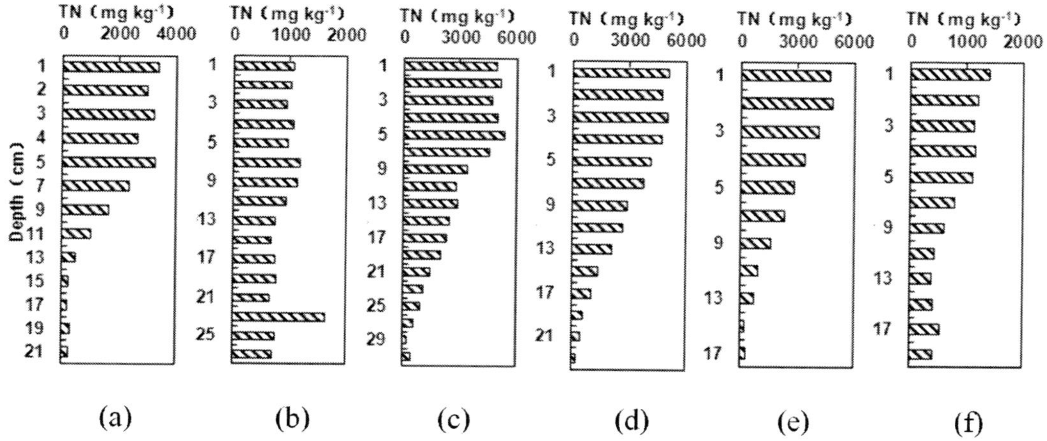

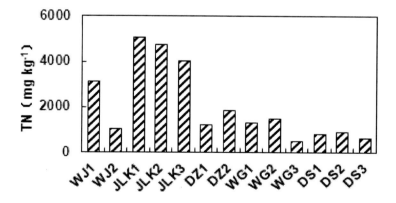

Figure 4. The vertical distribution of TN of sediment core. (a.WJ1, b. WJ2, c. JLK1, d. JLK2, e. JLK3, f. DZ1).

TN clearly decreased with sediment depth except WJ2 (Fig.4). The maximum value of TN in each sediment cores was presented in the upper 5cm sediments and below the 15~20cm the concentration of TN remained relatively constant low value. It is noteworthy that the nutrients elements, including P and N, in the WJ2 sediment core were both showed relatively instantly value. It is probably because that WJ2 located in the south part of Wujin Lake where was in the center of Wujin Park. It was became an artificial pond to some extent and had few water flow exchange since 1970`s.

Figure 5. The distribution of TN of surface sediment in five lakes.

The concentrations of TN in surface sediments in Jiulongkou Lake were higher than other lakes (Fig. 5). In the Jiulongkou Lake, the southern part (JLK1) and centre part (JLK2) had higher TN value than northern part (JLK3). The concentration of TN of surface sediment in the northern part of Wujin Lake was significantly higher than southern part. The concentrations of TN of surface sediments in Desheng Lake were lower than other lakes.

The vertical distribution trend of TOC in sediments cores was similar as TP and TN. The maximum value of TOC presented in the upper 3cm sediment and decreased until 15~20cm depth. Below the 15 to 20cm the concentration of TOC kept constantly value. The value of TOC in the surface sediment (0~5cm) was much higher than bottom sediment (25-30cm). WJ2 still had relatively constant value in the whole core.

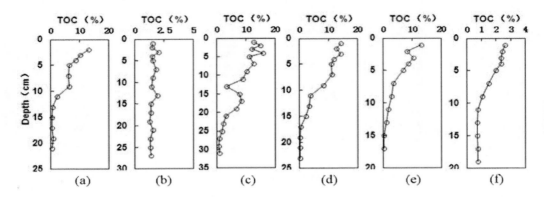

Figure 6. The vertical distribution of TN of sediment core. (a.WJ1, b. WJ2, c. JLK1, d. JLK2, e. JLK3, f. DZ1).

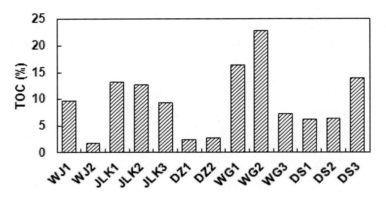

Figure 7. The distribution of TOC of surface sediment in five lakes.

3.4. Total Organic Carbon Distribution in Sediment Cores and Surface Sediments

The concentration of TOC of surface sediment had significantly differences between the study lakes (Fig 7). The surface sediment of Jiulongkou Lake and Wugong Lake had higher concentration of TOC than other lakes sediment.

4. DISCUSSIONS

Based on the former researches and historical material, the sedimentary rate of study lakes was around 0.4 cm year^{-1}[19, 20]. According to above sedimentary rate the upper 5cm sediment was deposited from mid-1990s until now. The 5cm to 15cm depth sediment in study lakes was deposited from 1970s to mid-1990s. The sediment below 15cm was deposited before 1970s.

The concentration of TP in sediment could be considered as an indicative indicator for regional change. The degree of sediment contaminate could be evaluated by the concentration of TP. It was divided into 3 parts: heavy contaminate degree (TP >1300 mg kg^{-1}), moderate contaminate degree (500 mg kg^{-1} <TP < 1300 mg kg^{-1}) and none contaminate degree (TP < 500 mg kg^{-1}) [21]. Based on the above evaluation standard, the sediment of Lixia River Basin lakes suffered contaminant in different degrees. The sediment of Wujin Lake was suffered moderate polluted in the upper 10~13cm, and suffered few polluted below the 15cm depth. The sediment of southern part (JLK1) and centre part (JLK2) of Jiulongkou Lake were suffered moderate pollution in the upper 10cm depth. The northern part (JLK3) of Jiulongkou Lake was suffered moderate pollution in the upper 5cm sediment. The concentration of TP in Dazong Lake was relatively lower than the other sites (Fig. 2 and Fig. 3). The surface sediment of Wugong Lake and Desheng Lake were suffered moderate pollution, some part even suffered heavy pollution. In all of the sediment below the 10~15cm depth, the concentration of TP was less than 500 mg kg^{-1} and kept constantly low value. It is presented that the amount of P flow from basin was increasing in recent years, especially the upper 10cm sediment which responded the period after 1980s.

As we known, IP was composed by NAIP and AP. AP is an important part of IP, which usually comes from clastic rocks and authigenic [22]. The former had significantly relationship with the erosion degree of catchment. The latter had relationship with calcium phosphate compound or the P which co-precipitation with calcium carbonate. AP had a relatively constant value in sediment. It was belonged to the P fractions which buried in sediment [23]. Therefore, there was none obviously vertical variation on the core sediments except WJ1 (Fig.2). Fig.2 showed that the concentration of TP in the top sediment was around 10 times higher than the concentration of TP in the bottom sediment. However, the concentration of IP in different depth had much smaller difference. The concentration of IP of top sediment was 1.2~2.9 times higher than bottom sediment. In the sediment core of WJ2, there was little difference between the concentration of IP in top sediment and bottom sediment. It was illustrated that along with the increasing density of anthropogenic disturbance in catchment, the erosion density became more and more seriously, which induced clastic rocks increased, either. Meanwhile, in the high P inflow lakes, the AP fraction of sediment could be accumulated by the co-precipitation of Ca^{2+}. However, this increased trend was much smaller than TP, NAIP and OP. It was showed that the AP had relatively lower senility of inflow P from basin than other fractions of P.

The sewage discharge could enhance the combination between the phosphate and Fe/Al oxide/hydrogen chloride, therefore the concentration of NAIP in sediment could considered as an important index for pollution [24]. In this chapter, the concentration of NAIP was decreased in the upper 15cm with depth (Fig.2). It was maybe induced by the vertical variation of Eh [25, 26]. Since the decrease of oxygen value could induce the decrease of oxidation-reduction potential at the same time. The Fe^{3+} was attempting to reduce to Fe^{2+} and the P which combined with Fe^{3+} will be released. Therefore the NAIP decreased with depth. Below the 15cm depth, the Eh value of sediment had a little affected by the oxidation-reduction potential, the concentration of NAIP in the bottom sediment was affected by the active iron transportation in the deeper sediment. In the bottom sediment, the active iron could be transport in following types. 1) sulfate reduced to S^{2-} and then the iron oxide react with S^{2-}. The reaction product was FeS and further became FeS_2. Both FeS and FeS_2 were difficulty soluble; 2) became firm iron oxide crystal such as hematite (Fe_2O_3); 3) changed to the mineral which was hard to extracted by chemical reagent, such as siderite or ferrosilicate; 4) acted as electron acceptor in the process of organic carbon decomposition by bacterial [27]. The active iron lost the combination ability of active P after above transportation. Then the P will be released. Therefore, the concentration of NAIP in the deeper depth usually lowers than the upper sediment [28]. Meanwhile, the concentration of NAIP was affected by the composition of organic matter. In the bottom sediment, the mineralized decomposition of organic matter was conducted by anaerobic bacterial. It was enhance the OP transformed to inorganic soluble P and produced Fe-P with iron in the interstitial water. The increase of Fe-P induced the increase of NAIP. Fig.2 showed that the concentration of NAIP in the WJ2 sediment around 15cm increased with depth, where had opposite trend of OP. It maybe the result that the mineralized decomposition of OP by anaerobic bacterial.

Besides IP fractions, the sediment of Lixia River Basin lakes had amounts of OP. The organic matter of sediment primarily came from humics and unstable organic compounds. It had significantly affected by sewage discharge and agricultural runoff. It was presented that the OP of sediment was sensitive to the sewage discharge and agricultural runoff to some extent. Fig. 2 showed that the concentration of OP was decreased with depth in most of sampling sediments. The decreasing trend was showed obviously in the upper 15cm sediment. It was illustrated that the sewage discharge and agricultural runoff was increased from the 70`s of last century. The percentage of IP and OP to TP in different depth sediment reflected the source of P had significantly variation either. The ratio of IP to TP was increased with depth in most sites. However, the ratio of OP to TP was increased with depth (Table 3). It was reflected that the OP input was increased and the IP had relatively origins in the sedimentary environment. The ratio of IP to OP reflects the retention time of lake [29]. The lower it is the higher retention time is. The ratio of IP to OP of surface sediment was lower than deeper sediment. It showed that the retention time of study lakes was increased year by year. It maybe induced by the anthropogenic disturbance activities such as the establishment of hydraulic engineering, reclaimiation and so on.

Table 2. IP/TP and OP/TP in sediment cores from Lixia River Basin lakes unit: %

Depth	WJ1		WJ2		JLK1		JLK2		JLK3		DZ1	
	IP/TP	OP/TP	IP/TP	OP/TP	IP/TP	OP/TP	IP/TP	OP/TP	IP/TP	OP/TP	IP/TP	OP/TP
0~5cm	71.18	25.35	81.06	18.94	43.91	55.05	51.61	49.97	53.93	43.47	70.60	34.76
5~15cm	72.63	22.16	86.30	13.70	46.82	45.24	61.72	43.51	63.20	26.00	72.85	32.10
15~30cm	55.36	34.01	89.17	11.95	61.35	37.86	64.55	33.25	52.55	69.32	68.60	21.59

In order to figure out which fractions of P was more sensitivity to the anthropogenic activity, the surface sediment of study lakes in other two seasons (summer: May and winter: Dec) were sampled and determined. Fig. 8 showed that the percentage of major fractions of P (AP, NAIP and OP) to TP in three seasons. The Wujin Lake had relatively higher concentration of AP and the IP was the most important component of TP. Since WJ1 had been dredged in summer, the surface sediment was the deeper sediment of WJ1 actually. The deeper sediment usually had higher AP concentration, so the percentage of AP to TP became higher in the summer and winter season. The vertical distribution of P fractions kept constantly in WJ2 (Fig.2 (b)). It was maybe WJ2 was located in a pond where little hydraulic exchange had. The source of P primarily came from authigenic clastic which was the major source of AP. Therefore, the percentage of AP to TP kept high value in all of the three seasons. The percentage of OP to TP in Jiulongkou Lake was higher than other sampling sites in all of the year. The average value was 53.62% which was a little higher than the percentage of IP to TP. It indicated that Jiulongkou Lake was accepted amounts of polluted materials from catchment and the ecosystem was under a relatively dangers stage. The percentage of AP, NAIP and OP to TP were basically equivalent in the sediment of Dazong Lake. It was worthy of note that the NAIP and OP were easy to release to the overlying water and adopted by phytoplankton further. Therefore the bioavailable P concentration of sediment in Dazong Lake was relatively higher, the eutrophication problem cannot be ignored either. The percentage of OP to TP of Wugong Lake was lower than the percentage of AP to TP and NAIP to TP. It was indicated that the Wugong Lake had suffered limited polluted by agriculture. However, there was high density aquaculture in the Wugong Lake. Amounts of feed and waste were deposited in the bottom of lake and induced the concentration of NAIP increased year by year. The percentage of NAIP of Desheng Lake was significantly higher than the percentage of AP to TP and OP to TP, especially in Aug and Dec. Based on the regular aquaculture cycle, the fishing feed was increased from June and reached highest amount in July and August, then the breeding cycle continued until the end of Dec. It indicated that the NAIP could reflect the polluted degree of sediment in the aquaculture lakes.

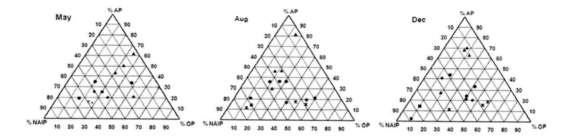

Figure 8. The percentage of AP, NAIP and OP to TP of surface sediment of study lakes in three seasons triangular diagram (Square: Wujin Lake, Triangle: Jiulongkou Lake, Circular: Dazong Lake, Diamond: Wugong Lake and Snowflakes: Desheng Lake).

Generally speaking, the sewage discharge and aquaculture had significantly affected on the concentration of P fraction and the percentage of P fractions to TP. Concretely, the sewage discharge had significantly affected on the increased concentration of OP and the percentage of OP to TP. The aquaculture pollution had affected on the increased concentration of NAIP, which induced by amounts of unused feed and waste deposited. In the process of P fractions deposited, some particulate organic material, which adsorbed by P fractions, was deposited in the sediment and mineralization at the same time. The decomposition of the organic matter enhanced the activity intensity of microorganism. The oxygen concentration was decreased and the sediment environment became anoxic. Therefore, the process of deaminase and sulfur reduction was promoted. Those reaction processes could enhance inorganic nutrient such as N and P released from sediment to overlying water [30]. Meanwhile, the NAIP had solubilization effect on many compounds under anaerobic environment, and the release of P was primarily come from the digestion and decomposition effect of OP. The accumulation of OP always represented the higher rate of P buried [31]. Since the reconstruction of bacterial, OP was considered as the major soluble phosphate source of sediment pore water [32]. Therefore, the NAIP and OP of sediment usually considered as an origin source of P and could be release P further under anaerobic environment, which could aggravate the eutrophication degree of lakes [33, 34]. For the little hydraulic exchange lakes (for example: the southern part of Wujin Lake), The AP which originated from authigenic clastic became the most important fractions of TP.

The vertical distribution of TN of sediment was divided into three sections as TP. The concentration of TN in the upper 5cm sediment was higher than other depth sediment and fluctuated frequently. The concentration of TN from 5cm to 15cm depth was decreased with depth gradually. Below the 15cm depth, the concentration of TN was kept stable value. This part of sediment could be considered as stable settlement section. It was worthy noticed that the WJ2 site as a special study site, the concentration of TP and TN had little vertical variation, there was none significantly difference of nutrient content between the surface sediment and bottom sediment.

The concentration of TN variation was affected by the biological disturbance and hydraulic disturbance. The biological disturbance was induced by the ingestion, building tubes, hole and other actions of zoobenthos, especially the trophic sedimentary large animal [27]. The hydraulic disturbance was due to the re-suspension and re-settlement of sediment which was induced by the hydraulic condition of lake flows. The unstable value of TN in surface sediment (settlement fluctuation section) was usually induced by those disturbances. In the degradation decreased section, the biological disturbance was still had affect on the distribution of TN. However, the disturbance of anthropogenic played an important role in the distribution of TN. The discharge from industry, agricultural and aquaculture to lakes was increased significantly. Therefore, the concentration of TN was kept increasing in these depth. Below the 15cm depth, the sedimentary environment was entered into stable accumulation section. The concentration of TN kept relatively stable and had little exchange of over-lying water. It was indicated that the polluted inflow from basin had little difference in each year before the 1970s.

The carbon of sediment was divided into organic carbon and inorganic carbon. Among those two fractions of carbon, the organic carbon came from the animals and plants. However, the inorganic carbon came from the minerals. The body of plants and animals was deposited in sediment and decomposed by biochemistry process or diagenesis process. All of the above processes were transferred the body of organism to organic carbon in sediment. Therefore, the concentration of TOC not only reflected the initial productivity of lake and the organic matter content of sediment, it also indicated the preserve ability of sediment [35]. The concentration of organic carbon was depended on the inflow amount from catchment and the initial productivity of lake [36]. The ratio of C to N was applied to distinguish the origin source of sediment organic matter. Many researches suggested that when the C/N higher than 14, the organic matter of sediment primarily came from catchment, when the C/N lower than 6, the organic matter of sediment came from endogenous input, and when the C/N was ranged from 6 to 14, the organic matter had mixture input origins [37, 38].

The vertical distribution of TOC in study sediment cores was similar as TP and TN. Fig. 9 showed the vertical profile of C/N in sediment cores.

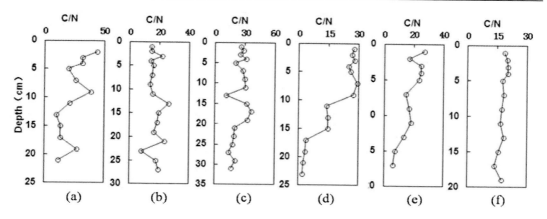

Figure 9. The vertical distribution of C/N of study sediment cores. (a.WJ1, b. WJ2, c. JLK1, d. JLK2, e. JLK3, f. DZ1).

As mentioned above, the vertical variation of C/N reflected the variation of origin source of organic matter in Lixia River Basin to some extent. From the 1970s, the industry, agricultural and aquaculture was developed rapidly, the garbage was discarded near the off-lake and the sewage was discharged into the lakes directly, lots of bank slope was developed as agriculture land which induced seriously soil erosion problem. The ratio of C to N was higher than 14 in the 0~15 cm depth sediment, which indicated that the organic matter was primarily came from catchment inflow [37, 38]. It was also showed the anthropogenic affect on the lake environment. Besides indicating the origin source of organic matter, the ratio of C/N could reflect the plant types of organic matter. Previous researches showed that the C/N was higher than 20 of fiber bundle plants (grasses, shrubs and trees et. al) and ranged from 4 to 10 of none fiber bundle plants (phytoplankton et. al). For aquatic organism, the phytoplankton usually had higher C/N than zooplankton [39-42]. In other words, the sediment had lower C/N was indicated that the organic came from fiber bundle plants of terrestrial was much lower than the productivity of lake (phytoplankton et. al). However, the sediment had higher C/N was indicated that it received amounts of fiber bundle plants debris from terrestrial. For example, the Jiulongkou Lake had flourish fiber bundle plants such as reed, the surrounding catchment was used by agricultural land and had relatively high plants coverage. Therefore, the C/N of Jiulongkou Lake in upper sediment was higher than 20. The Dazong Lake had over aquatics breed, a little emerged plant, lower plants coverage and high density phytoplankton. Therefore, the C/N of Dazong Lake in upper sediment was less than 20. For the different area in the same lake, the C/N had sensitive response to plant type either. For example, the northern part of Wujin Lake (WJ1) had flourish reed and surrounding lots of trees, therefore, the C/N of sediment was higher than 20 in the upper 15cm depth. However, the southern part of Wujin Lake (WJ2) had low plant coverage in surrounding area, the C/N of sediment was lower than 20. The C/N was decreased with depth in most of sediment vertical profiles. It worthy noted that the C/N had increased trend in some depth of sediment cores. This maybe induced by the catastrophic flood or lake migration. The surrounding area of off-lake became water area by flood bring and the phytoplankton became the primary plant [43]. For example, the Jiulongkou Lake was suffered a 50 years frequency flood in 1991. Therefore, the C/N of 5~7cm depth sediment was increased with depth in JLK1 and JLK2 sites. It was indicated that the off-shore area was became the lake by flooding. The fiber bundle plants debris decreased and the phytoplankton debris increased. Therefore, the C/N was increased with dept. The C/N of surface sediment was affected by organic decomposition to some extent. In the previous stage of diagenetic process, the component of organic matter could be decomposed selectively, which induced the change of C/N. Generally speaking, the organic nitrogen of sediment could be decomposed firstly by bacterial. Therefore, whether aerobic decomposition or anaerobic decomposition, the N compounds will be decomposed faster than TOC. Along with the increased anthropogenic activities, the input of TOC in the deeper sediment (response to the old times) was significantly lower than the surface sediment (response to recent years), the C/N was decreased either [44, 45].

Three periods of human-induced eutrophication are evident in the cores that recorded nearly one hundred years of sediment accumulation in Lixia River Basin lakes. The first period of eutrophication in the study lakes record started around 1930s and ended 1970s which corresponded to the sediment below 15cm depth. This period could be considered as the background value of sedimentary evolution of Lixia River Basin. The sedimentary environment of this period presented following characteristics: the concentration of biogeochemical elements was low and the eutrophication phenomenon was not obviously. This period could be named as stable accumulation period. The second period of eutrophication in the study lake record started around 1970s and ended around mid-1990s which corresponded to the 5cm to 15cm depth sediments. This period could be considered as degradation decreased period. In the 1970s, the agricultural and industry of Lixia River Basin was in the initial stage of development and had majior development in the next 20 years. The surface area of lake was decreased significantly induced by reclamation, enclosure culture or other human disturbance. The concentration of TP (including OP and NAIP), TN and TOC were increased with decreased depth, and C/N values was further increased either. The nutrient and organic matter was accumulated and the degree of pollution of sediment was more seriously. The third period spanned from mid-1990s until now which corresponded to upper 5cm sediments. In this period the intensity of human disturbance was higher than the previous periods. It was represented settlement fluctuation period. As described above, the concentration of TP, TN and TOC had significantly higher value than other depths. Along with the rapid development of Lixia River Basin, the inflow had relatively high concentration and amounts of nutrients, the content of TP, TN and TOC was higher in this period. The maximum values of all of the biogeochemical elements were appeared in this period. It indicated that the pollution of study lakes had not be affectively controlled and restored in present. There had obviously difference between the sediment above the 15cm depth and below the 15cm depth. It showed that the sedimentary environment had significantly changed from the 1970s to 1980s. The response of sedimentary environment to the anthropogenic disturbance affect was very sensitive.

CONCLUSION

In this chapter, the spatial and vertical distribution of five P fractions and other two biogeochemical elements (TN and TOC) in sediment of Lixia River Basin lakes were measured. All of the biogeochemical elements (C, N, and P) had similar vertical distribution of sediment. The upper 5cm was the settlement fluctuation period. The concentration of the biogeochemical elements was high. The sediment of 5 to 15cm depth was considered as degradation decreased period, the concentration of the biogeochemical elements was decreased with depth. The sediment below the 15cm was named as stable accumulation period. The concentration of the biogeochemical elements was kept relatively stable low. Considered the results of the biogeochemical elements (carbon and nitrogen), the viewpoint "Three Stages" of the lakes in Lixia River Basin sedimentary environment was proposed, which can define three periods, before 1970s, from 1970s to 1990s and after 1990s. The first period was considered as the background period of the lakes in study area. The second period was the time when industry and agricultural begin to develop and the polluted material flowed into lakes more and more. During the third period, the industrial, agricultural and fishery developed quickly, the lakes in Lixia River Basin had been subjected to various pollutant sources and led to the serious pollution and hyper-eutrophication.

Among all the P fractions, TP, NAIP and OP were more sensitive to the anthropogenic impact than AP and IP. Furthermore, NAIP had significant relationship with fishery pollution and OP had significant relationship with other polluted from basin inflow respectively. The concentration of P fractions and TN was not only affected by the anthropogenic activity, it also affected by the sedimentary environment such as Eh, biological disturbance and hydraulic disturbance. The enhanced anthropogenic P input to study lakes since the 1970s caused increased primary productivity, which is represented by higher TOC and C/N in the sediments.

ACKNOWLEDGMENTS

The authors are grateful to all participants in the project for their discussions of the research. The study was supported by National Natural Science Foundation of China (No. 50879018).

REFERENCES

[1]   Correll D. The role of phosphorus in the eutrophication of receiving waters: a review[J]. *J Environ Qual,* 1998(27):261-266.

[2]   Smith V, Tilman G, Nekola J. Eutrophication: Impacts of excess nutrient inputs on freshwater, marine, and terrestrial ecosystems[J]. *Environ Pollut,* 1999(100):179-196.

[3]   Routh J, Meyers P A, Gustafsson Ö, et al. Sedimentary geochemical record of human-induced environmental changes in the Lake Brunnsviken watershed, Sweden[J]. *Limnology and Oceanography,* 2004(49):1560-1569.

[4]   Liu E, Shen J, Zhang E, et al. A geochemical record of recent anthropogenic nutrient loading and enhanced productivity in Lake Nansihu, China[J]. *J Paleolimnol,* 2010(44):15-24.

[5]   Meyers P. An Overview of Sediment Organic Matter Records of Human Eutrophication in the Laurentian Great Lakes Region[J]. *Water, Air, & Soil Pollution: Focus,* 2006,6(5):453-463.

[6]   Das S K, Routh J, Roychoudhury A N, et al. Elemental (C, N, H and P) and stable isotope ($\delta^{15}N$ and $\delta^{13}C$) signatures in sediments from Zeekoevlei, South Africa: a record of human intervention in the lake.[J]. *J Paleolimnol,* 2008(39):349-360.

[7]   Holtan H L. Phosphorus in sediment, water and soil: an overview[J]. *Hydrobiologia,* 1988,170:19-34.

[8]   Hua Z, Zhu X, Wang X. Study on bioavailability of Selenastrum capricornutum influenced by released phosphorus[J]. *Acta Scientiae Circumstantiae,* 2000,20(1):100-105.

[9]   Karst T L, Smol J P. Paleolimnological evidence of limnetic nutrient concentration equilibrium in shallow, macrophyte-dominated lake[J]. *Aquatic Sciences,* 2000,62:20-38.

[10]   Fan C., Wang C. *Enviromental geochemistry and eutrophication in the lakes of the lower Yangze region[M]. Beijing*: Science Press, 2007.

[11]   Zhang R, Wu F, Liu C, et al. Characteristics of organic phosphorus fractions in different trophic sediments of lakes from the middle and lower reaches of Yangtze River region and Southwestern Plateau, China[J]. *Environ Pollut,* 2008(152):366-372.

[12]   Zhang Y, Xia J, Liang T, et al. Impact of water projects on river flow regimes and water quality in Huai River basin[J]. *Water Resour Management,* 2010(24):889-908.

[13]   Zhang Y, Liu L, Wang J, et al. *An index of river health for river plain network regions, India,* 2009[C].

[14]   Liu L, Zhang Y, Efting A, et al. Modeling bioavailable phosphorus via other phosphorus fractions in sediment cores from Jiulongkou Lake, China[J]. *Environ Earth Sci,* 2011.

[15]   Jin X, Tu Q. The standard investigation methods of the lake eutrophichation[M]. Beijing: *China Environmental Science Press,* 1990.

[16]   González Medeiros J J, Pérez Cid B, FernándeZ Gómez E. Analytical phosphorus fractionation in sewage sludge and sediment samples[J]. *Anal Bioanal Chem,* 2004,381:873-878.

[17]   Ruban V, Brigault S, Demare D, et al. An investigation of the origin and mobility of phosphorus in freshwater sediments from Bort-Les-Orgues reservoir, France[J]. *Journal of Environmental Monitoring,* 1999,1:403-407.

[18]   Goltermann H, Sly P, Thomas R. Study of the relationship between water quality and sediment transport[M]. *Paris: Technical Papers in Hydrology UNESCO,* 1983.

[19]   Zhang Y. *Study on the mechanism sedimentary environment response and biotic response of shallow lakes to anthropologic impacts in plain river-net area* [D]. Nanjing: Hohai University, 2011.

[20]   He H, Ding H, Zhang Z, et al. *Grain-size characteristics and their enviromental signifiance of Hongze Lake sediments[J].* 2005,25(5):590-596.

[21]   Liu H, Jin X, Jing Y. Enviromental dredging technology of lake sediment[J]. *Engineering Science,* 1990,1(1):81-84.

[22]   Ruban V, López-Sánchez J F, Pardo P, et al. Harmonized protocol and certified reference material for the determination of extractable contents of phosphorus in freshwater sediments − A synthesis of recent works[J]. *Fresenius J Anal Chem,* 2001,370:224-228.

[23] Gonsiorczyk T, Casper P, Koschel R. Phosphorus-binding forms in the sediment of an oligotrophic and an eutrophic hardwater lake of the Baltic Lake District (Germany)[J]. *Water Science and TechnologyEutrophication Research State-of-the Art: Inputs, Processes, Effects, Modelling, Management, Specialist Symposium dedicated to Lambertus Lijklema,* 1998,37(3):51-58.

[24] Hou L, Liu M, Xu S, et al. Species of phosphorus in core sediments from the Changjiang estuary and its environmental significance[J]. *Marine Environmental Science,* 2001,20(2):7-12.

[25] Jensen H S, Thamdrup B. Iron-bond phosphorus in marine sediments as measured by bicarbonate-dithionite extraction[J]. *Hydrobiologia,* 1993,253:47-59.

[26] Ruttenberg K C. Development of a sequential extration method for different forms of phosphorus in marine sediments[J]. *Limnology and Oceanography,* 1992,37:1460-1482.

[27] Du H, Li J, Huang C, et al. Vertical distributions of nitrogen and phosphorus in sediment cores of Zhelin Bay[J]. *Marine Sciences,* 2007,31(6):43-51.

[28] Krom M D, Berner R. Adsorption of phosphate in anoxic marine sediments[J]. *Limnology and Oceanography,* 1980,25(5):797-806.

[29] Avilés A, Becerra J, Palomo L, et al. Distribution of different phosphorus fractions in the sediment of palmones river(southern Spain) during a dry season[J]. *Limnetica,* 2000,19:31-38.

[30] Dahlbacr B, Gunnarsson L A H. Sedimentation and sulfate reduction under amussel culture [J]. *Mar. Bio.,* 1981,63:269-275.

[31] Clavero V, Izquierdo J J, Palomo L, et al. Water management and climate changes increases the phosphorus accumulation in the small shallow estuary of the Palmones River (southern Spain)[J]. *Sci Total Environ,* 1999,228:193-202.

[32] Berner R A. *Early diagenesis. A theorical approach*[M]. Princenton: Princenton Press, 1980.

[33] Van Capellen P V, Gallard J F. Biochemical dynamics in aquatic sediments[J]. *Rev Mineralogy,* 1996,34:336-376.

[34] Furrer G, Von Gunten N. Steady-state modelling of biogeochemical processes in columns with aquifer. 1 speciation and mass balances[J]. *Chem Geol,* 1996,133:15-28.

[35] Wang S. *Hulun Lake: The palaeolimnology study*[M]. Hefei: China Science and Technology University Press, 1995.

[36] Kelts K. Environments of deposition of lacustrine petroleum source rocks:an introduction[J]. *Lacutrine Petroleom Source,* 1988,40:3-26.

[37] Bordowsky O K. Accumulation of organic matter in bottom sediments[J]. *Marine Geology,* 1965,3:32-82.

[38] Flemer D A, Robert B B. Particulate carbon;nitrogen relation in northern Chesapeake Bay[J]. *Fish Res Board Canada,* 1971,28:911-918.

[39] Ishiwatari R, Ogura K, Horie S. Organic geochemistry of a lacustrine sediment (Lake Haruna, Japan) [J]. *Chemical Geology,* 1980,29:261-280.

[40] Talbot M R. A review of palaeohydrological interpretation of carbon and oxygen isotopic rations in primary lacustrine carbonate[J]. *Chem Geol,* 1990,80(4):261-279.

[41] Meyers P A, Ishiwatari R. Lacustrine organic geochemistry−an overview of indicators of organic matter sources and diagenesis in lake sediments [J]. *Organic Geochemistry,* 1993,20(7):867-900.

[42] Mayer L. Surface area control of organic carbon accumulation in continental shelf sediments[J]. *Geochimica et Cosmochimica Acta,* 1994,58(4):1271-1284.

[43] Andrew S C. *Paleolimnlogy--The history and evolution of lake systems*[M]. New York: Oxford University Press, 2003.

[44] Seki H, Skelding J, Parsons T R. Observation on the decomposition of a marine sedimen[J]. *Linmnol Oceanogr,* 1968,8(3):440-447.

[45] Fagane L, Planinc R, Pezdic J. Marine geology of the Gulf of Trieste (northern Adriatic): Geochem Aspect[J]. *Mar Geol,* 1991,99(1-2):93-108.

In: Phosphorus: Properties, Health Effects and the Environment   ISBN: 978-1-62081-399-7
Editors: Ming Yue Chen and Da-Xia Yang   © 2012 Nova Science Publishers, Inc.

Chapter 6

APPLICATION OF THE STANDARDS, MEASUREMENTS AND TESTING PROGRAMME AND X-RAY POWDER DIFFRACTION TO STUDY PHOSPHORUS SPECIATION IN SEDIMENTS FROM BAIHUA LAKE, CHINA

Mei Jin[1,2,], Jiwei Hu[1], Liya Fu[1] and Miao Jia[1]*

[1]Guizhou Provincial Key Laboratory for Information System of Mountainous Areas and Protection of Ecological Environment, Guizhou Normal University, Guiyang City, Guizhou Province, China

[2]School of Chemistry and Materials Science, Guizhou Normal University, Guiyang City, Guizhou Province, China

ABSTRACT

The distribution characteristics of phosphorus speciation in 17 surface sediment samples collected from Baihua Lake, one of the five drinking water sources for Guiyang City in southwest China, were investigated using the Standards, Measurements and Testing (SMT) programme and X-ray powder diffraction (XRD). In the study area, the total phosphorus (TP) concentrations varied from 591.57 to 2374.80 mg/kg with the mean concentration of 1604.02 mg/kg (dry weight), and it was evident that the phosphorus level in the sediments was generally higher than in other eutrophic lakes such as Chaohu Lake and Xihu Lake. The results of the two methods, the SMT and XRD, demonstrated the presence of different phosphorus species in the lake sediments. The results of the SMT protocol indicated that the average percentages of inorganic phosphorus (IP), organic phosphorus (OP), iron/aluminum-bound phosphorus (Fe/Al-P) and calcium-bound phosphorus (Ca-P) were 67.33%, 30.53%, 39.38% and 27.41%, respectively. Notably, the concentrations of inorganic phosphorus (IP) were higher than that of OP, and the IP consisted mainly of Fe/Al-P. The high concentrations of Fe/Al-P, a major and direct source of phosphorus release, might play an important part in accelerating eutrophication of water bodies. The present XRD analysis showed that AlPO4 was found in all sediment samples among phosphorus species. Further statistical analyses of the

* E-Mail: jwhu@gznu.edu.cn (J.H.), E-Mail: jinmeimei1985102@163.com (M.J.).

results revealed significant and positive correlations between phosphorus species in sediments, and the four cluster levels were obtained. Additionally, remediation measures were briefly evaluated for the lake considering its pollution conditions and distinctive environmental features.

1. INTRODUCTION

Baihua Lake (E 106°27'- 106°34', N 26°35'- 26° 42'), a man-made reservoir built in the 1960s, is located in Qingzhen County and only 16 km west of Guiyang City, the capital of Guizhou Province in southwest China [1-3]. Baihua is a deep lake lying between mountains in an area with typical carbonate rock (Karst) terrain in Yungui Plateau. The mean depth of the lake is approximately 12 meters, with the greatest depth up to 45 meters [4]. The lake covers a surface area of 14.5 km^2 and holds 1.82×10^8 m^3 of water. Baihua Lake is one of the five drinking-water sources for approximately 3 million people in Guiyang, and it is a multi-functional water body that is also used for flood control, shipping, and fishery [5, 6].

Phosphorus, a mineral nutrient, often limits primary production in many freshwater ecosystems [7-9], and it is generally regarded as one of the most important limiting nutrients for accelerated eutrophication [10-13]. Lake sediment, an important part of water environment, can act as either a sink or a source for phosphorus [14-16]. Under normal conditions, sedimentation of phosphorus via particulates exceeds the amount released by sediments, causing a net accumulation over time. However, under certain conditions, release of phosphorus from sediments may be large enough to cause, or at least perpetuate, the eutrophication process [17]. Bengtsson demonstrated that although 98% of the external phosphorus load had been diverted from Lake Sodra Bergundasjon in Sweden, it remained eutrophic due to the high rate of phosphorus regeneration from its sediments [18]. Consequently, sediment phosphorus most obviously plays an important role in accelerating eutrophication of water bodies.

With the development of various industries and agricultures in the surrounding areas, Baihua Lake has been polluted seriously by phosphorus, nitrogen, organic matter and heavy metals. At present, the lake is already in a eutrophic state, and phosphorus has been one of the main factors [19]. The eutrophication has sometimes caused algal blooms, fish suffocation and other undesired effects [20]. Some algae can produce toxins that have been associated with human health problems [21]. Therefore, it is necessary to analyze sediment phosphorus, especially the role of which should be considered. However, not all phosphorus is bio-available. The total phosphorus (TP) concentration is not enough to indicate the potential risk. Thus, in this investigation, phosphorus forms were studied based on the Standards, Measurements and Testing (SMT) programme proposed by the European Commission [22]. The SMT protocol leads to obtaining five phosphorus fractions: iron/aluminum-bound phosphorus (Fe/Al-P) bound to Al, Fe and Mn oxyhydrates; calcium-bound phosphorus (Ca-P); inorganic phosphorus (IP); organic phosphorus (OP) and TP. The concentration of the Fe/Al-P fraction can be used for the estimation of both short-term and long-term available phosphorus in sediments and it is a measure of available algal phosphorus [23]. Conversely, Ca-P is a relatively stable, inter and non-bioavailable phosphorus fraction [24]. The most important inorganic phosphorus pools seem to be Fe/Al-P and Ca-P [25]. Most methods of phosphorus determination are based on the reaction of phosphorus with an acidified molybdate reagent to yield a phosphomolybdate heteropolyacid, which is then reduced to an intensely coloured blue compound and determined spectrophotometrically [26, 27].

At present, eutrophication problem of Baihua Lake has received much attention from governments and environmental researchers. Hitherto, Jiang et al. [19] and Wang et al. [28] have investigated the chemical species of phosphorus in sediments from Baihua Lake, using a sequential extraction technique reported by Jin et al.. However, to the best of our knowledge, few of studies on the chemical species of phosphorus in sediments from Baihua Lake have been conducted employing SMT programme and X-ray powder diffraction (XRD), a non-destructive and rapid analytical technique primarily used for phase identification of crystalline materials that can provide information regarding unit cell dimensions [29]. The objectives of this research were to study the distribution characteristics of phosphorus speciation using the SMT programme and XRD, to make a statistical analysis on test data for interpretation of possible origins of the phosphorus loadings and transformation mechanism of the phosphorus species, and finally to provide relevant data for the management of the lake. Additionally, remediation measures were briefly evaluated for the lake considering its pollution conditions and distinctive environmental features.

2 MATERIALS AND METHODS

2.1. Sampling

The sediment samples used in this study were collected during June 2011 in Baihua Lake with a grab-sampler. Superficial sediment samples were taken at Dachong (DC), Yueliangwan (YLW), Meituwan (MTW), Pingpu (PP), Guanyinshanzhuang (GYSZ), Laojiutu (LJT), Jiangjiapu (JJP), Yapengzhai (YPZ), Tishuizhan (TSZ), Longtan (LT), Jinyinshan (JYS), Dahewan (DHW), Pijiangou (PJG), Baifan (BF), Chafanzai (CFZ), Tangchong (TC) and Maixihekou (MXHK), which were selected based on the size, shape, and water flowing direction of the lake (Figure 1). The precise collection sites were located in situ using a global positioning system (GPS). Each sediment sample was obtained by mixing three to four sediments collected near the sampling locations. Samples were put in the glass bottles (1000 cm^3 volume) that were cleaned with 5% HCl (v/v) and 5% HNO$_3$ (v/v), and immediately transported to the laboratory. In our laboratory, the sediments were centrifuged and the supernatant were discarded. After air-dried at room temperature, the sediment samples were ground to < 100 mesh for analysis.

2.2. Instruments and Reagents

The following instruments were used in this research: (1) GPS-72 from American Garmin Corporation made in Taiwan, (2) UV-Visible spectrophotometer (Cary 100 Bio) by Varian Corporation from USA, (3) X-ray diffractometer (X'pert PRO) produced by PANalytical Corporation in Holland, (4) Immersion oscillator (SHZ-C) by Shanghai Medical Instruments Corporation from China, (5) Water purification system (Nex Power 2000) from Human Corporation in Korea. All reagents used in this research were made in China. The hydrochloric acid (HCl), sulfuric acid (H$_2$SO$_4$) and nitric acid (HNO$_3$) were guaranteed reagent (GR) grade. All of the other reagents used were analytical reagent (AR) grade. Deionized water was prepared by the water purification system presented above.

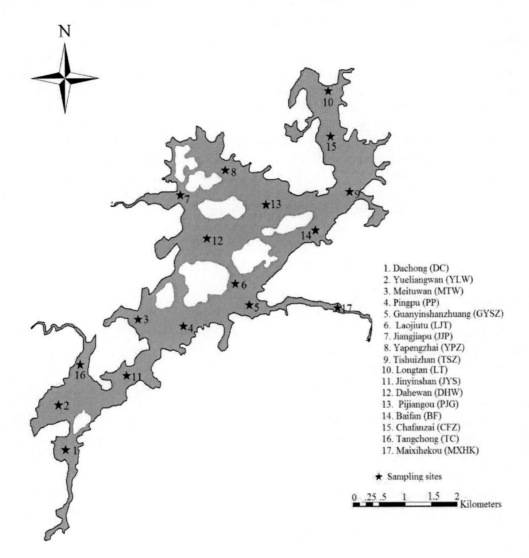

1. Dachong (DC)
2. Yueliangwan (YLW)
3. Meituwan (MTW)
4. Pingpu (PP)
5. Guanyinshanzhuang (GYSZ)
6. Laojiutu (LJT)
7. Jiangjiapu (JJP)
8. Yapengzhai (YPZ)
9. Tishuizhan (TSZ)
10. Longtan (LT)
11. Jinyinshan (JYS)
12. Dahewan (DHW)
13. Pijiangou (PJG)
14. Baifan (BF)
15. Chafanzai (CFZ)
16. Tangchong (TC)
17. Maixihekou (MXHK)

★ Sampling sites

Figure.1: Distribution of sampling sites in Baihua Lake.

2.3. Analytical Procedures of TP and Phosphorus Forms

In this investigation, TP and phosphorus forms were studied based on SMT protocol, the process of which was shown in Figure 2.

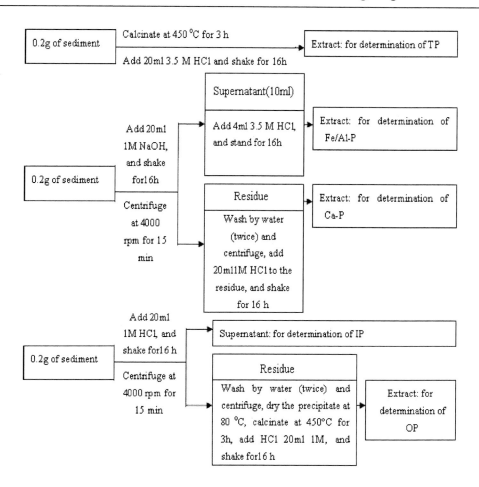

Figure 2. SMT protocol for phosphorus forms in freshwater sediment.

At the end of each extraction, the extract was separated from the solid residue by centrifugation at 4000 rpm (round per minute) for 15 min. Then, the supernatant was decanted and collected for analysis, and the residue was discarded. Meanwhile, a blank was prepared and replicate samples were analyzed in a similar way.

2.4. Study of Phosphorus Forms in Sediments from Baihua Lake by XRD

In this study, XRD was also used to analyze phosphorus forms in sediments from Baihua Lake. Briefly, each sediment sample described above was pressed into a 1.3-cm-diameter sample plexiglass holder well of 1 mm thickness. The analysis of XRD adopted a multifunctional sample stage MPSS (vertical system), with the scan speed of 32°/min, the tension of 40 kV, the current of 40 mA and the step size of 0.0167°. The original data were rectified based on the Jade program to eliminate Kα, and then obtain the XRD patterns of the whole samples. In combination with the database, the major chemical compositions were obtained.

3 RESULTS AND DISCUSSION

3.1. Distribution of TP and Phosphorus Forms in Sediments from Baihua Lake

According to the SMT protocol, TP could be represented by the sum of OP and IP, and IP could be divided into Fe/Al-P and Ca-P. These relations could be described by the following formula: TP = OP + IP, and IP = Fe/Al-P + Ca-P. Generally, the recovery rate was 97.2%-103.2% for TP, and 95.5%-104.7% for IP in most cases in the present work, and this recovery rate was reasonable [30]. The TP concentrations and phosphorus forms in sediments from Baihua Lake were shown in Table 1. In this study, it is obvious that there were notably high recovery rates for TP and IP, and most recovery rates were within the range described above.

In the study area, the TP concentrations varied from 591.57 to 2374.80 mg/kg (Table 1), with the mean concentration of 1604.02 mg/kg, whereas the TP concentrations in sediments from Chaohu Lake in Anhui Province and Xihu Lake in Fujian Province, China, ranged from 450 to 560 mg/kg and from 750 to 900 mg/kg, respectively [31, 32]. Obviously, it was evident that the phosphorus level in the sediments from Baihua Lake was generally higher than those from Chaohu Lake and Xihu Lake, which are both eutrophic lakes. In order to make pollution condition of the whole lake more intuitive, the kriging interpolation was conducted by ArcGIS software (Figure 3). It can be found in Table 1 and Figure 3 that the largest value of TP turned up at the TC sampling site, followed by the TSZ sampling site. While, at site of MTW, the TP had the lowest content. This is probably attributable to the fact that near the site of TC, there was a pig farm. Its effects on phosphorus loading are relatively significant. At the TSZ sampling site, domestic sewage from the Baiyun area might be the main reason leading to the high concentration of TP.

In all sediment samples, the concentration of IP ranged from 355.74 mg/kg to 1863.75 mg/kg, with the highest concentration observed at TC, and the lowest observed at MTW. Fe/Al-P (bio-available fraction of phosphorus), a major and direct source of phosphorus release, might play an important part in accelerating eutrophication of water bodies. It was considered to be primarily from industrial wastewater and urban swage discharges. As shown in Table 1, the concentration of Fe/Al-P ranged from 184.40 mg/kg to 1243.60 mg/kg, with the highest and the lowest concentration observed at TC and MTW, respectively. The highest concentration is approximate 7 times the lowest. This wide concentration range showed that the influence of human activity on different regions were different. Ca-P (non-bioavailable phosphorus fraction) was considered to be related to the local geology. The highest concentration of Ca-P was observed at CFZ, and the lowest was observed at JJP. In comparison with Fe/Al-P, the narrow concentration range of Ca-P exhibited that Ca-P was relatively stable, which was agreed with its source. OP (bio-available fraction of phosphorus), considered to be primarily from rural agricultural cultivation and fertilization, is an important phosphorus fraction buried in the sediment. It might be released to the overlying water, and thus directly affects the availability levels of dissolved phosphorus for primary production [33]. For OP, the concentration varied from 231.54 mg/kg to 571.40 mg/kg. The highest and the lowest concentration were also observed at TC and MTW, respectively.

Table 1. The TP concentrations and phosphorus forms in sediments (dry weight) and recovery rates

Sample number	Fe/Al-P		Ca-P		IP		OP		TP	(Fe/Al-P+ Ca-P)/IP	(IP+OP)/TP
	mg/kg	%	mg/kg	%	mg/kg	%	mg/kg	%	mg/kg	%	%
1	671.18	43.82	409.04	26.71	1083.83	70.77	434.95	28.40	1531.54	99.67	99.17
2	947.67	49.34	483.80	25.19	1379.68	71.83	494.77	25.76	1920.76	103.80	97.60
3	184.40	31.17	156.63	26.48	355.74	60.13	231.54	39.14	591.57	95.86	99.27
4	362.08	32.43	260.82	23.36	636.59	57.01	425.22	38.08	1116.60	97.80	95.10
5	677.19	38.24	471.07	26.60	1166.57	65.88	561.63	31.72	1770.85	98.40	97.60
6	694.48	36.16	727.15	37.86	1390.98	72.42	475.30	24.75	1920.76	102.20	97.16
7	285.53	38.97	144.50	19.72	444.21	60.63	271.46	37.05	732.66	96.80	97.68
8	777.51	41.21	546.97	29.00	1317.75	69.85	547.33	29.01	1886.63	100.51	98.86
9	941.61	42.08	732.81	32.75	1650.57	73.76	544.57	24.34	2237.77	101.44	98.09
10	538.36	37.49	302.61	21.07	823.38	57.34	496.42	34.57	1436.05	102.10	96.08
11	852.43	45.39	424.79	22.62	1319.84	70.28	514.79	27.41	1878.04	96.80	97.70
12	963.32	50.54	422.70	22.18	1370.28	71.90	491.23	25.77	1905.88	101.10	97.70
13	700.82	42.47	432.52	26.21	1114.42	67.53	509.77	30.89	1650.30	101.70	98.40
14	338.43	33.39	303.21	29.91	657.92	64.90	358.22	35.34	1013.63	97.50	100.20
15	787.17	37.76	848.41	40.70	1668.11	80.02	474.08	22.74	2084.68	98.05	102.76
16	1243.60	52.37	548.73	23.11	1863.75	78.48	571.40	24.06	2374.80	96.20	102.5
17	202.30	16.64	395.33	32.52	630.82	51.89	485.69	39.95	1215.73	94.74	91.80
Mean	656.95	39.38	447.71	27.41	1110.26	67.33	464.02	30.53	1604.02	99.10	98.10

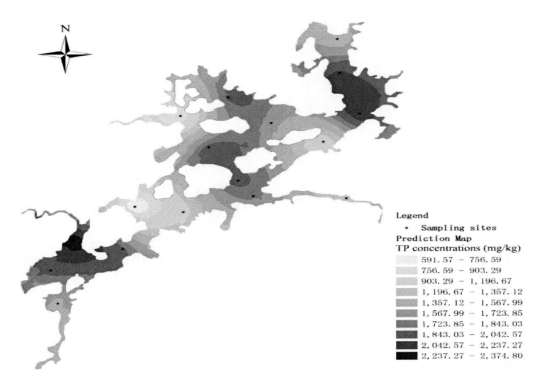

Figure 3. Kriging map of distribution of TP in sediments from Baihua Lake.

As shown in Table 1, it was clear that the average percentages of IP, OP, Fe/Al-P and Ca-P were 67.33%, 30.53%, 39.38% and 27.41%, respectively. Notably, the concentrations of IP were higher than that of OP, and the IP consisted mainly of Fe/Al-P. The high concentrations of Fe/Al-P might be related to the environmental conditions of Baihua Lake. The lake has a relatively short history (45 years), and is still in the stage of the accumulation of sediments [28]. Iron oxide or hydroxide minerals, abundant in sediment, can easily adsorb phosphatic ions (PO_4^{3-}). Therefore, although in calcareous regions with high concentration of Ca, the concentrations of Fe/Al-P in Baihua Lake are found to be still high compared with those of Ca-P. Additionally, human activities might be another reason leading to the high concentrations of Fe/Al-P. In order to obtain the specific reason, further studies are needed to be done.

Table 2. Correlation coefficients between Fe/Al-P, Ca-P, IP, OP and TP in sediments from Baihua Lake

	TP	IP	Fe/Al-P	Ca-P	OP
TP	1				
IP	0.983**	1			
Fe/Al-P	0.932**	0.944**	1		
Ca-P	0.845**	0.858**	0.649**	1	
OP	0.870**	0.772**	0.739**	0.652**	1

** Correlation is significant at the 0.01 level (two-tailed).

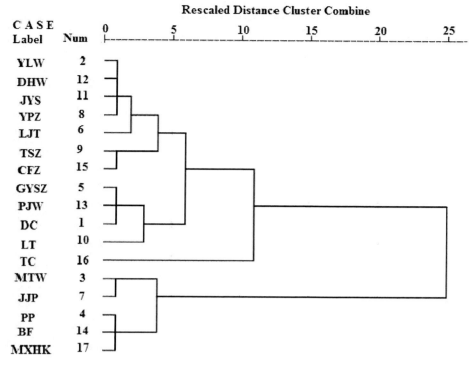

Figure 4. Dendrogram plot of HCA for phosphorus and its species in sediments from Baihua Lake.

Table 3. Major compositions of sediment from Baihua Lake

Sampling sites	Major compositions
DC	SiO2, CaCO3
YLW	SiO2, CaCO3
MTW	SiO2, CaCO3
PP	SiO2, CaCO3
GYSZ	SiO2, CaCO3, [Mg0.03Ca0.97][CO3]
LJT	SiO2, CaCO3, [Mg0.03Ca0.97][CO3]
JJP	SiO2, CaCO3, C15H11ClN2O2
YPZ	SiO2, CaCO3
TSZ	SiO2, CaCO3, [Mg0.03Ca0.97][CO3]
LT	SiO2, CaCO3
JYS	SiO2, CaCO3
DHW	SiO2, CaCO3
PJG	SiO2, CaCO3
BF	SiO2, CaCO3
CFZ	SiO2, CaCO3
TC	SiO2, CaCO3
MXHK	SiO2, CaCO3

Table 4. Phosphorus species in 17 sediment samples from Baihua Lake by XRD

Sample number	Phosphorus species
1	$AlPO_4$, $Fe(PO_4)$, $C_2H_8NO_4P$, $Li[Fe_{0.06}Mn_{0.94}][PO_4]$, $LiMnPO_4$, $NaHPO_3NH_2$, $KNaCa_2(PO_4)_2$, $Cs_4P_2O_7$, PON, $MgSiP_2$, CeP_2O_7, $Na_3Mn(PO_4)(CO_3)$, $Ga_6Na_4(PO_3F)_6O_2$, $Hf(HPO_4)_2$, $Zn_2P_2O_7$, $Nd_2Ni_7P_4$
2	$AlPO_4$, $Fe(PO_4)$, PON, $NaHPO_3NH_2$, $KNaCa_2(PO_4)_2$, $LiMnPO_4$, $BaCrP_2O_7$, $[Br_3P(OH)](AsF_6)$, $H_3PW_{12}O_{40}.29H_2O$, $SrIr_2P_2$, $Bi_{0.5}Sb_{1.5}(PO_4)_3$, $Hf(HPO_4)_2$, $Rb_3Nd(PO_4)_2$, $LiMgPO_4$, $Ga(PO_4)$, $CrPO_4$
3	$AlPO_4$, $Fe(PO_4)$, $Fe_{1.176}(PO_4)(OH)_{0.57}(H2O)_{0.43}$, $CaH_2NO_3PO_4.H_2O$, $MgAlPO_5$, $Be(PO_3)_2$, $Fe_{1.21}(PO_4)[F_{0.45}(OH)_{0.18}(H2O)_{0.37}]$, $Cs_7Ti_3P_7O_{27}$, $Fe_5(PO_4)_4(OH)_3.2H_2O$, $C_4H_{12}O_6P_2$, $C_4H_{12}O_5P_2$
4	$AlPO_4$, $Fe(PO_4)$, $LiMnPO_4$, $Hf(HPO_4)_2$, $PbHPO_4$, $Nd_2Ni_7P_4$, ErPdP, $RbTh_2(PO_4)_3$, $Pb_4BiO_4PO_4$, $SrIr_2P_2$, $[Br_3P(OH)](AsF_6)$, $BaCrP_2O_7$
5	$AlPO_4$, $Fe(PO_4)$, $K_2Na(AlP_2)$, $Zn_2P_2O_7$, $(Ca, Ce, La)PO_4.H_2O$, $Bi_{0.5}Sb_{1.5}(PO_4)_3$, $Rb_3Eu(PO_4)_2$, $Ca_6Na_4(PO_3F)_6O_2$, $NaCuPO_4$, $KBaPO_4$, $CuAlP_2Se_6$, $Pb_4BiO_4PO_4$, $NaPO_3NH_3$, $PbHPO_4$, $K_2Na(AlP_2)$
6	$AlPO_4$, $Fe(PO_4)$, $Li[Fe_{0.06}Mn_{0.94}][PO_4]$, $C_2H_8NO_4P$, $LiMgPO_4$, $Cu(H_2PO_2)_2$, $Hf(HPO_4)_2$, $NaHPO_3NH_2$, $Rb_3Nd(PO_4)_2$, $[Br_3P(OH)](AsF_6)$, $LiMnPO_4$, $Bi_{0.5}Sb_{1.5}(PO_4)_3$, $PbHPO_4$, $NaPO_3NH_3$, $BiSb_3(PO_4)_6$
7	$AlPO_4$, $Fe(PO_4)$, $C_4H_{12}O_6P_2$, $C_2H_8NO_4P$, $C_{12}H_{33}N_2O_4P.H_2O$, $(Fe, Mn)_2(PO_4)F$, CeP_2O_7, UP_2O_7, $Ag(ZnPO_4)$, $Fe_5(PO_4)_4(OH)_3.2H_2O$, Ce_2NiP_4, $Zn_2P_2O_7$, $Nd_2Ni_7P_4$, $Bi_{0.5}Sb_{1.5}(PO_4)_3$, $Hf(HPO_4)_2$, $BiSb_3(PO_4)_6$
8	$AlPO_4$, $Fe(PO_4)$, $Fe_{1.176}(PO_4)(OH)_{0.57}(H2O)_{0.43}$, $LiMnPO_4$, $Zn_2P_2O_7$, $NaCuPO_4$, $K_2Ni(P_2O_7)$, Li_3PO_4, CsMnP, $BiSb_3(PO_4)_6$, $Rb_3Eu(PO_4)_2$, $[Br_3P(OH)](AsF_6)$, $PbHPO_4$, $Bi_{0.5}Sb_{1.5}(PO_4)_3$, $BiSb_3(PO_4)_6$, $Be(HPO_4)(H_2O)$
9	$AlPO_4$, $Fe(PO_4)$, $[Li_{0.834}Fe_{0.055}]MgPO_4$, $CH_6O_5P_2$, $(Zn, Ca)Al_2P_2H_6O_{12}.3H_2O$, Na_3PO_4, $PbHPO_4$, $Mo_3Ni_2P_{1.167}$, $LiMgPO_4$, Li_3PO_4, $Zn_2P_2O_7$, $Bi_{0.5}Sb_{1.5}(PO_4)_3$, $BiSb_3(PO_4)_6$, $Rb_3Nd(PO_4)_2$
10	$AlPO_4$, $Fe(PO_4)$, $LiMnPO_4$, $CaDPO_4(D_2O)_2$, $[Li_{0.834}Fe_{0.055}]MgPO_4$, $Li[Fe_{0.06}Mn_{0.94}][PO_4]$, CaP, $CH_6O_6P_2$, $CH_6O_5P_2$, $KNaCa_2(PO_4)_2$, $Zn_4(P_2N_4)_3S$, $Hf(HPO_4)_2$, $SrIr_2P_2$, $LiMgPO_4$, $PbHPO_4$, $Rb_3Nd(PO_4)_2$
11	$AlPO_4$, $LiMnPO_4$, PON, $CrPO_4$, $Li[Fe_{0.06}Mn_{0.94}][PO_4]$, $(Al_{0.29}Ga_{0.71})(PO_4)$, $Zn_4(P_2N_4)_3S$, $Ga(PO_4)$, $Bi_{0.5}Sb_{1.5}(PO_4)_3$, $Rb_3Nd(PO_4)_2$, $Hf(HPO_4)_2$, $BiSb_3(PO_4)_6$
12	$AlPO_4$, $Fe(PO_4)$, $CaDPO_4(D_2O)_2$, $(Al_{0.29}Ga_{0.71})(PO_4)$, $NaPO_3NH_3$, $Ba_{10}(PO_4)_6S$, $BiSb_3(PO_4)_6$, $LiMgPO_4$, $Hf(HPO_4)_2$, $LiMnPO_4$, $Cr(NH_4)HP_3O_{10}$, $Hf(HPO_4)_2$, $Bi_{0.5}Sb_{1.5}(PO_4)_3$, $BiSb_3(PO_4)_6$, $Rb_3Nd(PO_4)_2$
13	$AlPO_4$, $CaDPO_4(D_2O)_2$, $Ba_5(PO_4)_3Cl$, $CsAl_3(P_3O_{10})_2$, $BaCr(P_2O_7)$, $NaAl(P_2O_7)$, $Li[Fe_{0.06}Mn_{0.94}][PO_4]$, $Ba_{10}(PO_4)_6S$, $Ba_5(PO_4)_3(OH)$, $LiMnPO_4$, $CrPO_4$, $Bi_{0.5}Sb_{1.5}(PO_4)_3$, $BiSb_3(PO_4)_6$
14	$AlPO_4$, $Fe(PO_4)$, $C_4H_{12}O_5P_2$, $C_4H_{12}O_6P_2$, YbPtP, LuPtP, $KNaCa_2(PO_4)_2$, $LiMgPO_4$, $Hf(HPO_4)_2$, $Cu(H_2PO_2)_2$, $NaPO_3NH_3$, $Zn_2P_2O_7$, $Bi_{0.5}Sb_{1.5}(PO_4)_3$, $BiSb_3(PO_4)_6$, $NaPO_3NH_3$, $NaHPO_3NH_2$, $Nd_2Ni_7P_4$
15	$AlPO_4$, $Fe(PO_4)$, Li_3PO_4, $Rb_3Nd(PO_4)_2$, $Hf(HPO_4)_2$, $KNaCa_2(PO_4)_2$, $Li[Fe_{0.06}Mn_{0.94}][PO_4]$, $LiMnPO_4$, $NaPO_3NH_3$, $LiMgPO_4$, $NaHPO_3NH_2$, $PbHPO_4$
16	$AlPO_4$, $Fe(PO_4)$, $CaDPO_4(D_2O)_2$, $Nd_2Ni_7P_4$, $Pb_4BiO_4PO_4$, $SrIrP_2$, $C_2H_8NO_4P$, $Bi_{0.5}Sb_{1.5}(PO_4)_3$, $NaPO_3NH_3$, $NaHPO_3NH_2$, $Rb_3Nd(PO_4)_2$, $BiSb_3(PO_4)_6$, $Zn_2P_2O_7$, $LiMgPO_4$, $Hf(HPO_4)_2$
17	$AlPO_4$, $Fe(PO_4)$, $Fe_3(PO_4)_2$, $Ca_4Ir_8P_7$, $Ca_6Na_4(PO_3F)_6O_2$, $CuAlP_2Se_6$, $SrMn_2(PO_4)_2$, $Rb_3Eu(PO_4)_2$, $GaPO_4$, $KBaPO_4$, $Zn_2(P_2Se_6)$, $RbPO_3$, $PbHPO_4$, $Zn_2P_2O_7$, $(Al_{0.29}Ga_{0.71})(PO_4)$, $Hf(HPO_4)_2$

Correlations between phosphorus and its species in sediments from Baihua Lake were analyzed, with the results shown in Table 2. The Pearson correlation coefficient between Fe/Al-P, OP, Ca-P and TP were 0.932, 0.870, 0.845 (P<0.01), respectively. It was clear that Fe/Al-P, OP and Ca-P all showed significant positive correlations with TP. The results indicated that an increase in the TP concentrations was mainly caused by increased Fe/Al-P, and then OP, which was in accordance with the previous research [34]. However, Ca-P also played an important role in the increase of the TP concentrations. For phosphorus forms, significant positive correlations (P<0.01) between OP and Fe/Al-P, as well as Ca-P demonstrated that both Fe/Al-P and Ca-P might be affected by OP. Fe/Al-P also showed significant positive correlations (P<0.01) with Ca-P. This might be attributed to the phosphate solubilizing bacteria that could transform insoluble phosphate into the bio-available forms mentioned above. However, owing to the different sources of Fe/Al-P and Ca-P, the Pearson correlation coefficient was relatively small.

Hierarchical cluster analysis (HCA), a statistical method for identifying relatively homogeneous clusters of cases based on measured characteristics was carried out in the present research as well. The dendrogram of HCA regarding phosphorus and its species in sediments from Baihua Lake was shown in Figure 4. It can be seen that the 17 locations in this survey can be divided into 4 groups. The first group contains 7 locations: YLW, DHW, JYS, YPZ, LJT, TSZ and CFZ; the second group contains 4 locations: GYSZ, PJW, DC and LT; the third group contains 1 location: TC; the fourth group contains 5 location: MTW, JJP, PP, BF and MXHK. It is obvious that the pollution status of all locations belonging to one cluster is similar. The farther the distance between two clusters, the greater the discrepancy of pollution intensity in the sediments. Hence, according to the results of HCA in our investigation, it is inferred that the distribution of phosphorus in sampling sites of one group is affected by the same factors which needs further studies.

3.2. Determination of Phosphorus Forms in Sediments from Baihua Lake by XRD

XRD was used to determine mineralogy of crystalline phases of all samples for which there was adequate crystalline sediment for analysis. The major compositions and phosphorus species of 17 sediment samples from Baihua Lake were presented in Tables 3 and 4, respectively. It seemed from Table 3 that the major compositions of all sediment samples from Baihua Lake included SiO_2 and $CaCO_3$. As shown in Table 4, XRD analysis demonstrated the existence of phosphorus species in sediments from Baihua Lake, including TP, IP, OP, Fe/Al-P and Ca-P, which partly confirmed the results of SMT. Furthermore, $AlPO_4$ was found in all sediment samples among phosphorus species, which was probably related to the discharge of Guizhou Aluminum Company around the lake. However, Ca-P was found only in part of sediment samples. This might be attributable to the ligand competition between PO_4^{3-} and CO_3^{2-} in the sediments, which would decrease the availability of binding sites on calcic complex, because the major compositions of all sediment samples from Baihua Lake included $CaCO_3$.

3.3. Methods of Controlling Phosphorus Release from Sediments

Some remediation measures for controlling the release of phosphorus from the sediment have been put forward, e.g. dredging and sediment capping [35]. Dredging is the removal of accumulated lake sediments. In consideration of the high cost, environmental impact and public acceptance, dredging will not be a feasible method [36]. Furthermore, at the bottom of Baihua Lake, there are probably caves and underground rivers which can transport phosphorus pollutants to other places to cause unknown consequences for a long period of time [4]. Consequently, dredging is not considered to be useful for Baihua Lake. For sediment capping, contaminated sediments remaining in place at the site are covered by stable layers of sediment, gravel, rock, and synthetic materials. Indeed, a research showed that the calcite barrier can control phosphorus release from sediments [37]. With capping approach, the cost is relatively high due to the need for a long term monitoring and maintenance to prevent contaminants from migrating. Thus, a new method should be developed for this drinking-water source.

CONCLUSION

In summary, the results of the XRD analysis showed that $AlPO_4$ was found in all sediment samples among phosphorus species. The SMT protocol demonstrated that TP consisted mainly of IP, and the IP consisted mainly of Fe/Al-P. The high concentration of Fe/Al-P indicated a significant risk of phosphorus release. Thus, in addition to curtailing external sources of phosphorus, some remediation measures should be taken to control the release of phosphorus from lake sediments, an internal source of phosphorus. As a result of the distinctive environmental features of Baihua Lake, more feasible methods are needed.

ACKNOWLEDGMENTS

This work was supported by the National Natural Science Foundation of China (Grant No. 20967003) and by the Government of Guiyang City (Project No. [2010] 5-2).

REFERENCES

[1]   J. Luo, L.Y. Fu, J. W. Hu, Z. W. Yu, C. Liu, S. M. Duan and X. F. Jin, "Estimation of organochlorine pesticides and dioxin-like PCBs in surface sediments from Baihua Lake", *Advanced Materials Research*, vol. 233-235, pp. 2988-2993, 2011.

[2]   L.Y Fu., J. Luo, J.W. Hu, Q. Wu, X.F. Huang and L.F. Tian, "Estimation of Organochlorine Pesticides (DDT and HCH) in Surface Sediments from Baihua Lake", Selected Proceedings of the Fifth International Conference on Waste Management and Technology (ICWMT 5), pp. 534-538, 2010.

[3]   J. J. Deng, X. F. Huang, J. W. Hu, C. X. Li, Y. Yi and J. Long, "Distribution of several microorganisms and activity of alkaline phosphatase in sediments from Baihua Lake", *Asia-Pacific Journal of Chemical Engineering*, vol. 4, pp. 711-716, 2009.

[4]   X. F. Huang, J. W. Hu, J. J. Deng, C. X. Li, J. Long and F. X. Qin, "Heavy-metals pollution and potential ecological risk assessment of sediments from Baihua Lake", *International Journal of Environmental Health Research*, vol. 19, pp. 405-419, 2009.

[5]   X. F. Huang, J. W. Hu, J. J. Deng, C. X. Li and F. X. Qin, "Speciation of heavy metals in sediments from Baihua Lake and Aha Lake", *Asia-Pacific Journal of Chemical Engineering*, vol. 4, pp. 635-642, 2009.

[6]   W. Shen, J. W. Hu, L. Y. Fu, and M. Jin, "Distribution of several microorganisms in sediments from Baihua Lake", *Advanced Materials Research*, vol. 396-398, p. 1923, 2011.

[7]   H. W. Paerl, L. M. Valdes, A. R. Joyner and M. F. Piehler, "Solving problems resulting from solutions: evolution of a dual nutrient management strategy for the eutrophying Neuse River Estuary, North Carolina", *Environmental Science and Technollogy*, vol. 38, pp. 3068-3073, 2004.

[8]   W. J. Surridge, A. L. Heathwaite and A. J. Baird, "The release of phosphorus to porewater and surface water from river riparian sediments", *Journal of Environmental Quality*, vol. 36, pp. 1534-1544, 2007.

[9]   D. L. Correll, "The role of phosphorus in the eutrophication of receiving waters: A review", *Journal of Environmental Quality*, vol. 27, pp. 261-266, 1998.

[10] D. J. Conley, H. W. Paerl, R. W. Howarth, D. F. Boesch, S. P. Seitzinger, K. E. Havens, C. Lancelot and G. E. Likens, "Controlling eutrophication: nitrogen and phosphorus", *Science*, vol. 323, pp. 1014-1015, 2009.

[11] C. J. Penn and R. B. Bryant, "Phosphorus solubility in response to acidification of dairy manure amended soils", *Soil Science Society of America Journal*, vol. 72, pp. 238-243, 2008.

[12] S. L. Chinault and G. A. O'Connor, "Phosphorus release from a biosolids-amended sandy spodosol", *Journal of Environmental Quality,* vol. 37, pp. 937-943, 2008.

[13] K. Ádám, T. Krogstad, F. R. D. Suliman and P. D. Jenssen, "Phosphorous sorption by filtralite P-small scale box experiment", *Journal of Environmental Science Health*, vol. 40, pp. 1239-1250, 2005.

[14] T. Gonsiorczyk, P. Casper, and R. Koschel, "Phosphorus binding forms in the sediments of an oligotrophic and an eutrophic hardwater lake of the Baltic district (Germany)", *Water Science and Technology*, vol. 37, p. 51, 1998.

[15] F. C. Wu, H. R. Qing and G. J. Wan, "Regeneration of N, P and Si near the sediment/water interface of lakes from southwestern China plateau", *Water Research*, vol. 35, p. 1334, 2001.

[16] P. A. Moore, K. R. Reddy and D. A. Graetz, "Phosphorus geochemistry in the sediment-water column of a hypereutrophic lake", *Journal of Environmental Quality,* vol. 20, pp. 869-875, 1991.

[17] L. J. Lennox, "Lough Ennel: Laboratory studies on sediment phosphorus release under varying mixing, aerobic and anaerobic conditions", *Freshwater Biology*, vol. 14, pp. 183-187, 1984.

[18] L. Bengtsson, "Phosphorus release from a highly eutrophic lake sediment", *Verh International Verein Limnology*, vol. 19, pp. 1263-1271, 1975.

[19] C. H. Jiang, J. J. Deng and J. W. Hu, "Phosphorus speciation in sediments from Lakes Baihua and Aha with a typical karstic environment, China", *Advanced Materials Research*, vol. 113-114, pp. 420-424, 2010.

[20] G. J. Wan, "Environmental process of the deep- water lakes and approach to the protection of water resources on the Yunnan-Guizhou Plateau", *Engineering Sciences*, vol. 11, pp. 60-71, 2009. (in Chinese).

[21] K. Kotut, A. Ballot and L. Krienitz, "Toxic cyanobacteria and their toxins in standing waters of Kenya: implications for water resource use", *Journal of Water and Health*, vol. 4, pp. 233-245, 2006.

[22] V. Ruban, J. F. López-Sánchez, P. Pardo, G. Rauret, H. Muntau and P. Quevauviller, "Harmonized protocol and certified reference material for the determination of extractable contents of phosphorus in freshwater sediments-a synthesis of recent works", *Fresenius' Journal of Analytical Chemistry*, vol. 370, pp. 224-228, 2001.

[23] Q. X. Zhou, C. E. Gibson and Y. M. Zhu, "Evaluation of phosphorus bioavailability in sediment of three contrasting lakes in China and the UK", *Chemosphere*, vol. 42, pp. 221-225, 2001.

[24] C. H. Jiang, J. W. Hu, X. F. Huang, C. X. Li, J. J. Deng, J. Zhang and F. Liu, "Phosphorus speciation in sediments of Lake Hongfeng, China", *Chinese Journal of Oceanolgy and Limnology*, vol. 29, pp. 53-62, 2011.

[25] H. L. Golterman, *The chemistry of phosphate and nitrogen compounds in sediments*: Kluwer Academic Publishers, 2004.

[26] J. Murphy and J. P. Riley, "A modified single solution method for the determination of phosphate in natural waters", *Analytica Chimica Acta*, vol. 27, pp. 31-36, 1962.

[27] I. D. McKelvie, D. M. W. Peat and P. J. Worsfold, "Techniques for the quantification and speciation of phosphorus in natural waters", *Analytical Proceedings including Analalytical Communications*, vol. 32, pp. 437-445, 1995.

[28] Y. C. Wang, G. J. Wan, S. L. Wang, S. H. Li and R. G. Huang, "Forms of phosphorus in sediments of Lake Baihua and Lake Hongfeng, Guizhou", *Acta Mineralogica Sinica*, vol. 20, pp. 273-278, 2000. (in Chinese)

[29] C. H. Jiang, D. Wu, J. W. Hu, F. Liu, X. F. Huang, C. X. Li and M. Jin, "Speciation of phosphorus in sediments from Lake Hongfeng using chemical fractionation and X-ray powder diffraction, China", *Chinese Science Bulletin*, vol. 56, pp. 2098-2108, 2011.

[30] P. Pardo, G. Rauret and J. F. Lopez-sanchez, "Shortened screening method for phosphorus fractionation in sediments: A complementary approach to the standards, measurements and testing harmonised protocol", *Analytica Chimica Acta*, vol. 508, pp. 201-206, 2004.

[31] Q. H. Huang, D. H. Wang, C. X. Wang, M. Ma and Z. J. Wang, "Relation between phosphorus forms in the sediments and lake eutrophication", *China Environmental Science*, vol. 23, pp. 583-586, 2003. (in Chinese).

[32] Y. P. Su, D. X. Zheng, Y. T. Zhuang, G. Li, W. Z. Lin and L. Q. Xue, "Phosphorus fractionations in sediments from eutrophicated lakes in Fujian Province", *Journal of Agro-Environmental Science*, vol. 24, pp. 362-365, 2005. (in Chinese).

[33] G. Edlund, R. Carman, "Distribution and diagenesis of organic and inorganic phosphorus in sediments of the Baltic proper", *Chemosphere*, vol. 45, p. 1053, 2001.

[34] V. Ruban, S. Brigault, D. Demare and A. M. Philippe, "An investigation of the origin and mobility of phosphorus in freshwater sediments from Bort-Les-Orgues Reservoir, France", *Journal of Environmental Monitoring*, vol. 1, pp. 403- 407, 1999.

[35] K. Siong and T. Asaeda, "Does calcite encrustation in chara provide a phosphorus nutrient sink", *Journal of Environmental Quality*, vol. 35, pp. 490-494, 2006.

[36] C. Kinaci, B. Inanc, A. F. Aydin, E. Yuksel, M. F. Sevimli, O. Arikan and D. Topacik, "Quality of the bottom sediment prior to dredging in the Golden Horn of Istanbul", *Journal of Environmental Science Health*, vol. A39, pp. 365-374, 2004.

[37] J. W. Lin, Z. L. Zhu, J. F. Zhao and Y. H. Zhan, "Influencing factors of calcite active barrier system to control phosphorus release from sediments", *Environmental Science*, vol. 29, pp. 121-126, 2008. (in Chinese).

In: Phosphorus: Properties, Health Effects and the Environment   ISBN: 978-1-62081-399-7
Editors: Ming Yue Chen and Da-Xia Yang   © 2012 Nova Science Publishers, Inc.

Chapter 7

PHOSPHORUS COMPLEX OF PORPHYRINS

Kazutaka Hirakawa

Department of Basic Engineering (Chemistry), Faculty of Engineering, Shizuoka
University, Johoku 3-5-1, Naka-ku, Hamamatsu, Shizuoka, Japan

ABSTRACT

Phosphorus complexes of porphyrins demonstrate unique character. Porphyrin, a
macrocyclic compound, is an important ligand for most atoms. Various metal ions are
captured by the central nitrogens of a porphyrin ring through a coordinate bond. Some
nonmetallic atoms can also bind to the central nitrogens. Phosphorus is an important
nonmetallic central atom of porphyrin and can form a relatively stable complex. In
general, the structure of a phosphorus complex of porphyrin is sterically hindered.
Phosphorus porphyrin has a relatively small redox potential of one-electron reduction.
Therefore, the photoexcited state of a phosphorus porphyrin is a strong oxidant. This
electron accepting ability is advantageous for a photo-induced electron transfer reaction.
In addition, porphyrins are used as photosensitizers of photodynamic therapy, which is a
promising treatment of cancer. Since phosphorus porphyrins can oxidize biomolecules,
such as protein and DNA, through photo-induced electron transfer, they have been
studied as potential photosensitizers for photodynamic therapy.

1. INTRODUCTION

Phosphorus can be used as a central atom of porphyrin. Porphyrin, a macrocyclic
compound, is an important ligand for almost all atoms. Various metal ions, in particular, are
captured by the central nitrogens of porphyrins through a coordinate bond (Figure 1). Some
nonmetallic atoms can also bind to the central nitrogens. Phosphorus is an important
nonmetallic central atom of porphyrin, and a relatively stable complex can be formed with it.
In general, organic phosphorus compounds are highly toxic. However, a phosphorus complex
of porphyrin is not toxic. One of the most important characters of phosphorus porphyrin
(P(V)porphyrin) is its high electron-accepting ability. In the case of photochemical reactions,
P(V)porphyrins act as the electron acceptor. Therefore, various studies about photo-induced

electron transfer to P(V)porphyrins have been reported. Porphyrins are used as photosensitizer of photodynamic therapy (PDT), which is a promising treatment of cancer. P(V)porphyrins have been studied as potential photosensitizers for PDT [1-3]. Photosensitizers of PDT damage biomolecules of cancer cells through the mechanism mediated by reactive oxygen formation, and P(V)porphyrin can damage biomolecules directly through an electron transfer reaction. In this chapter, the photochemical and potential medicinal properties of phosphorus complexes of porphyrins are briefly reviewed.

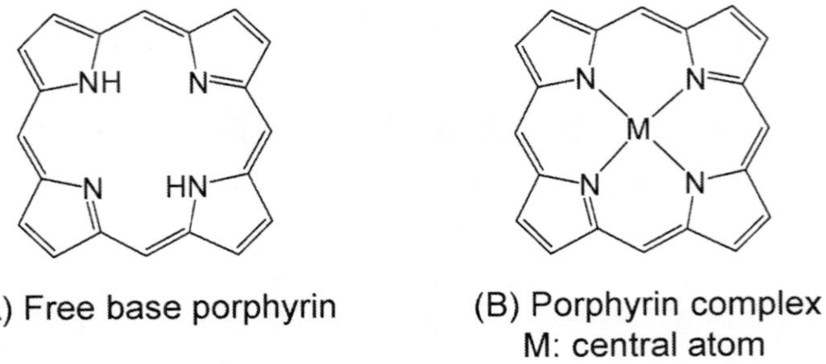

(A) Free base porphyrin

(B) Porphyrin complex
M: central atom

Figure 1. Free base and complex of the porphyrin ring.

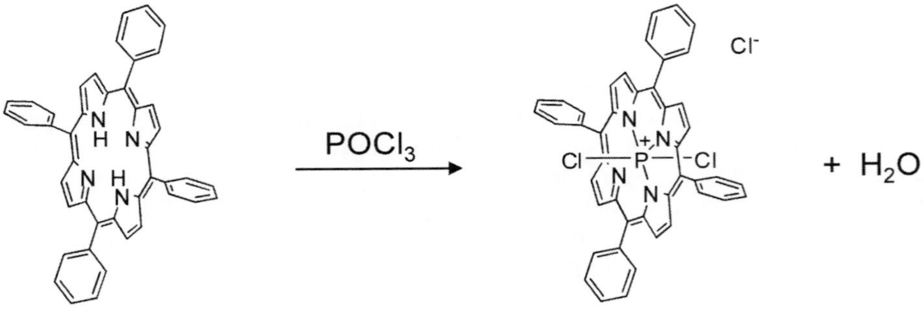

$$POCl_3 + 3H_2O \longrightarrow H_3PO_4 + 3HCl$$

Figure 2. Scheme of the introduction of a phosphorus atom into tetraphenyl porphyrin.

2. PHOSPHORUS ATOM INTRODUCTION INTO A PORPHYRIN RING

2.1. Protocol of the Phosphorus Introduction

A general protocol of phosphorus introduction into porphyrin follows the procedure shown in Figure 2. This is a synthesis method of dichloroP(V)tetraphenylporphyrin chloride (Cl$_2$P(V)P) from free-base tetraphenylporphyrin [4]. A free-base porphyrin is dissolved in dry pyridine, and almost 60-fold (molar quantity) phosphorus oxychloride (POCl$_3$) is added to the solution. This solution will be refluxed during 24 – 48 hours. Since the byproduct of this reaction is hydrogen chloride (HCl), bubbling nitrogen can purge the HCl gas and enhances the reaction. The preparation of P(V)porphyrin can be monitored by change in color. The brownish color of free-base porphyrin changes to dark green or dark blue when phosphorus is introduced. A light green solution may be due to the protonation of central nitrogen. The completion of this reaction is confirmed by absorption spectrum measurement and thin layer chromatography. After the reaction, the solvent pyridine and residual POCl$_3$ can be removed by vacuum evaporation. Solid products can be purified by column chromatography, using silica gel and chloroform-methanol as eluents. In general, the yield of the phosphorus introduction is high (almost unity).

2.2. Substitution of the Axial Ligand of Central Phosphorus

The axial chlorine connecting with the central phosphorus atom can be easily substituted by an alkoxy group. The reaction between Cl$_2$P(V)P and alcohol successfully produces symmetrically substituted dialkoxyP(V)porphyrin [5-8]. The asymmetrical substitutions with the hydroxyl group and the alkoxy group are possible by using silver nitrate in the acetonitrile/water mixing solvent (Figure 3) [9]. Stirring the solution containing dichloroP(V)tetrakis(n-butoxyphenyl) porphyrin chloride, 1-pyrenebutanol, and silver nitrate induces the formation of hydroxyl-pyrenebutoxyP(V)porphyrin (Py-POH) (Figure 4) [10].

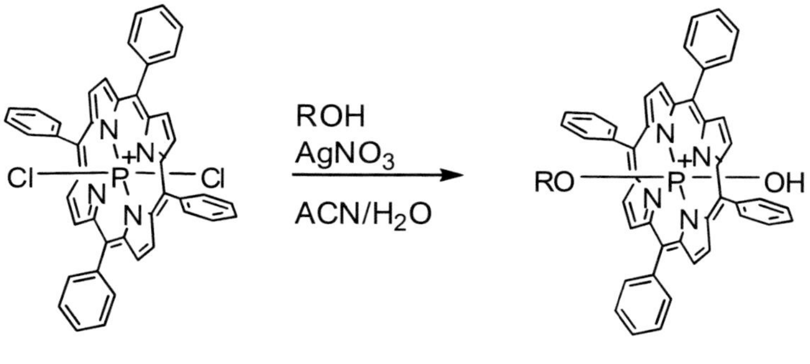

Figure 3. Scheme of the asymmetrical synthesis of P(V)porphyrin derivatives in acetonitrile (ACN)/water.

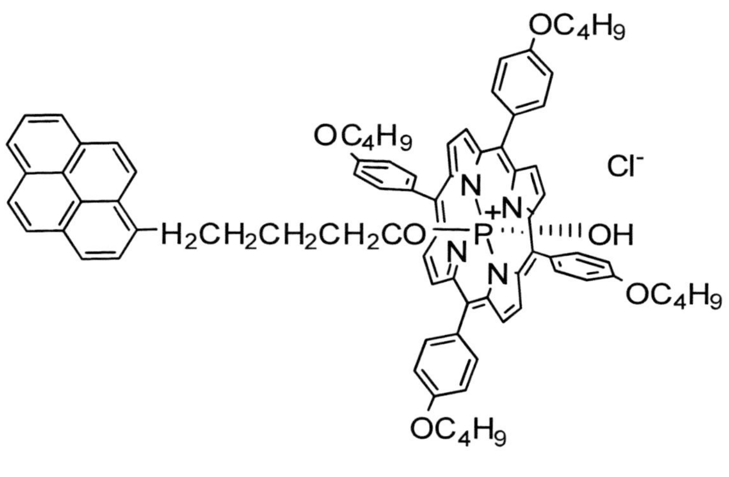

Figure 4. Structure of hydroxy(1-pyrenebutoxy)P(V)porphyrin.

3. Chemical Properties of P(V)Porphyrins

3.1. General Property of P(V)Porphyrins

The P(V)porphyrin is a strong electron acceptor by the central cationic phosphorus atom. Its strength as an electron acceptor depends on the electron affinity of an axial ligand connected at the central phosphorus atom of the P(V)porphyrin. In general, photoexcited high-valent metalloporphyrins have high oxidation ability compared with low-valent metalloporphyrins or free-base porphyrins [8, 11]. Therefore, P(V)porphyrins are advantageous for an oxidative charge transfer reaction. For example, the oxidation potential of tetraphenylporphyrin P(V) complexes (1.4-1.8 V vs. saturated calomel electrode (SCE) in acetonitrile) [8, 11] is higher than that of guanine (1.24 V) [12], indicating that photoexcited P(V)porphyrins have the potential to oxidize DNA through photo-induced electron transfer. Therefore, P(V)porphyrin may potentially damage biomacromolecules through dual mechanisms, electron transfer and reactive oxygen generation [13]. In addition, P(V)porphyrins can be dissolved in both organic solvents and aqueous media, suggesting that this photosensitizer has affinity for a phospholipid cell membrane and can disperse in a cell.

3.2. Control of Electron Transfer and Energy Transfer in Photoexcited P(V)Porphyrin

Excitation energy transfer and photo-induced electron transfer are essential processes for molecular systems involved in photo-information operations and photosynthesis [14-22]. Various studies on the control of these processes have been reported [14-20]. For example, a series of molecular photonic gates based on switching the electronic state of a molecule by the pH and ion strength of a solvent has been reported [16-19]. In the case of P(V)porphyrin, competition between energy transfer and electron transfer in the photo-excited pyrene to the P(V)porphyrin in bispyrenylP(V)porphyrins has been reported [8]. These processes were selected by the solvent's polarity. This selection of electronic transition processes is caused by the control of the electron transfer rate and depends on the energy level of the charge transfer state. The P(V)porphyrin is a strong electron acceptor by the central cationic phosphorus atom [4, 23]. The strength as an electron acceptor depends on the electron affinity of an axial ligand connected at the central phosphorus atom of the P(V)porphyrin. Therefore, controlling the condition of the axial ligand leads to control of the electron affinity of the P(V)porphyrin and control of energy transfer and electron transfer. For this purpose, a changeable axial ligand is considered to be a key component. In the case of the dihydroxyP(V)porphyrin, the electronic condition of the π-electron system and the electron affinity is changed by acid dissociation of the axial hydroxyl groups [24]. This characteristic can be used for the external control of the electron affinity by the pH of the surroundings.

Reports have been made on the external control of energy transfer and electron transfer from the pyrene moiety to the P(V)porphyrin ring by the change in conditions of the axial hydroxyl group using Py-POH (Figure 4) [10]. The fluorescence intensity of the pyrene moiety of Py-POH was markedly quenched by the porphyrin ring. The energy transfer from the pyrene to the porphyrin was confirmed by the fluorescence excitation spectrum measurement. Electron transfer is also possible energetically. It has been reported that competition between the energy transfer and the electron transfer in the photoexcited pyrene-P(V)porphyrin system is possible [8]. The calculated critical distance of energy transfer from the photoexcited pyrene moiety to the P(V)porphyrin through dipole-dipole interaction (Förster mechanism) is 42 Å [25]. This critical distance of energy transfer (R_0) was calculated from the following equation:

$$R_0^6 = \frac{9000 \ln 10 \kappa^2 \Phi_{Py \to Py}^0}{128\pi^5 N_A n^4} \int F(\nu)\varepsilon(\nu)\nu^{-4} \, d\nu$$

(1)

where κ is the geometrical factor, N_A is the Avogadro constant, n is the refractive index, $F(\nu)$ is the normalized fluorescence spectrum of the pyrene moiety, $\varepsilon(\nu)$ is the absorption spectrum of the P(V)porphyrin ring, and ν is the wavenumber. Because the center-to-center distance between the pyrene moiety and the porphyrin ring is 8.5 Å, a high yield of energy transfer reasonably occurs in this molecular system. On the other hand, it was reported that the electron transfer rate constant from photoexcited pyrene to a tetraphenylporphyrinP(V) complex separated by butoxy chain is 1.8×10^9 s^{-1} in dichloromethane, and the energy transfer competed with the electron transfer [8]. The competition between the energy transfer and the electron transfer should be reasonable phenomenon in the molecular system of Py-POH.

P(V)porphyrin has a strong electron affinity due to the positive charge from a central phosphorus cation [26]. The pK_a of the axial hydroxyl group of Py-POH was estimated to be 9.5 and can be dissociated in an alkali solution. Fluorescence quantum yields of the porphyrin moiety increased, depending on the pH of the solvent. These results can be reasonably explained. The electron affinity of the P(V)porphyrin is decreased through neutralization of the positive charge of the central phosphorus by the negative charge from the acid dissociation of the axial hydroxyl group, which results in the suppression of the intramolecular electron transfer. This suppression of electron transfer makes energy transfer the predominant process (Figure 5).

The control of photophysical processes, such as energy transfer and electron transfer, is an important theme. The combination of porphyrin and pyrene is useful for this purpose, because both processes of energy transfer and electron transfer are possible from the photoexcited state of the pyrene [8, 27]. The control of the energy transfer and electron transfer is also important for the medicinal application of photochemistry [28-30].

In summary, energy transfer to porphyrin competes with electron transfer to porphyrin in the photo-excited state of the pyrene of Py-POH. The axial hydroxyl group of Py-POH was dissociated with pK_a = 9.5, and the energy transfer became the predominant process. The switching of energy transfer and electron transfer was based on the change of electron affinity of the P(V)porphyrin moiety by the acid dissociation of the axial hydroxyl group. This study has shown that external control of intramolecular energy transfer and electron transfer is possible by changing the condition of the axial hydroxyl group by interaction with the surroundings.

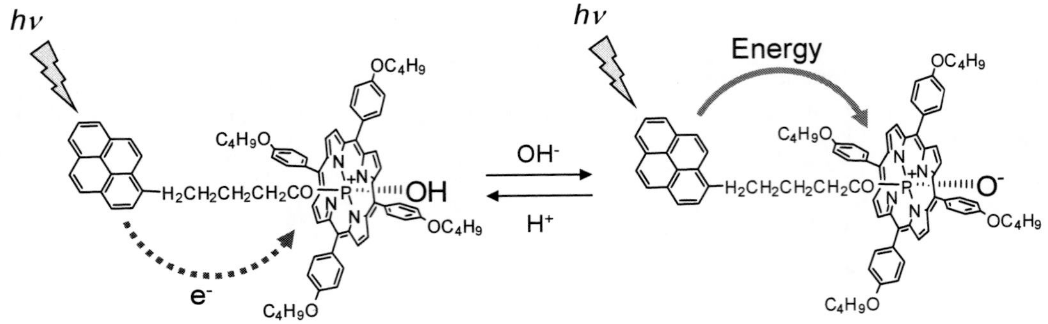

Figure 5. Schematic diagram of the control of energy transfer and electron transfer by the pH of a solvent.

4. POTENTIAL MEDICINAL APPLICATION OF P(V) PORPHYRINS

4.1. Medicinal Application of Porphyrin: Photodynamic Therapy

Porphyrins are important compounds as photosensitizers of PDT [1-3]. PDT, which is a relatively new treatment for cancer, employs a photosensitizer and visible light to produce oxidative stress in cells and ablate cancerous tumors. PDT is also used to treat some nonmalignant conditions that are generally characterized by the overgrowth of unwanted or abnormal cells. Human tissue has relatively high transparency for visible light, especially red light, and visible light hardly demonstrates side effects. The general procedure of PDT is as follows: 1) administration of a photosensitizer (drug), 2) photo-irradiation to photosensitizer, and 3) photosensitized damage of cancer biomacromolecules. This photodamage leads to cell death of the tumor via apoptosis or necrosis. In general, photoexcited drugs induce biomacromolecule damage through the type I mechanism (electron transfer), the type II mechanism (reactive oxygen generation), or both (Figure 6) [31-33]. In the type I mechanism, one electron is transferred from the biomolecules, such as the DNA base or amino acid residue of protein, to photoexcited sensitizers, resulting in the modification of these biomolecules. In the case of DNA damage, consecutive guanine residues are selectively oxidized in the double strand [31,33]. This mechanism requires relatively large oxidative activity for photoexcited sensitizers. Therefore, various ultraviolet photosensitizers can damage biomacromolecules via the type I mechanism. However, visible-light photosensitizers rarely induce biomacromolecule damage through this mechanism [31].

In general, the type II mechanism involves the generation of singlet oxygen ($^1O_2$) from photoexcited sensitizers to molecular oxygen through energy transfer. Molecular oxygen has two low-lying singlet excited states, $^1\Delta_g$ and $^1\sum_g^+$, at 0.98 eV (95 kJ mol^{-1}) and 1.63 eV (158 kJ mol^{-1}), respectively, above the ground triplet state ($^3\sum_g^-$) [34]. Since the lifetime of $^1\sum_g^+$ is very short, its contribution to DNA damage is negligible, but $^1\Delta_g$ (hereinafter $^1O_2$) is an important reactive species. $^1O_2$ is easily generated by visible light [31], and is considered as an important reactive species of PDT. The energy transfer reaction can be expressed as follows:

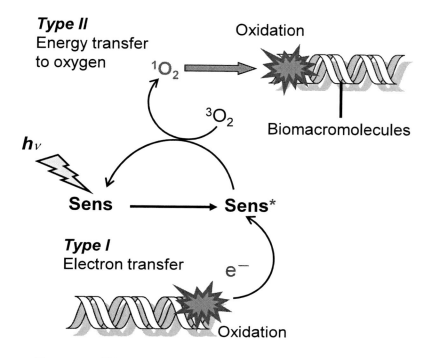

Figure 6. Mechanism of biomacromolecule damage through the type I and type II mechanisms.

$$^1Sens + h\nu \rightarrow {}^1Sens* \tag{2}$$

$$^1Sens* \rightarrow {}^3Sens* \tag{3}$$

$$^3Sens* \, (^1Sens*) + {}^3O_2 \rightarrow {}^1Sens + {}^1O_2 \, (^1\Sigma_g^+ \text{ or } {}^1\Delta_g) \tag{4}$$

$$^1O_2 \, (^1\Sigma_g^+) \rightarrow {}^1O_2 \, (^1\Delta_g) \tag{5}$$

where ^1Sens represents the ground state photosensitizer, $^1Sens*$ is the singlet excited state photosensitizer, and $^3Sens*$ is the triplet excited state photosensitizer. The spin multiplicity of molecular oxygen (triplet state) changes into the singlet state via this energy transfer. Since this process must proceed through electron exchange (Dexter mechanism) [35], contact between the excited photosensitizer and molecular oxygen is important for $^1O_2$ generation. $^1O_2$ is an unstable excited state and undergoes physical quenching by its surroundings. The lifetime of $^1O_2$, which is relatively short ($2 \sim 4$ µs) in H_2O, is greatly elongated in D_2O (~ 70 µs) [36, 37]. Consequently, DNA damage via the type II mechanism can be enhanced in D_2O compared with H_2O. $^1O_2$ is capable of oxidation in various biomolecules. Critical sites of generated $^1O_2$ include mitochondria and phospholipid membranes [1-3]. In the case of DNA damage, guanines are selectively oxidized by $^1O_2$.

Porphyrins have a relatively strong absorption band around the red region. Furthermore, porphyrins can easily generate $^1O_2$, an important reactive oxygen species of PDT, to photosensitize biomolecule oxidation. In addition, P(V)porphyrin is advantageous for both the type I and type II mechanisms.

4.2. Protein Damage Photosensitized by P(V)Porphyrin

Photosensitized protein damage by P(V)porphyrin derivatives (PEtG$_2$ and PPrG$_2$) (Figure 7) was reported [38, 39]. Absorption spectrum measurement demonstrated the binding interaction of P(V)porphyrins with human serum albumin (HSA), a water-soluble protein. Photo-irradiated P(V)porphyrins damaged the amino acid residue of HSA, resulting in the decrease of fluorescence intensity from tryptophan and tyrosine residues. P(V)porphyrins photosensitized $^1O_2$ generation, and the contribution of $^1O_2$ to the HSA damage was confirmed. However, an $^1O_2$ quencher, sodium azide (NaN$_3$), could not completely inhibit HSA damage. This can be explained by the contribution of the electron transfer mechanism to HSA damage. Indeed, the fluorescence of P(V)porphyrins was quenched by HSA, supporting the electron transfer mechanism. These results suggest that the phototoxic effect of P(V)porphyrins may be conserved under lower oxygen concentrations, such as those in cancer cells, by dual photodamaging mechanisms: $^1O_2$ generation and oxygen-independent electron transfer.

Photosensitized $^1O_2$ generation by PEtG$_2$ and PPrG$_2$ was confirmed using near-infrared luminescence measurement, and the yield was estimated to be relatively large (0.83 in H$_2$O for both P(V)porphyrins). The redox potential of one-electron reduction of these P(V)porphyrins in singlet excited states (S$_1$) is about 1.5 V vs. SCE, suggesting that oxidation of tryptophan (oxidation potential: 1.0 V vs. SCE) is energetically possible. A transient absorption measurement showed that the electron transfer takes place to the S$_1$ and not to the triplet excited state (T$_1$). These findings advocate that P(V)porphyrins can induce damage to biomolecules via dual mechanisms: $^1O_2$ generation and electron transfer.

The mechanism of HSA damage photosensitized by P(V)porphyrins is summarized in Figure 8. Photoexcited P(V)porphyrins (S$_1$ state) oxidize amino acid residues of HSA through electron transfer within the S$_1$ lifetime (4~5 ns). The formed charge transfer state possibly undergoes further reaction with water or oxygen molecules, resulting in the formation of non-fluorescent decomposed products. An alternate process is intersystem crossing from the S$_1$ to T$_1$ state. The lifetime of the T$_1$ state, which was estimated from the time profile of $^1O_2$ emission [39], was 1.6 μs. In the presence of sufficient molecular oxygen, $^1O_2$ can be generated through energy transfer from the T$_1$ state of P(V)porphyrins within the T$_1$ state lifetime. During this time frame (about 4.1 μs), generated $^1O_2$ oxidizes amino acids.

In conclusion, a porphyrin P(V) complex demonstrated relatively high photo-oxidative activity via electron transfer in the condition of low oxygen concentration that takes place in cancer cells.

4.3. DNA Damage Photosensitized by P(V)Porphyrin

DNA is an important potential target of PDT. Indeed, cellular DNA damage photosensitized by porphyrin derivatives has been reported [40, 41]. The photosensitized DNA damage caused by a derivative of the P(V)porphyrin dihydroxoP(V) tetraphenylporphyrin (POH$_2$) (Figure 9) was reported [13]. Water-solubility of POH$_2$ is relatively high due to the axial hydroxyl groups. The study of near-infrared emission measurements demonstrated that photosensitized $^1O_2$ generation by POH$_2$ is relatively small compared with other P(V)porphyrin derivatives (quantum yield: 0.28 in ethanol). The quantum yield of $^1O_2$ generation was determined by comparing the infrared emission intensity by the photosensitizer with that of methylene blue, a reference photosensitizer [42].

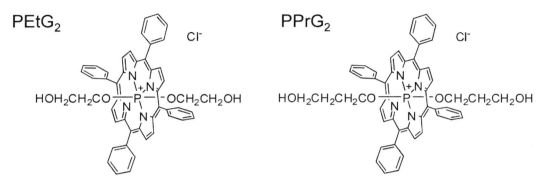

Figure 7. Structures of PEtG$_2$ and PPrG$_2$.

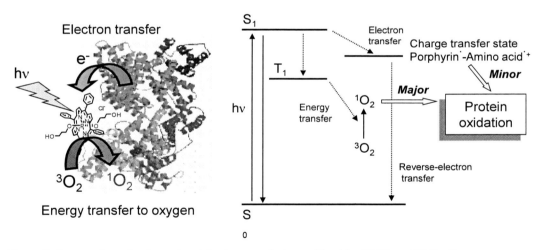

Figure 8. Proposed mechanism of protein damage photosensitized by PEtG$_2$ or PPrG$_2$. Because P(V)porphyrin is a cation, the radical pair of the neutral P(V)porphyrin radical (Porphyrin$^.$) and the amino acid cation radical (Amino acid$^{.+}$) was formed through electron transfer.

The absorption spectrum of POH$_2$ was broadened slightly by the addition of calf thymus DNA (double-stranded DNA). This spectral broadening was explained by a static interaction between POH$_2$ and DNA. Since the tetraphenylporphyrin P(V) complex is sterically hindered, POH$_2$ should bind to DNA externally rather than by intercalation or groove-binding. In addition, partial intercalation of POH$_2$ into double-stranded DNA might be possible. POH$_2$ shows S$_2$ and S$_1$ fluorescence at ca. 430 and 602 nm, respectively. The S$_2$ and S$_1$ fluorescence quantum yields of POH$_2$ were decreased through an interaction with DNA, suggesting quenching of photoexcited POH$_2$ through electron transfer from DNA. The lifetime of porphyrin S$_2$ is very short (a few ps), which supports the static interaction between POH$_2$ and

DNA. The photo-oxidative property of P(V)porphyrin derivatives via electron transfer has been reported [8, 10]. The quenching efficiency of S_2 fluorescence was larger than that of S_1 fluorescence, possibly due to the lower reduction potential of S_2. Fluorescence quenching suggests that photoexcited POH_2 has the ability to damage DNA through the electron transfer.

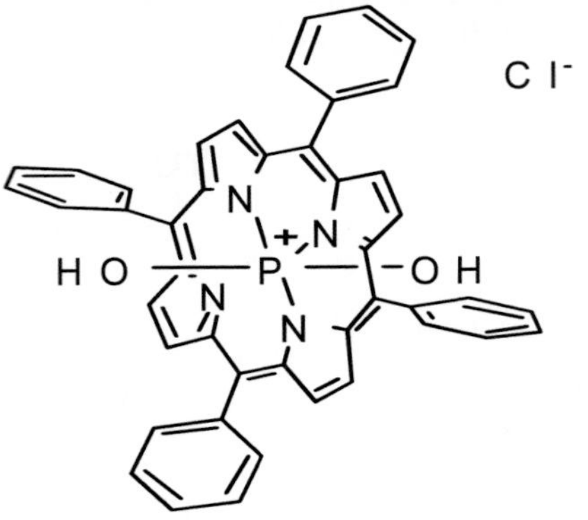

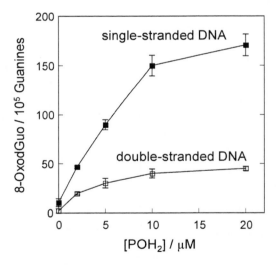

Figure 9. Structure of POH_2.

Figure 10. Formation of 8-oxodGuo induced by photoexcited POH_2. The reaction mixtures contained 100 μM/base-pair calf thymus DNA and POH_2 in 100 μL of a 4 mM sodium phosphate buffer (pH 7.8). The vertical axis indicates 8-oxodGuo formation on 10^5 bases of guanines.

Under aerobic conditions, POH_2 photosensitized damage was more severe for single-stranded DNA than for double-stranded DNA. Photoexcited POH_2 damaged every guanine residue in single-stranded DNA. HPLC measurements confirmed the formation of 8-oxo-7,8-dihydro-2'-deoxyguanine (8-oxodGuo) and showed that the yield of 8-oxodGuo in single-stranded DNA is larger than it is in double-stranded DNA (Figure 10). Guanine-specific DNA damage and the enhancement in single-stranded DNA suggest that $^1O_2$ generation mainly contributes to the mechanism of DNA photodamage by POH_2. On the other hand, photosensitized damage at consecutive guanines was much less pronounced in double-stranded DNA. Because consecutive guanines act as a hole trap, this DNA-damaging pattern suggests the partial involvement of photo-induced electron transfer [31]. However, DNA damage by electron transfer was not a main mechanism, possibly due to reverse electron transfer.

It is reported that reaction of guanine with $^1O_2$ leads to the formation of 8-oxodGuo as a major oxidized product [43, 44] (Figure 11). Formed 8-oxodGuo undergoes further oxidation by $^1O_2$ [45]. The quenching of the S_1 and S_2 fluorescence of POH_2 by DNA supported the electron transfer mechanism. The cation radical on the consecutive G sequence arises from either initial electron abstraction of this guanine by photoexcited POH_2 or through hole transfer from a relatively distant one-electron oxidized nucleobase [12]. The formed guanine cation radicals may react with a water molecule to form the C-8 OH adduct radical [45, 46]. This radical may be converted into a 2,6-diamino-4-hydroxy-5-formamidopyrimidine (FapyGua) residue through a reducing process [45, 46, 47]. On the other hand, competitive oxidation of the 8-hydroxy-7,8-dihydroguanyl radical, which may be achieved by molecular oxygen, gives rise to 8-oxodGuo [45, 48-50] and other oxidized products (e.g. imidazolone, oxazolone). Imidazolone and oxazolone may also be primary oxidation products that arise from the conversion of the deprotonated form of the guanine radical cation after O_2 or $O_2^{\cdot-}$ addition.

In summary, this study has demonstrated that photoexcited POH_2 induces guanine-specific damage, mainly through $^1O_2$ generation, and that electron transfer partially contributes to DNA damage. These mechanisms can damage other biomacromolecules, such as proteins and the phospholipid membrane, and may contribute to the PDT effect. The interaction between a porphyrinoid sensitizer and DNA appears to affect the mechanism of photosensitized DNA damage. Since the lifetime of $^1O_2$ is very short in a cell, DNA-binding interaction is important for the $^1O_2$-mediated PDT mechanism. On the other hand, photo-induced electron transfer can occur from the photoexcited state of POH_2.

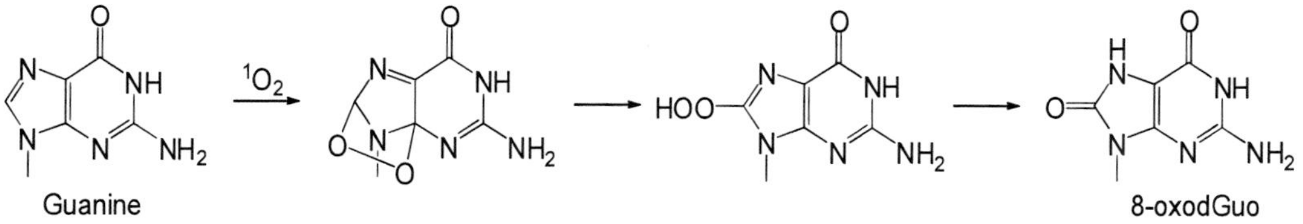

Figure 11. Formation of 8-oxodGuo through oxidation of guanine by $^1O_2$.

CONCLUSION

The character of the porphyrin ring is controlled by the central atom. A phosphorus complex of porphyrin is sterically hindered and has high electron-accepting ability. This ability is especially important for photo-induced electron transfer reaction. The photoexcited state of P(V)porphyrin is a strong oxidant. For this characteristic, P(V)porphyrin is studied as a photosensitizer of PDT to oxidize biomacromolecules of cancer cells through photo-induced electron transfer.

REFERENCES

[1]   Dolmans, D. E. J. G. J.; Fukumura, D. and Jain, R. K. (2003). Photodynamic therapy for cancer. *Nat. Rev. Cancer*, 3, 380-387.

[2]   Ackroyd, R.; Kelty, C.; Brown, N. and Reed, M. (2001). The history of photodetection and photodynamic therapy. *Photochem. Photobiol.*, 74, 656-669.

[3]   Moan, J. and Peng, Q. (2003). An outline of the hundred-year history of PDT. *Anticancer Res.*, 23, 3591-3600.

[4]   Marrese, C. A. and Carrano, C. J. (1983). Synthesis, characterization, and electrochemistry of (5,10,15,20-tetraphenylporphinato)dichlorophosphorus(V) chloride. *Inorg. Chem.*, 22, 1858-1862.

[5]   Segawa, H.; Kunimoto, K.; Nakamoto, A. and Shimidzu, T. (1992). Synthesis of axial dialkoxy phosphorus(V)porphyrin derivatives-novel hypervalent phosphorus compounds. *J. Chem. Soc. Perkin Trans. 1*, 939-940.

[6]   Susumu, K.; Segawa, H. and Shimidzu, T. (1995). Synthesis and photochemical properties of the orthogonal porphyrin triad composed of free-base and phosphorus(V) porphyrins. *Chem. Lett.*, 929-930.

[7]   Rao, T. A. and Maiya, B. G. (1995). 'Axial-bonding type' hybrid porphyrin trimers: design, synthesis and modulation of redox and photophysical properties. *J. Chem. Soc., Chem. Commun.*, 939-940.

[8]   Hirakawa, K. and Segawa, H. (1999). Excitation energy transfer and photo-induced electron transfer in axial bispyrenyl phosphorus porphyrin derivatives: factors governing the competition between energy and electron transfer processes under the existence of intramolecular π-π interaction. *J. Photochem. Photobiol. A: Chem.*, 123, 67-76.

[9]   Kunimoto, K.; Segawa, H. and Shimidzu, T. (1992). Selective synthesis of unsymmetrical dialkoxyphosphorus(V) tetraphenylporphine derivatives by stepwise substitution of axial position. *Tetrahedron lett.*, 33, 6327-6330.

[10]   Hirakawa, K. and Segawa, H. (2010). Acid dissociation of axial hydroxyl group of hydroxy(1-pyrenebutoxy)-phosphorus(V) porphyrin controls the intramolecular excitation energy transfer. *Photochem. Photobiol. Sci.*, 9, 704-709.

[11]   Inoue, H.; Okamoto, T.; Kameo, Y.; Sumitani, M.; Fujiwara, A.; Ishibashi, D. and Hida, M. (1994). Photochemical epoxidation of cyclohexene sensitized by tetraphenylporphyrinatoantimony(V) in the presence of water acting both as an electron and an oxygen donor. *J. Chem. Soc. Perkin Trans. 1*, 105-111.

[12]   Lewis, F. D. and Wu, Y. (2001). Dynamics of superexchange photoinduced electron transfer in duplex DNA. *J. Photochem. Photobiol. C: Photochemistry Rev.*, 2, 1-16.

[13]   Hirakawa, K.; Kawanishi, S.; Hirano, T. and Segawa, H. (2007). Guanine-specific DNA oxidation photosensitized by the tetraphenylporphyrin phosphorus(V) complex via singlet oxygen generation and electron transfer. *J. Photochem. Photobiol. B: Biol.*, 87, 209-217.

[14]   Lehn, J. M. (1988). Supramolecular chemistry-scope and perspectives molecules, supermolecules, and molecular devices. *Angew. Chem. Int. Ed. Engl.*, 27, 89-112.

[15] Lehn, J. M. (1990). Perspectives in supramolecular chemistry - from molecular recognition towards molecular information processing and self-organization. *Angew. Chem. Int. Ed. Engl.*, 29, 1304-1319.

[16] de Silva, A. P.; Uchiyama, S.; Vance, T. P. and Wannalerse, B. (2007). A supramolecular chemistry basis for molecular logic and computation. *Coordination Chem. Rev.*, 251, 1623-1632.

[17] de Silva, A. P.; Gunaratne, H. Q. N. and McCoy, C. P. (1993). A molecular photoionic AND gate based on fluorescent signaling. *Nature*, 364, 42-44.

[18] de Silva, A. P.; Gunaratne, H. Q. N. and Maguire, G. E. M. (1994). 'Off–on' fluorescent sensors for physiological levels of magnesium ions based on photoinduced electron transfer (PET), which also behave as photoionic OR logic gates. *J. Chem. Soc. Chem. Commun.*, 1213-1214.

[19] de Silva, A. P.; Gunaratne, H. Q. N. and McCoy, C. P. (1997). Molecular photoionic AND logic gates with bright fluorescence and "Off–On" digital action. *J. Am. Chem. Soc.*, 119, 7891-7892.

[20] de Silva, A. P.; Dixon, I. M.; Gunaratne, H. Q. N.; Gunnlaugsson, T.; Maxwell, P. R. S. and Rice, T. E. (1999). Integration of logic functions and sequential operation of gates at the molecular-scale. *J. Am. Chem. Soc.*, 121, 1393-1394.

[21] Wasielewski, M. R. (1992). Photoinduced electron transfer in supramolecular systems for artificial photosynthesis. *Chem. Rev.*, 92, 435-461.

[22] Wasielewski, M. R. (2009). Self-assembly strategies for integrating light harvesting and charge separation in artificial photosynthetic systems. *Acc. Chem. Res.*, 42, 1910-1921.

[23] Fuhrhop, J. H.; Kadish, K. M. and Davis, D. G. (1973). The redox behavior of metallo-octaethylporphyrins. *J. Am. Chem. Soc.*, 95, 5140-5147.

[24] Gouterman, M.; Sayer, P.; Shankland, E. and Smith, J. P. (1981). Porphyrins. 41. phosphorus mesoporphyrin and phthalocyanine. *Inorg. Chem.*, 20, 87-92.

[25] Förster, T. (1948). Zwischenmolekulare energiewanderung und fluoreszenz. *Ann. Physik*, 437, 55-75.

[26] Takeuchi, Y.; Hirakawa, K.; Susumu, K. and Segawa, H. (2004). Electrochemical determination of charge transfer direction of center-to-edge phosphorus(V) porphyrin arrays. *Electrochemistry*, 7, 449-451.

[27] Hirakawa, K.; Saito, K. and Segawa, H. (2009). Anomalously selective quenching of S2 fluorescence from upper excited state of zinc 5-(1'-pyrenyl)-10,15,20-triphenylporphyrin derivatives through intramolecular charge transfer state. *J. Phys. Chem. A*, 113, 8852-8856.

[28] Cló, E.; Snyder, J. W.; Ogilby, P. R. and Gothelf, K. V. (2007). Control and selectivity of photosensitized singlet oxygen production: challenges in complex biological systems. *ChemBioChem*, 8, 475-481.

[29] Hirakawa, K.; Kawanishi, S. and Hirano, T. (2005). The mechanism of guanine specific photo-oxidation in the presence of berberine and palmatine: activation of photosensitized singlet oxygen generation through DNA-binding interaction. *Chem. Res. Toxicol.*, 18, 1545-1552.

[30] Hirakawa, K. and Hirano, T. (2008). The microenvironment of DNA switches the activity of singlet oxygen generation photosensitized by berberine and palmatine. *Photochem. Photobiol.*, 84, 202-208.

[31] Hirakawa, K. in (2008). DNA damage through photo-induced electron transfer and photosensitized generation of reactive oxygen species. in New Research on DNA Damage, Chapter 9, pp. 197-219, Nova Science Publishers Inc., New York.

[32] Foote, C. S. (1991). Definition of type I and type II photosensitized oxidation. *Photochem. Photobiol.*, 54, 659.

[33] Kawanishi, S.; Hiraku, Y. and Oikawa, S. (2001). Sequence-specific DNA damage induced by UVA radiation in the presence of endogenous and exogenous photosensitizers. *Curr. Probl. Dermatol.*, 29, 74-82.

[34] DeRosa, M. C. and Crutchley, R. J. (2002). Photosensitized singlet oxygen and its applications. *Coordination Chem. Rev.*, 233-234, 351-371.

[35] Dexter, D. L. (1953). A theory of sensitized luminescence in solids. J. *Chem. Phys.*, 21, 836-850.

[36] Ogilby, P. R. and Foote, C. S. (1983). Chemistry of singlet oxygen. 42. Effect of solvent, solvent isotopic substitution, and temperature on the lifetime of singlet molecular oxygen ($^1\Delta_g$). *J. Am. Chem. Soc.*, 105, 3423-3430.

[37] Hirakawa, K.; Hirano, T.; Nishimura, Y.; Arai, T. and Nosaka, Y. (2011). Control of singlet oxygen generation photosensitized by meso-anthrylporphyrin through interaction with DNA. *Photochem. Photobiol.*, 87, 833-839.

[38] Hirakawa, K.; Ebara, Y.; Hirano, T. and Segawa, H. (2009). Photo-damage of human serum albumin by porphyrin P(V) complex through electron transfer and singlet oxygen generation. *J. Jpn. Soc. Laser Surgery and Medicine*, 29, 372-378.

[39] Hirakawa, K.; Kikuchi, R.; Segawa, H.; Hirano, T.; Okazaki, S. and Nosaka, Y. (2010). Oxygen-independent photosensitizer: phosphorus(V)porphyrin. *Photomed. Photobiol.*, 32, 15-16.

[40] Besaratinia, A.; Bates, S. E.; Synold, T. W. and Pfeifer, G. P. (2004). Similar mutagenicity of photoactivated porphyrins and ultraviolet A radiation in mouse embryonic fibroblasts: involvement of oxidative DNA lesions in mutagenesis. *Biochemistry*, 43, 15557-15566.

[41] Woods, J. A.; Traynor, N. J.; Brancaleon, L. and Moseley, H. (2004). The effect of photofrin on DNA strand breaks and base oxidation in HaCaT keratinocytes: a comet assay study. *Photochem. Photobiol.*, 79, 105-113.

[42] Usui, Y. and Kamogawa, K. (1974). Standard system to determine the quantum yield of singlet oxygen formation in aqueous solution. *Photochem. Photobiol.*, 19, 245-247.

[43] Cadet, J.; Berger, M.; Buchko, G. W.; Joshi, P. C.; Raoul, S. and Ravabnat, J.-L. (1994). 2,2-diamino-4-[(3,5-di-o-acetyl-2-deoxy-β-D-erythro-pentofuranosyl)amino]-5-(2H)-oxazolone: a novel and predominant radical oxidation product 3',5'-di-o-acetyl-2'-deoxyguanosine. *J. Am. Chem. Soc.*, 116, 7403-7404.

[44] Gasparutto, D.; Ravanat, J.-L.; Gerot, O. and Cadet, J. (1998). Characterization and chemical stability of photooxidized oligonucleotides that contain 2,2'-diamino-4-[(2-deoxy-D-erythro-pentofuranosyl)amino]-5(2H)-oxazolone. *J. Am. Chem. Soc.*, 118, 10283-10286.

[45] Burrows, C. J. and Muller, J. G. (1998). Oxidative nucleobase modifications leading to strand scission. *Chem. Rev.*, 98, 1109-1151.

[46] Steenken, S. (1989). Purine bases, nucleoside, and nucleotides: aqueous solution redox chemistry and transformation reactions of their radical cation and e- and OH adducts. *Chem. Rev.*, 89, 503-520.

[47] Pouget, J. P.; Douki, T.; Richard, M. J. and Cadet, J. (2000). DNA damage induced in cells by gamma and UVA radiation as measured by HPLC/GC/-MS and HPLC-EC and Comet assay. *Chem. Res. Toxicol.*, 13, 541-549.

[48] Douki, T. and Cadet, J. (1999). Modification of DNA bases by photosensitized one-electron oxidation. *Int. J. Radiat. Biol.*, 75, 571-581.

[49] Kasai, H.; Yamaizumi, Z.; Berger, M. and Cadet, J. (1992). Photosensitized formation of 7,8-dihydro-8-oxo-2'-deoxyguanosine (8-hydroxy-2'-deoxyguanosine) in DNA by riboflavin: a nonsinglet oxygen-mediated reaction. *J. Am. Chem. Soc.*, 114, 9692-9694.

[50] Cullis, P. M.; Malone, M. E. and Merson-Davies, L. A. (1996). Guanine radical cations are precursors of 7,8-dihydro-8-oxo-2'-deoxyguanosine but are not precursors of immediate strand breaks in DNA. *J. Am. Chem. Soc.*, 118, 2775-2788.

INDEX

A

abatement, 123
abstraction, 189
accounting, 130
acetic acid, 16, 20
acetone, 4, 12
acetonitrile, 14, 181, 182
acid, vii, 1, 8, 10, 11, 12, 14, 18, 20, 22, 23, 24, 25,
    26, 29, 30, 31, 32, 33, 34, 37, 38, 39, 41, 42, 43,
    45, 46, 48, 49, 50, 51, 55, 56, 57, 64, 65, 166,
    182, 183, 187
acidic, 10, 11, 12, 14, 29, 30, 39, 42
acidity, 10
activation energy, 97
active site, 29, 35, 69, 70, 80
acylation, 11
additives, 2, 40
adhesives, 39
ADP, 43
adsorption, 43
aggregation, 30, 127
agriculture, 155, 157
alanine, 33, 34, 36, 43
alcohols, 12, 20
aldehydes, 3
algae, 118, 119, 120, 126, 132, 141, 164
algorithm, ix, 117, 124, 133, 139
aliphatic amines, 3
alkenes, 13, 57
alkylation, 4, 10, 19
aluminium, 54, 65, 66, 74
amalgam, 15
amine, vii, 1, 2, 3, 4, 6, 7, 8, 10, 14, 16, 18, 19, 20,
    21, 22, 24, 29, 35, 38, 39, 40, 74
amine derivatives, vii, 1
amine group, vii, 1, 10, 19, 20, 22, 24, 40
amines, 12, 17, 18, 20, 21, 23, 25, 28, 38, 42, 44, 45,
    47, 48, 50

amino, vii, 1, 2, 6, 16, 20, 21, 22, 23, 26, 29, 31, 32,
    33, 34, 35, 36, 37, 40, 41, 42, 43, 44, 45, 46, 48,
    49, 50, 51, 184, 186, 187, 192
amino acid, vii, 1, 16, 22, 31, 32, 33, 34, 35, 40, 41,
    48, 50, 184, 186, 187
amino acids, vii, 1, 16, 22, 31, 32, 33, 34, 35, 40, 41,
    48, 186
amino groups, 16, 29
ammonia, ix, 17, 20, 29, 117, 118, 139
ammonium, 30, 32, 33, 37, 120
amorphous polymers, 85
anaerobic bacteria, 154
aniline, 18
anti-cancer, 6
anticancer drug, 36
antimony, 41
antitumor, 36, 44, 45, 46, 50
antitumor agent, 46
apoptosis, 184
aquaculture, 155, 156, 157
aquatic systems, vii, ix, 117, 119, 121, 123, 126,
    138, 139, 141
arginine, 35, 46, 49
aromatic rings, 36
Asia, 174, 175
aspartic acid, 22, 51
asymmetric synthesis, 48
atomic distances, 102, 103
atomic orbitals, 105, 108
atoms, vii, viii, x, 3, 23, 26, 29, 30, 38, 53, 54, 60,
    64, 70, 75, 81, 88, 95, 96, 97, 98, 99, 100, 101,
    102, 103, 104, 105, 107, 108, 109, 110, 112, 113,
    179
ATP, 43

B

backscattering, 110, 111

bacteria, 132, 133, 142, 143, 173
band gap, 103, 107, 108
base, 13, 23, 30, 38, 42, 45, 50, 127, 129, 180, 182, 184, 188, 190, 192
basicity, vii, 1, 35, 38
Beijing, 160
beneficial effect, 61
benzene, 37, 48, 60
bicarbonate, 161
bioavailability, 146, 160, 176
biochemistry, 156
biological activity, vii, 1, 20, 37, 38, 40
biological control, 142
biological processes, 126
biological systems, 191
biologically active compounds, vii, 1
biomass, 118, 119, 120, 121, 122, 126, 134, 136, 140, 143
biomolecules, x, 179, 180, 184, 185, 186
biotic, 140, 141, 160
bonding, viii, 31, 32, 95, 107, 108, 109, 110, 115, 190
bonds, viii, 2, 18, 87, 95, 100, 101, 102, 104, 105, 110, 112
boron /phosphorus co-doped single wall carbon nanotubes (B-PSWNTs), viii, 95
branching, 70
breakdown, 96
breast cancer, 36
breathing, 73
breeding, 155
butadiene, 66, 67, 68, 69, 70, 71, 72, 74, 75, 76, 77, 79, 80, 81, 82, 83, 88
butadiene polymerization, 74

C

Ca^{2+}, 153
cadmium, 29
calcium, x, 39, 153, 163, 164
calcium carbonate, 153
calibration, ix, 86, 117, 139
calixarenes, 37
cancer, x, 35, 36, 179, 180, 184, 186, 189, 190
cancer cells, 35, 36, 180, 186, 189
CaP, 172
capillary, 49
carbon, vii, viii, ix, 3, 6, 9, 10, 15, 16, 19, 20, 21, 23, 25, 28, 29, 32, 34, 39, 45, 53, 54, 56, 58, 59, 60, 61, 62, 63, 64, 65, 78, 84, 85, 95, 96, 97, 98, 99, 100, 101, 102, 103, 104, 105, 112, 113, 115, 132, 145, 146, 147, 148, 154, 156, 159, 161, 162

carbon atoms, 32, 58, 60, 85, 97, 100, 101, 102, 103, 104
carbon monoxide, viii, 53, 54, 56, 59, 62, 63
carbon nanotubes, vii, viii, 95, 97, 98, 99, 104, 105, 112, 115
carbon tetrachloride, 39
carboxyl, 30, 31, 32, 37, 39
carboxylic acid, 36, 39, 50
carboxylic acids, 50
catalysis, 20, 63, 64, 87
catalyst, 3, 4, 6, 14, 15, 16, 18, 20, 22, 28, 37, 39, 44, 46, 50, 54, 55, 56, 57, 58, 59, 60, 61, 62, 63, 65, 66, 67, 68, 69, 70, 74, 75, 77, 78, 79, 83, 87, 88
catalytic activity, 55, 58, 60, 61, 62, 63, 66, 74, 75
catalytic system, 55, 57, 62, 63, 64, 66, 82
catchments, 146
cathepsin G, 36, 49
cation, 30, 183, 187, 189, 192
C-C, 16
cell death, 184
challenges, 191
chemical, viii, 54, 95, 96, 97, 108, 109, 110, 113, 115, 126, 132, 142, 146, 154, 165, 167, 176, 192
chemical inertness, 96
chemical stability, 192
chemical vapor deposition, 97
China, v, ix, 95, 114, 115, 145, 146, 159, 160, 161, 163, 164, 165, 168, 174, 175, 176
chiral group, 78
chirality, 97, 98, 99
chlorine, 181
chlorobenzene, 85
chloroform, 39, 181
chlorophyll, 118, 119, 120, 121, 124, 127, 128, 129, 130, 132, 134, 135, 140, 143
cholinesterase, 35, 43
chromatography, 35, 181
chromium, viii, 53, 54, 66, 74, 75, 77, 80, 82, 85, 87, 88
City, ix, 163, 164, 174
clarity, 125
cleavage, 42
climate, 161
climate change, 161
closure, 27
cluster analysis, 173
clusters, 173
C-N, 27
cobalt, viii, 29, 43, 53, 54, 66, 67, 68, 69, 70, 71, 73, 77, 80, 83, 85, 86, 88
color, 180
commercial, 55, 67, 88
community, 140

compatibility, 96
competition, 173, 182, 183, 190
compilation, vii, 134
complexity, 133
complications, 140
composition, ix, 20, 117, 118, 132, 139, 140, 146, 154
compounds, vii, 1, 2, 6, 7, 10, 12, 13, 19, 20, 21, 22, 24, 26, 29, 31, 33, 35, 36, 38, 39, 40, 47, 49, 50, 54, 55, 56, 66, 74, 85, 87, 155, 158, 179, 184, 190
comprehension, 88
computation, 99, 103, 112, 191
condensation, 6, 15
conductance, viii, 96, 98, 110, 111, 113
conduction, 98, 101, 103, 105, 107, 110, 112
conductivity, viii, 95, 96, 97, 101, 102, 103, 113
configuration, 5, 23, 28, 31, 37, 65
conjugation, 27
conserving, 98, 99
construction, 140
contaminant, 153
convergence, 99
cooling, 24
coordination, 29, 31, 35, 55, 57, 62
copolymer, 56, 57, 58, 63
copolymerization, vii, viii, 53, 54, 55, 56, 57, 58, 60, 61, 62, 63, 64, 85, 87, 88
copolymerization rate, 56
copolymers, viii, 53, 54, 55, 56, 64, 88
copper, 28, 29, 30
correlation, 75, 99, 124, 128, 129, 173
correlation coefficient, 128, 173
correlation function, 99
correlations, 173
cost, 123, 133, 174
covalent bond, 101, 102
covering, 129, 139
crystal structure, 75
crystalline, 21, 54, 67, 71, 73, 74, 85, 86, 88, 165, 173
crystallinity, 86
crystallization, 71
crystals, 99, 100, 101
cultivation, 168
culture, 158, 161
CV, ix, 117, 122, 139
CVD, 97, 98
cyanide, 29
cycles, 16, 88
cycling, 140
cyclodextrins, 3, 49
cytotoxicity, 45

D

damages, 102, 112
database, 167
DDT, 174
decomposition, 126, 154, 155, 158, 162
defects, 97
deformation, 110
degradation, 121, 156, 158, 159
dendrogram, 173
denitrification, ix, 117, 118, 121, 123, 132, 133, 139, 143
Denmark, 129
density function theory (DFT), viii, 95
density functional theory, 97
dentin, 39
deposition, ix, 96, 98, 101, 117, 121, 123, 133, 139, 146, 161
depth, 122, 124, 125, 126, 127, 129, 146, 147, 149, 151, 152, 153, 154, 156, 157, 158, 159, 164
derivatives, vii, 1, 2, 7, 8, 11, 12, 16, 17, 20, 21, 22, 30, 31, 35, 36, 37, 40, 42, 44, 46, 47, 48, 49, 50, 51, 63, 88, 181, 186, 188, 190, 191
detection, ix, 117, 139
DFT, viii, 95, 97, 99, 112
diamond lattice integrity, viii, 95
diamonds, 97, 100, 101, 102, 103
diatoms, 120, 139, 142
diene polymerization, 66, 73, 77, 78, 81, 82, 83, 88
dienes, 47, 65, 66, 72, 74, 77, 78, 79, 80, 84, 86
diffraction, ix, 163, 165, 176
diffusion, 110, 118, 132, 139
digestion, 148, 156
dihydroxyphenylalanine, 33, 34
dioxin, 174
dioxin-like PCBs, 174
discharges, 121, 168
discrimination, 49
dispersion, 109, 110
displacement, 20, 99
dissociation, 62, 63, 182, 183, 190
distillation, 18
distribution, ix, 39, 42, 100, 110, 111, 112, 126, 142, 146, 149, 150, 151, 152, 154, 156, 157, 158, 163, 165, 170, 173
DNA, x, 179, 182, 184, 185, 186, 187, 188, 189, 190, 191, 192, 193
DNA damage, 184, 185, 186, 188, 189, 192, 193
DNA lesions, 192
DNA strand breaks, 192
dominance, 141, 142, 143
donors, 29, 64, 96
dopants, 98, 110

doping, vii, viii, 95, 97, 101, 102, 103, 104, 108, 111, 112, 113
double bonds, 84
drawing, 62
drinking water, ix, 163
drug delivery, 35
drugs, 35, 36, 184
DSC, 71, 72, 77, 87

E

ecology, 118
ecosystem, 133, 141, 142, 143, 146, 155
electric charge, 97, 100, 101
electric field, ix, 96, 98, 108, 111, 112, 113
electrical conductivity, 112, 113
electrical properties, vii
electrochemistry, 190
electron, vii, viii, x, 1, 2, 9, 13, 20, 23, 24, 27, 29, 30, 32, 61, 70, 95, 96, 97, 102, 103, 105, 107, 110, 111, 154, 179, 182, 183, 184, 185, 186, 187, 189, 190, 191, 192, 193
electronic structure, viii, 95, 97, 98, 99, 101, 109, 112
electrons, 20, 97, 98, 99, 101, 102, 103, 105, 110, 113
electrophoresis, 49
e-mail, 1
emission, 186, 187
enamel, 39
enantiomers, 3, 49
energy, viii, 10, 95, 97, 98, 99, 100, 101, 102, 103, 104, 105, 106, 107, 108, 109, 110, 111, 112, 182, 183, 184, 185, 186, 190
energy transfer, 182, 183, 184, 185, 186, 190
engineering, 154
environment, ix, 38, 62, 96, 126, 136, 142, 145, 146, 147, 154, 155, 156, 157, 158, 159, 160, 164, 175
environmental change, 159
environmental conditions, 144, 146, 170
environmental impact, 174
environmental issues, vii
environmental protection, 4
environments, 96
enzyme, 35
enzymes, 35, 36, 49
EPR, 30
equilibrium, 24, 62, 118, 160
erosion, 127, 153
ester, 18, 20, 24, 26, 39
etching, 45
ethanol, 4, 18, 187
ethers, 13

ethylene, 8, 17, 21, 26, 55, 56, 57, 59, 60, 61, 63, 66
European Commission, 148, 164
evaporation, 181
evidence, 62, 77, 141, 160
evolution, 146, 158, 162, 175
excitation, 182, 190
extinction, 124
extraction, 29, 31, 32, 33, 34, 38, 39, 41, 148, 161, 165, 167

F

farms, 144
feedstocks, 88
Fermi level, 105, 106, 107
fertilization, 168
fiber, 97, 157
fibroblasts, 192
filament, 98
films, viii, 73, 95, 96, 101, 102, 112
financial, 41
financial support, 41
Finland, 132
fish, 126, 140, 144, 164
fishing, 155
fixation, ix, 117, 121, 122, 132, 133, 138, 139, 141, 142, 143, 144
flame, 2, 40
flocculation, 127, 140
flooding, 157
fluorescence, 182, 183, 186, 187, 189, 191
fluorine, 46, 49
food, 126
footwear, 73
force, 99, 146
formaldehyde, 5
formation, viii, 2, 3, 6, 9, 12, 14, 16, 17, 18, 19, 20, 21, 22, 23, 24, 25, 26, 27, 28, 30, 31, 32, 33, 35, 73, 79, 80, 81, 82, 83, 95, 97, 98, 103, 112, 146, 180, 181, 186, 188, 189, 192, 193
formula, 57, 62, 101, 103, 104, 111, 168
fragments, 3, 7, 8, 22, 29, 30, 33, 34, 37
France, v, 53, 160, 176
free ligands, vii, 53
freshwater, 125, 127, 134, 138, 141, 146, 159, 160, 164, 167, 176
fruits, 73
functionalization, 55

G

garbage, 157
gel, 181

geology, 162, 168
geometry, 27, 58, 99, 100, 103, 108, 109
Germany, 161, 175
global climate change, 146
glycine, 11
glycol, 35
gold nanoparticles, 30, 51
governments, 165
GPC, 69, 70, 71, 72, 87
GPS, 165
graphite, 97, 104, 105, 108
grasses, 157
gravity, 118, 133, 147
green alga, 142, 143
growing polymer chain, 78
growth, 134, 136, 143
growth rate, 134, 136, 143
growth temperature, 134
guanine, 182, 184, 188, 189, 191
guidance, 119
Gulf of Trieste, 162
gutta-percha, 66

H

halogen, 23
halogens, 36
hardness, 96
harvesting, 191
health, vii, 160
health effects, vii
heavy metals, 45, 164, 175
hemisphere, 130
heptane, 69, 87
heterogeneity, 149
histidine, 33
history, 54, 88, 146, 162, 170, 190
homocysteine, 36
homogeneity, 101
homogeneous catalyst, 74
homopolymerization, 83
host, 35, 37
human, viii, 35, 49, 95, 146, 158, 159, 160, 164, 168, 170, 186, 192
human activity, 146, 168
human health, viii, 95, 146, 164
human neutrophil elastase, 49
hybrid, 47, 105, 190
hybridization, 98, 104, 105, 107, 108, 109, 110, 112
hydrocarbons, 55
hydrogen, 6, 20, 31, 32, 33, 35, 100, 153, 180
hydrogen atoms, 100
hydrogen bonds, 20, 32, 33, 35

hydrogen chloride, 153, 180
hydrogenation, 15, 16
hydrolysis, 6, 8, 10, 14, 20, 22, 23, 30
hydrophilicity, 39
hydrophobicity, 33, 34
hydroxide, 170
hydroxyl, 4, 8, 10, 31, 33, 44, 181, 182, 183, 187, 190
hydroxyl groups, 4, 182, 187
hypertrophy, 127
hypotensive, 20, 40
hypothesis, 83, 119

I

ideal, 101
identification, 88, 165
improvements, 97
impurities, 29, 97, 105, 106, 109
in vitro, 42, 45, 46
in vivo, 48
India, 160
industries, 96, 164
industry, viii, ix, 29, 73, 95, 145, 156, 157, 158, 159
inflation, 101, 103
information processing, 191
ingestion, 156
inhibition, 35, 46
inhibitor, 35
injuries, viii, 95
inorganic phosphorus (IP), x, 163, 164
insertion, 78, 80, 81, 82, 84, 85
integrated circuits, 113
integrity, viii, 95, 113
interface, 34, 112, 175
intervention, 160
intrinsic viscosity, 59
ion exchangers, 45
ion-exchange, 29
ionic polymerization, 65
ionization, 97
ions, 30, 33, 98, 99, 100, 102, 170, 191
IR spectra, 69, 71
IR spectroscopy, 3
iron, x, 48, 124, 153, 163, 164
iron transport, 153
irradiation, 49, 184
isolation, 4, 39, 57
isomerization, 24, 25, 27
isomers, 6, 26, 27, 65
isoprene, 65, 66, 73, 76, 77, 79, 80, 81, 82
isotactic sequences, 81, 82
isotope, 160

issues, 2
Italy, 53

J

Japan, 142, 161, 179

K

Kenya, 176
keratinocytes, 192
ketones, 3, 37, 39, 50
kinetics, 32
Korea, 165

L

lakes, ix, x, 122, 125, 134, 135, 136, 138, 139, 140, 141, 142, 143, 145, 146, 147, 150, 151, 152, 153, 154, 155, 156, 157, 158, 159, 160, 163, 168, 175, 176
lamination, 140
lanthanide, vii, 53, 66
lattices, 98, 100, 101, 102, 103, 112
lead, 7, 9, 15, 107
lifetime, 56, 184, 185, 186, 187, 189, 192
ligand, x, 7, 30, 31, 54, 55, 56, 57, 58, 59, 60, 61, 62, 63, 64, 65, 66, 68, 69, 71, 75, 77, 79, 80, 81, 82, 83, 84, 88, 115, 173, 179, 182
light, 124, 129, 141, 147, 181, 184, 191
light conditions, 129
liquids, 3, 4
lithium, 23, 96
localization, 48, 111
low temperatures, 138
luminescence, 186, 192
Luo, 114, 174
lying, 156, 164, 184
lysine, 35, 46

M

macrocyclic compound, x, 22, 179
magnesium, 191
magnetic field, 111
magnitude, 32, 132
man, 164
management, 119, 123, 125, 141, 161, 165, 175
manufacturing, 88
manure, 175
marine environment, 141, 143
mass, ix, 117, 118, 121, 133, 139, 141, 146, 161

materials, 2, 40, 54, 85, 99, 124, 155, 165, 174
matter, 124, 140, 141, 154, 156, 157
measurement, 97, 122, 133, 181, 183, 186
measurements, 122, 133, 141, 176, 187, 188
mechanical properties, 55
media, 3, 49, 57, 63, 130, 182
median, 127, 128, 129, 131, 134, 135, 136, 138
medicine, 35, 96
melting, 21, 54, 71, 88
melting temperature, 71
membranes, 33, 34, 43, 185
metal complexes, vii, 29, 53, 54
metal ion, vii, x, 1, 29, 41, 43, 179
metal ions, vii, x, 1, 41, 43, 179
metallocenes, 88
metals, 8, 29, 30, 31, 36, 39, 55, 99, 175
meth, 20, 39, 45
methanol, 8, 27, 56, 60, 61, 63, 64, 181
methyl group, 25, 28, 82
methyl groups, 25
methylene blue, 187
microorganism, 155
microorganisms, 174, 175
microstructure, viii, 53, 54, 66, 67, 68, 69, 71, 80, 88
microstructures, 65
migration, 157
mineralization, 126, 155
mitochondria, 185
mixing, 7, 57, 105, 165, 175, 181
modelling, 42, 86, 140, 141, 161
models, ix, 41, 117, 133, 139, 143, 144
moderators, 129
modifications, 192
molecular oxygen, 184, 185, 186, 189, 192
molecular structure, 67, 68
molecular weight, 55, 56, 57, 58, 62, 69, 70, 71, 72, 84, 85, 86, 88
molecular weight distribution, 69, 70, 71, 72
molecules, 2, 63, 186, 190
momentum, 110
monomers, 45, 57, 65, 66, 72, 73, 80, 88
mosaic, 35
Moscow, 142
mucus, 133
mutagenesis, 192
MWD, 60

N

nanoelectronics, viii, 95
nanoparticles, 3, 30
nanotube, viii, 95, 97, 98, 103, 106
Nd, 66

necrosis, 184
neutral, 31, 55, 57, 100, 187
nickel, 22, 29, 30, 55
nitrite, 122
nitrobenzene, 39
nitrogen, vii, ix, 1, 2, 3, 9, 11, 12, 13, 19, 20, 25, 26, 27, 29, 30, 31, 32, 35, 36, 38, 43, 62, 63, 76, 96, 97, 117, 118, 119, 120, 121, 122, 123, 128, 132, 133, 134, 136, 138, 139, 140, 142, 143, 144, 145, 146, 147, 148, 158, 159, 161, 164, 175, 176, 180
nitrogen compounds, 176
nitrogen fixation, 119, 121, 122, 123, 132, 133, 134, 140, 142, 144
NMR, 5, 24, 28, 37, 42, 45, 58, 61, 62, 69, 70, 71, 72, 73, 76, 77, 78, 85, 86, 87
N-N, 62, 63
non-apatite P (NAIP), ix, 145
non-polar, 39
norbornene, 84, 85, 86, 87, 88
North America, 140
North Sea, 128
nucleophiles, 14
nucleophilicity, 11
nucleotides, 192
nuisance, 132
nutrient, vii, 118, 119, 121, 123, 129, 132, 133, 140, 141, 144, 147, 155, 156, 158, 159, 160, 164, 175, 176
nutrient concentrations, 129
nutrients, ix, 117, 118, 119, 121, 124, 126, 130, 132, 139, 142, 144, 147, 151, 158, 164

O

octane, 39, 59
OECD, 127, 144
OH, 31, 41, 172, 189, 192
olefins, 54, 56, 57, 87, 88, 89
oligomers, 55, 58
oligotrophic conditions, 128
one dimension, 97, 109, 110
operations, 143, 182
opportunities, 26
optimization, 99
orbit, 105
organic compounds, 41, 154
organic matter, 121, 126, 133, 154, 155, 156, 157, 158, 161, 164
organic P (OP), ix, 145, 148
organic phosphorus (OP), x, 163, 164
organic solvents, 3, 4, 21, 85, 182
organism, 156, 157
organophosphorus analogs, vii, 1, 40

oxidation, 153, 182, 185, 186, 189, 190, 191, 192, 193
oxidation products, 189
oxidative stress, 184
oxidize biomolecules, x, 179
oximes, 14, 15
oxygen, 9, 29, 35, 39, 55, 96, 126, 133, 139, 153, 155, 161, 184, 185, 186, 190, 191, 192, 193

P

Pacific, 142, 175
palladium, viii, 15, 16, 50, 53, 54, 55, 56, 57, 58, 59, 60, 61, 62, 63, 64, 65, 88
parallel, 109
participants, 159
patents, 55
peptide, 11, 16, 35, 46
peptides, 3, 35, 36
permeability, 43
PET, 191
petroleum, 161
pH, 30, 31, 122, 182, 183, 184, 188
pharmaceutical, 35
pharmaceuticals, 2, 40
pharmacologists, vii, 1
phenylalanine, 33
phosphate, ix, 117, 118, 120, 121, 139, 153, 156, 161, 173, 176, 188
phosphonic acids, vii, 1, 48
phosphorous, 110
phosphorus-doped concentration, viii, 95
phosphorylation, 6, 13, 35, 38, 42
photodynamic therapy, x, 179, 180, 190
photodynamic therapy (PDT), 180
photosensitizers, x, 179, 180, 184, 192
photosynthesis, 182, 191
photosynthetic systems, 191
physical properties, viii, 95, 97, 112
physicochemical methods, 33
physics, 114, 115
phytoplankton, 118, 119, 120, 121, 124, 126, 130, 132, 133, 142, 143, 155, 157
plane waves, 99
plankton, ix, 117, 124, 139
plant growth, 8, 36
plant type, 157
plants, 156, 157
platform, 34
Poland, 140
polar, 31, 39, 54, 58, 64, 88
polar groups, 31
polarity, 39, 182

polarization, 20
pollutants, 126, 174
pollution, viii, ix, x, 3, 95, 141, 145, 146, 153, 155,
    158, 159, 164, 165, 168, 173, 175
polyamines, 29
polybutadiene, 66, 67, 73, 82, 88
polydienes, 65
polyisoprene, 66, 78, 82
polyketones, 54, 55, 57, 63
polymer, vii, 53, 54, 55, 57, 58, 59, 60, 62, 63, 65,
    69, 70, 71, 72, 73, 74, 76, 77, 79, 80, 82, 87, 88
polymer chain, 54, 65, 69
polymer chains, 54
polymer materials, 88
polymer structure, vii, 53
polymerization, 54, 57, 58, 59, 65, 66, 67, 68, 69, 70,
    71, 72, 73, 74, 75, 76, 77, 78, 79, 80, 81, 82, 83,
    84, 85, 86, 87, 88, 89
polymerization mechanism, 54, 78, 79
polymerization temperature, 59, 71, 77, 87
polymerization time, 75
polymers, 2, 35, 40, 54, 65, 66, 68, 69, 70, 71, 72,
    73, 74, 75, 79, 80, 81, 82, 83, 84, 85, 86, 87, 88
polyolefins, 86
polystyrene, 86
pools, ix, 117, 139, 164
population, viii, 96, 98, 110, 112, 146
porphyrins, x, 179, 182, 185, 186, 190, 192
positive correlation, x, 164, 173
potassium, 39
potential photosensitizers, x, 179, 180
precipitation, 153
predation, 118, 140, 141
preparation, 43, 47, 50, 51, 57, 58, 59, 73, 85, 180
priming, 45
principles, 99
probability, 75
producers, 119
project, 159
proline, 39
promoter, 60
propane, 56, 57, 58, 59, 61, 65, 74
propylene, 23, 55, 57, 59, 60, 61, 66
prostate cancer, 36
protection, 176
proteins, 189
proton donating, vii, 1, 2, 29, 31
protons, 62
purification, 8, 38, 39, 165
purity, 16
pyrimidine, 4, 27, 51
pyrolysis, 98

Q

quantification, ix, 117, 121, 123, 138, 176
quantum mechanics, 99
quantum yields, 183, 187
question mark, 121, 133

R

race, 36, 46
radiation, 96, 192, 193
radicals, 189
radius, 100, 102, 103, 108
reactant, 4
reaction center, 38
reaction mechanism, 2, 17
reaction medium, 57
reaction rate, 58, 59
reactions, 2, 3, 4, 11, 12, 13, 17, 18, 20, 21, 25, 28,
    29, 50, 62, 63, 179, 192
reactive oxygen, 180, 182, 184, 185, 192
reactivity, 20, 35
reading, 78
reagents, 18, 26, 29, 38, 57, 165
receptors, 33, 37
recognition, 34, 191
reconstruction, 143, 156
recovery, 168, 169
recrystallization, 23
recycling, 126, 140
refractive index, 183
regenerate, 4
regeneration, 119, 121, 140, 164
regression, 124, 125, 128, 130, 134, 135, 137, 138,
    139, 140
regression line, 128, 135, 137, 139
regression model, 130, 140
relaxation, 96, 110
relevance, 85, 88
remedial actions, 119, 138
remediation, x, 164, 165, 174
repulsion, 30
requirements, 31, 96, 101, 113
researchers, 7, 67, 88, 165
residues, 184, 186
resins, 29, 45
respiration, 143
response, vii, ix, 145, 146, 147, 157, 158, 160, 175
rhodium, 55
riboflavin, 193
rings, 37
risk, 123, 164, 174, 175
risk assessment, 175

risks, 135
room temperature, 13, 14, 67, 165
routes, 84
Royal Society, 115
rubber, 66, 73
runoff, 154
Russia, 41

S

salinity, 122, 125, 126, 127, 129, 130, 131, 136, 137,
    138, 139
Salmonella, 36, 43
salts, 28, 29
saltwater, 133
samarium, 46
scatter, 124, 138, 139
scatter plot, 138
scattering, 97, 124
science, 141, 142
scope, 47, 51, 190
seafood, 73
sediment, ix, 124, 133, 146, 147, 148, 149, 150, 151,
    152, 153, 154, 155, 156, 157, 158, 160, 161, 163,
    164, 165, 167, 168, 170, 171, 172, 173, 174, 175,
    176, 177
sedimentation, ix, 117, 118, 121, 123, 124, 132, 133,
    139, 164
sediments, ix, x, 126, 139, 140, 145, 146, 147, 148,
    150, 151, 153, 154, 158, 159, 160, 161, 162, 163,
    164, 165, 167, 168, 169, 170, 171, 173, 174, 175,
    176, 177
selectivity, 31, 33, 34, 37, 56, 60, 88, 191
self-organization, 191
semiconductor, viii, 95, 96, 97, 98, 101, 103, 106,
    108, 112
semiconductors, viii, 96, 97, 99, 102, 109
senility, 153
sensitivity, 154
sensors, 97, 191
sequencing, 138
serum, 186, 192
serum albumin, 186, 192
sewage, 153, 154, 155, 157, 160, 168
shallow lakes, vii, 146, 160
shape, 97, 126, 165
showing, 57, 66, 88
shrubs, 157
side chain, 34, 65
side effects, 184
silica, 181
silver, 181
simulation, 125

simulations, 143
single crystals, 67
SiO2, 48, 171, 173
skeleton, 13, 38
sludge, 160
smoothing, 124
sodium, 18, 96, 186, 188
software, 98, 168
soil erosion, 146, 157
soil pollution, 141
solid state, 62
solidification, 88
solubility, 31, 63, 175, 187
solution, 14, 16, 18, 47, 62, 98, 176, 180, 181, 183,
    192
solvents, 39, 54, 62, 63, 67
sorption, 175
South Africa, 160
Spain, 161
specialists, vii, 1
speciation, ix, 161, 163, 165, 175, 176
species, vii, x, 1, 41, 50, 62, 63, 88, 132, 134, 136,
    163, 165, 171, 172, 173, 174, 184, 185, 192
spectroscopy, 5, 24, 28, 30, 37
spin, 28, 185
stability, 10, 30, 31, 32, 37, 57, 88, 96, 103, 104, 108
stabilizers, 2, 30, 40
Standards, Measurements and Testing (SMT), ix,
    163, 164
state, x, 27, 161, 164, 179, 182, 183, 184, 185, 186,
    189, 191
states, viii, 95, 97, 104, 106, 111, 184, 186
statistics, 128
stereoregular polymers, 66, 85, 88
stereospecificity, 66, 67, 74, 75, 88
stomach, 36
stress, 99
structural variation, 87
structure, viii, x, 7, 21, 24, 29, 31, 32, 33, 36, 50, 54,
    58, 65, 66, 68, 69, 70, 73, 77, 79, 80, 82, 83, 86,
    87, 88, 96, 97, 98, 99, 101, 103, 104, 105, 107,
    108, 109, 112, 146, 179
styrene, 57
substitution, 4, 12, 45, 54, 111, 190, 192
substitutions, 111, 181
substrate, 31, 32, 33, 37
substrates, vii, 1, 11, 23, 29, 32, 34, 41
succession, 140
sulfate, 153, 161
sulfur, 17, 96, 155
sulfuric acid, 166
suppression, 183
surface area, ix, 145, 158, 164

survival, 126
sustainable development, 146
Sweden, 117, 121, 123, 159, 164
SWNTs, viii, 96, 97, 98, 99, 103, 104, 105, 107, 108, 109, 110, 111, 112
symmetry, 104, 105, 109, 112
syndiotactic sequences, 73
syndiotacticity, 65
synthesis, vii, 2, 3, 4, 7, 9, 10, 11, 12, 13, 15, 16, 17, 22, 23, 26, 30, 31, 39, 40, 41, 42, 43, 44, 45, 46, 47, 48, 49, 50, 51, 54, 55, 57, 160, 176, 180, 181, 190
synthetic chemists, vii, 1
synthetic methods, 87

T

tacticity, 70, 73, 75, 81
Taiwan, 165
target, 3, 4, 6, 11, 15, 36, 186
techniques, 122, 138
technology, 96, 141, 160
temperature, 4, 12, 20, 24, 28, 60, 69, 70, 86, 88, 96, 97, 110, 122, 127, 128, 129, 130, 134, 135, 142, 192
tension, 167
terrestrial ecosystems, 159
test data, 165
testing, 176
tetrahydrofuran, 15
textbooks, 118
therapy, x, 179, 190
thin films, 96, 97, 101, 102, 103, 112, 113
thrombin, 42
thymus, 187, 188
time frame, 186
tissue, 184
titanium, 54, 88
tobacco, 35
toluene, 16, 39, 69, 70, 71, 72, 74, 77, 86, 87
total energy, viii, 95, 98, 101, 103, 104, 108, 112
total phosphorus (TP), ix, 117, 128, 139, 163, 164
transformation, 27, 165, 192
transformations, 25, 27, 143
transistor, 115
transition metal, vii, viii, 31, 53, 54, 55, 66, 73, 78, 84, 87, 88
transition temperature, 87
transmission, 142
transparency, 184
transport, vii, viii, 1, 31, 32, 34, 38, 41, 50, 96, 98, 110, 111, 113, 115, 118, 121, 127, 132, 133, 141, 147, 153, 160, 174

transport processes, 118, 121, 132, 141
transportation, 32, 41, 147, 154
treatment, x, 12, 14, 23, 96, 179, 180, 184
trifluoroacetate, 61
trifluoroacetic acid, 15, 23
triphenylphosphine, 88, 98
trophic state, 140
trypsin, 36, 49
tryptophan, 33, 186
tumor, 36, 184
tumor cells, 36
tumors, 184
turbulence, 127
turnover, 118, 121, 124
tyrosine, 33, 34, 186

U

UK, 176
UNESCO, 160
uniform, 111
urban, ix, 145, 168
urea, 16
USA, 89, 91, 145, 165
UV, 165

V

vacancies, 97, 102, 103, 112, 113
vacuum, 18, 181
valence, 98, 101, 103, 105, 107, 110
valine, 32
vanadium, 54
vapor, 98
variables, 122, 124, 125, 146
variations, 7, 38, 80, 101, 129, 130, 142
vector, 109
vegetables, 73
velocity, 128
vinyl monomers, viii, 54, 87
viscosity, 63

W

waste, 29, 155
waste water, 29
wastewater, 29, 168
water purification, 166
water quality, 124, 144, 160
water resources, 146, 176
watershed, 159
wear, 96

weight ratio, 127
wind power, 140
wind speed, 127
wind speeds, 127
workers, 20, 55

X-ray analysis, 24
X-ray diffraction, 33, 86
XRD, ix, 163, 165, 167, 172, 173, 174

Y

yield, ix, 3, 4, 6, 7, 13, 14, 15, 18, 63, 74, 77, 87, 117, 139, 165, 181, 183, 186, 187, 188, 192
ytterbium, 3, 50

Z

zeolites, 99
zinc, 15, 29, 30, 191
zirconium, 88
zooplankton, 118, 119, 126, 140, 157